The Life and Times of
DANIEL
GOOCH

Sir Daniel Gooch (Barraud's portrait of 1888)

The Life and Times of
DANIEL GOOCH

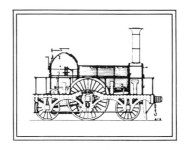

ALAN PLATT

ALAN SUTTON
1987

ALAN SUTTON PUBLISHING
BRUNSWICK ROAD · GLOUCESTER

First Published 1987

British Library Cataloguing in Publication Data

Platt, Alan
   The life and times of Daniel Gooch.
   1.   Gooch, Daniel 2.   Engineers—Great
   Britain—Biography 3.   Politicians—
   Great Britain—Biography
   I.   Title
   625.1'0092'4   TA140.G6

   ISBN 0–86299–317–2

Cover Credit   From the painting, *Rain, Steam and Speed*:
The Great Western Railway, of 1844 by J.M.W. Turner, The National Gallery, London. The painting depicts one of Daniel Gooch's *Fire Fly* locomotives. Inset is *Gorgon*, another of Gooch's seven-foot singles.

Typesetting and origination by
Alan Sutton Publishing Limited.
Printed in Great Britain

Contents

Preface

Daniel Gooch was born in 1816 of parents who were genteel but far from wealthy. When he was fourteen he started work at a vast, grim ironworks in Monmouthshire. At eighteen he took a post as a draughtsman at Dundee, proud that his wage of £1 a week made him independent of his widowed mother. He died, still in harness, at the age of seventy-three. In the fifty-five years of his professional life he made a fortune of three-quarters of a million pounds, an immense sum, the equivalent of perhaps thirty or forty millions today.

During the early days of the Great Western Railway, Gooch helped to save Isambard Brunel's career. He was Queen Victoria's first engine driver and became the 7-ft. gauge's most effective champion in struggles with George and Robert Stephenson and their narrow gauge faction. His locomotives, especially the magnificent *Iron Dukes*, were the fastest and most resplendent of their day. When Brunel's venture into Atmospheric Railways ended in failure, Gooch's money and engines came to the rescue. He was the leading spirit in making something approaching success of the *Great Eastern* steamship. His role in her most spectacular achievement, the laying of the Atlantic Telegraph Cable, gained him a baronetcy, the first to be awarded to an engineer. For twenty years he was an M.P., and a useful one, though he never spoke a word in the House. He was the Chairman of the Great Western Railway for twenty-four years, rescuing it from bankruptcy, presiding over its growth to the largest line in Britain and bearing the ultimate responsibility during the company's most hazardous enterprise, the construction of the Severn Tunnel.

As one of the most eminent Victorians, Gooch was known to royalty, to the great men of business, engineering and politics and to ordinary folk by the tens of thousands. His name is to be found in virtually every book on Nineteenth Century technology but his wider fame has faded. As a heroic engineer whose exploits bring us closer to our pasts he now deserves his due.

CHAPTER

1

Daniel Gooch was born just over a year after Waterloo. Beethoven, Turner and Sir Walter Scott were at the height of their powers. Jane Austen was writing of the mannerly peak of a neatly ordered society and John Constable was painting the lush countryside in which over half of the population still lived. But the Age of Elegance and of chess-board wars was nearly over. Already cotton spinning, coal and iron were so heavily industrialised that Britain was producing over a third of the world's manufactured goods. The most powerful upsurge of the Industrial Revolution, however, was yet to come.

So far the changes had brought little but misery to the working people. Good health was the greatest prize, and life was at its most precarious in the swarming towns. The Social Revolution, the inevitable counterpart of the growth of industry, was not yet under way. There was much to be done and for those with the wits, strength and tenacity to survive an era of great promise had dawned.

The characteristics which Daniel Gooch needed to sweep him to success came from the Longridges, a yeoman family which had flourished in the North of England for five generations. Two of his grandparents, his mother's father and his father's mother, were Longridges. It was his mother's father, Thomas Longridge, who had the greatest influence on his life.

Thomas Longridge had helped to build the industry fundamental to Britain's supremacy – ironmaking. He was born in 1751, the eldest of four sons. His great-grandfather, Michael Longridge, came to the North Country in the late seventeenth century, already wealthy enough to take the tenancy of five farms at Newburn-on-Tyne. Thomas's grandfather also was a farmer, but his father became a merchant. His mother was widowed when Thomas was only seven. She was left sufficiently well off to launch him as an ironmaster, a businessman skilled in the making and marketing of iron and iron products. Thomas married well, his wife being the daughter of a well-to-do shipowner on Wearside. She bore him four children, a boy and three girls.

Thomas Longridge became a partner in iron works at Sunderland and on Tyneside. He was involved with the important Hawks family, who had large foundries at Gateshead. When he was thirty-one he went into business with William Hawks, an ironmaster who had run the family business for nearly thirty years. The two bought the Bedlington Iron Works, a factory which was to become of great significance to both railways and the Gooches.

The village of Bedlington was some 12 miles north of Newcastle. It stood above the River Blyth, 4 miles from its mouth. Just to the east the river flowed through Blyth Dene, a wooded gorge where iron ore outcropped. With timber to provide charcoal for the primitive smelting processes and water power to drive the machinery, conditions were ideal for the development of an ironworks. By 1757 there were warehouses, a slitting mill and workshops for about forty nailers and by 1782, when Hawks and Longridge took over, 500 tons a year of iron rods and hoops were being turned out. The new owners were able to expand the business further, building rolling mills and a heavy forge.

1

Trade grew rapidly during the long wars with France.

In 1798 the bonds between the Hawks and the Longridges were strengthened when Thomas Longridge's eldest daughter married one of William's sons. Two years later a further business link developed, the impetus this time coming from Longridge.

Six years previously John Roebuck, the son of the founder of the famous Carron Ironworks in Scotland, had started a similar concern, the Devon Ironworks at Tillicoultry, east of Stirling. Roebuck soon found himself in difficulties and left the firm. Without him it did not prosper and so the remaining partners put it up for auction, but there were no bidders. Then a private purchaser appeared – Thomas Longridge. He offered them £5,000, £2,000 down and the rest at £250 a quarter. They accepted and Longridge, with William Hawks as one of his partners, took over.

Longridge had achieved a brilliant coup. Within a decade or so the Devon became the most lucrative of the Scottish ironworks, but he did not live to enjoy the success. In 1803, only three years after his masterly stroke, he died. Unfortunately he left no will. He had been a widower for some years and his uncharacteristic omission left at least one of his daughters in sore straits.

The bulk of Longridge's fortune was in his 'real estate', his freehold property and partnerships. The law was that this all passed to his heir-at-law, his eldest son, George Henry Longridge. His 'personal estate', the ready cash, linen, furniture and so on, went to his next of kin, his three daughters and George Henry. This was valued at £800, so that the girls were left with only £200 each. For the eldest, who had married the rich Hawks, this was no doubt a disappointment. For the youngest, Anna, who was single and just twenty, it was a disaster. She was dependant for a respectable income and marriage settlement on the charity of her brother, and words written in later years suggest that he was not generous to her.

How Anna spent the next two years is not known, but at some time she took the long coach ride south to stay with her father's cousin, Barbara, and her husband, who lived at 14 Queen Street, Kensington,

a mile or so beyond the outskirts of London.

Barbara's father was Michael Longridge, Thomas's uncle. He had married Mary Dorman, the daughter of a Newcastle doctor. The Longridges were proud of this match, as Mary could trace her ancestry back to Sir John Calverley, of Tudor times. Michael, however, was less successful in business than in wedlock. He became a brewer, but after only a few years went bankrupt. Fortunately his creditors were merciful and he was able to take a job as the book-keeper at a glassworks at Bishop Wearmouth. There was no money to launch his children into exceptional marriages or careers. His son left home at fourteen to be apprenticed to a sea captain. Barbara, his younger daughter, married a man who was not in a position to expect a wealthy wife – John Gooch. John, 'a truly upright and honest man', was in trade. He and Barbara had their trials, as four of their eight children died as infants, but by the time of Trafalgar, when Anna Longridge was visiting them, they were comfortably established in one of Kensington's Georgian terraces. Their son John, who was only four months older than Anna, and their teenage children, Matt and Barbara, enlivened the house.

The ripening of her friendship with young John Gooch soon solved Anna Longridge's problems. On 23 December 1805, at St. George's, Hanover Square, they became man and wife. Their first home was with John's parents.

Anna had married into a Suffolk family. Her father-in-law had been born in 1746 at Ringsfield, near Beccles. The parish registers prior to 1751 were destroyed, so that his antecedents can only be guessed at. Well-to-do Gooches were farming in the neighbourhood in the early seventeenth century and in the mid-eighteenth there were several families of the name in Beccles. On 2 December 1751, in the first pages of the surviving registers, the christening of Mary, the daughter of a husbandman called Daniel Gooch, was recorded. As this is the only entry for a Gooch for a decade it seems probable that he was his namesake's great-grandfather.

The first of John and Anna's children – eventually there were ten – arrived in 1807.

The couple were prospering, for soon afterwards they took the house next door. They then began unexplained wanderings, moving elsewhere in London for a few years and to Thorpe, in Surrey. After only a short time they went to Kidwelly, in South Wales. Finally, in late 1815 or early 1816, they made their way to the North of England.

After the deaths of Thomas Longridge and William Hawks, Bedlington Iron Works had passed into the hands of a London company, Gordon and Biddulph. Another branch of the Longridges became involved and soon Michael Longridge, who was Anna Gooch's cousin, became the managing partner. His second-cousin, John Gooch, had fallen on bad times in the severe slump which followed Waterloo. Michael Longridge's patronage gave him the post of book-keeper at the works and he settled at Bedlington 'happy in the enjoyment of an amiable and affectionate wife with whom I have possessed uninterrupted happiness, as regards our mutual affection'. Within less than a year their first five children, Barbara, Tom, Anna, John Viret and Jane, were joined by a sixth. On 24 August 1816, at about three in the morning, during an awful thunderstorm, Daniel Gooch drew his first breath.

CHAPTER

2

Gooch's first home was a cottage on the south side of Bedlington main street. The village, he said, was 'tolerably clean and large . . . with half a dozen good houses in it'. At its centre was the market cross, nearly opposite St. Cuthbert's church. Eastwards the narrow roadway slanted downhill to the river. To the west, where the Gooches lived, it widened to a broad avenue. The population was increasing steadily, reaching 1,900 by the end of the decade. The principal men of the ironworks, Michael Longridge and his works manager, John Birkinshaw, lived by the smoky factory, half a mile from the cross.

When he arrived John Gooch was far from well off. He could only afford to send Tom, his eldest boy, to the subsidised school which Michael Longridge had set up. Soon, however, his fortunes improved and Tom was sent to the best school in the neighbourhood, Mr Thompson's, at Crow Hall, two miles south of Bedlington.

Just before Daniel was two, Mary Ann, the seventh of the Gooch children, was born. John was continuing to prosper, as a

House occupied by the Gooches from about 1819 until 1831

4

Loading Birkinshaw's patent rails into a keel at Bedlington Iron Works in the 1820's

year or so later he took a much bigger house on the other side of the street. Daniel, who was only three, helped with the removal, struggling across with part of his cot.

The new house, larger and far grander than its neighbours, had nine boldly proportioned windows set about its broad front door, a fitting home for a man of standing in the little community. The last three Gooch children were born there, George Henry in 1820, Frances in 1823 and William Frederick in 1825. It still stands, now the King's Arms, a cheerful pub.

By the time that Daniel was four he was so mischievous that his mother packed him off to school. His teachers were the two young daughters of Gilbert Robson, gent, whose schoolroom was in a house by the cross. He stayed with them for three or four happy years and then followed his brothers to the larger and more daunting school on the other side of the Blyth.

In summer he walked through the fields, crossing the river by stepping stones, or rode, sharing a pony with his best friend, George Marshall. They had a two mile journey, easy enough for sturdy boys, but in the winter, when the waters raced high, they had to make a long detour westwards

to Hartford Bridge, a formidable seven-mile round trip. His education was no doubt similar to Tom's, who said that 'Latin or Greek were not taught me – but I made good progress in arithmetic and geometry, with a commencement in algebra'. Local tradition had it that he showed such marked mathematical ability that his friends were not surprised that within ten years of leaving the village he had achieved fame as an engineer.

Once school was over Daniel was free to do as he chose. So that he did not waste a minute of his Saturdays he often ate his breakfast the night before and tore out of the house long before anyone else was awake. On Sundays, however, church and catechism were the rule.

A familiar figure of Gooch's childhood was a bluff Northumbrian who used to take him onto his knee and tell him about coal mines and steam engines. This was George Stephenson, who knew John Gooch well. Stephenson's visits to Bedlington went back to 1814, when he had built his first locomotive. His boiler plates, wheels and axles had been forged at the ironworks. As the years passed his rising fame made him a regular customer. In 1820 he joined Thomas Mason as his partner in the Glebe

Colliery at Willow Bridge, a mile north of the village. Mason struck a bargain with Michael Longridge, offering cheap coal if he would build a wagonway from the Glebe to the ironworks, giving him access to the river.

Longridge had been impressed by a report describing experiments with wrought iron rails on tramroads instead of the customary cast iron. Scenting a new market he decided to try some on the line to the Glebe. His works manager, John Birkinshaw, succeeded in rolling rails with a tee shaped cross-section, which used the more expensive material economically whilst giving great strength. Birkinshaw patented his method, which was to prove of fundamental importance, as it applied steam power to the production of rails, enabling them to be mass produced when the tendrils of the railway system began to shoot out.

After some initial production difficulties the rails became a great success. On 28 June 1821 George Stephenson wrote that they were so much liked in the district that in a short time they would do away with cast iron railways altogether. Bedlington Iron Works were on to a winner.

Stephenson was then engaged on the survey of the Stockton and Darlington Railway. He and William Losh, of Losh, Wilson and Bell, the Newcastle ironfounders, had patented an improved form of cast iron rail in 1816. Stephenson saw Birkinshaw's invention as greatly superior to his own and so recommended the new rails for his splendid project. Losh was furious and they parted, which left Stephenson in an awkward predicament. The Stockton and Darlington Act empowered the company to use locomotives, the first time such a clause had been included in a railway Bill. Stephenson was determined that they would be the principal motive power on his line, but who would build them? Losh, Wilson and Bell were a closed chapter. Bedlington Iron Works had neither the expertise nor the facilities. Fenton, Murray and Wood of Leeds, who had previously built engines for the North-East, were no longer interested.

George Stephenson solved his problem with characteristic determination. On 23 June 1823 he went into partnership with his son Robert, Michael Longridge and two other businessmen as engine builders at Newcastle. Their firm, Robert Stephenson and Company, was the world's first locomotive business. Robert, though still not twenty, was made the managing partner.

Three months later Tom Gooch, who had just left school, went to Newcastle with his father to dine with George Stephenson. Afterwards the three signed indentures, binding Tom to Stephenson as a pupil for six years. He was launched into a career under a man of great note on Tyneside, though as yet little known elsewhere.

On Saturday 9 October 1824, when Daniel was barely eight, he was put onto the carrier's cart to go on his own to Newcastle to spend the weekend with his brother. On the Sunday morning they went to All Saints' Church. They listened to a band in the afternoon and attended Brunswick Chapel in the evening; 'Daniel', wrote Tom, 'was much amused.' As he grew older, however, his pastimes were less innocent and he and his friends were often in trouble.

George Marshall, his greatest companion, lived at a farmhouse just along the main street from the Gooches. The old ladies of the village often had to suffer their pranks. On winter evenings they would fill a cow's horn with old tar rope, put in a hot cinder and blow the acrid smoke through the key-holes into their cottages. Their escapades sometimes went too far. On one occasion they found some girls in the Marshalls' fields and tried to drive them out, but they only laughed. 'I had at the time a small frog in my hand,' said Gooch. 'As one of them opened her mouth in laughing rather wide, I slipped the frog into it.' She screamed and ran home, and a great hue and cry followed: 'There was a general inquiry into it the next day and we were threatened with a visit to Morpeth jail. I am not sure to this day whether she did or did not actually swallow the frog.'

Much more serious was what Daniel called "a game at hanging", which he and three of his friends tried. They used a ladder leaning against the Marshalls' hay rick as the gibbet, proposing to take turns as the victim. Gooch, significantly, was to be the last. When they strung up the first they

Loading wicker corves of coal underground

'thought it good fun to see him kick his legs about', but ran off when they heard the farm bailiff coming. He found the boy, black in the face and unconscious, and fortunately was able to revive him. 'We got into considerable hot water about this,' Gooch said.

John Gooch grew even more prosperous. On 12 March 1825 Tom noted that he had been at 'a retail iron warehouse which my father tried to carry on for a time on his own account in **connection** with the Bedlington Iron Works'. He made business trips, some of quite long duration, to places as far away as Liverpool, London and Dundee and was sufficiently well off to send his daughter Anna to a boarding school at Houghton-le-Spring. Daniel also benefitted, as his father gave him a lathe and a box of tools, a most expensive present. He took lessons in turning and became highly skilled, which triggered an interest in mechanics. He read books and carried out simple experiments, gaining a fair knowledge of natural philosophy and learning how steam engines worked.

When Gooch was twelve or so he began to spend many of his Saturdays underground at the Glebe, driving the pony trams. It was a fairly small pit which had cost Mason and Stephenson £1,400. Work started with the hewers, who lay naked on their sides, cutting the coal and loading it into wicker corves. These were dragged to the roadway by the older youths, who hoisted them by crane onto four-wheeled trams which were then drawn by the ponies along rough railways to the shaft bottom. We can imagine Daniel riding with a candle stuck in his capband, hailing the tiny trapper boys who crouched in the darkness to open the ventilation doors. 'In looking back at all the risks I ran at this pit,' he wrote, 'it is a wonder to me that I never met with an accident, but it was not in my nature at that time to have any fear, and I could never rest an hour at home.'

He also took a keen interest in the ironworks, where there were more dangers. Once he stumbled through an open trap-door in the engine house, falling into the hot-well where the condensate collected. As he gasped and shouted in the steaming water he was taken even nearer to drowning by the splashing at each stroke of the air pump.

Life in the village occasionally brought excitement. John Gooch was a churchwarden, one of the small group who kept the roads in repair, administered the poor law and maintained order. There was no police force, the only officer of the law being the parish constable, an elected and unpaid official. At Bedlington it was Robert Mitchell, the workhouse governor, who carried out this unpopular task. He and John Gooch, sometimes with Daniel in attendance, patrolled the lodging houses on the lookout for tramps. Authority, however, was tenuous.

The Gooches lived opposite an inn which was frequented by smugglers who rode south from Scotland on fast horses with kegs of illicit whisky slung from their saddles. If there was trouble the Bedlington folk took their side. One night a gang was cornered by the excisemen, who tried to drag them from their horses. Whilst the fight was going on the kegs stood by the roadside. Daniel and some of the other villagers stove them in, letting the evidence run to waste, much to the disgust of the customs officers.

After his twelfth birthday there was what he called 'a winter of great dread'. The Burke and Hare trial had taken place at Edinburgh and throughout the land people were afraid that murderers were abroad seeking dissection specimens. To foil the "resurrection men" a watch was kept on Bedlington churchyard after each burial. Burke was hanged on 28 January 1829, but Hare, who had turned King's evidence, was set free. Soon afterwards an evil-looking tramp arrived and the rumour spread that this was Hare. The whole village turned out to lynch him, but he was fleet of foot and escaped in the dark, followed by a hail of stones.

By the autumn of 1830 Gooch was a tall, slim youth ready to leave school. The careers of his two elder brothers were devel-oping well. Tom Gooch's apprenticeship had finished. He had worked as George Stephenson's only draughtsman and secretary and then as one of his resident engineers during the building of the Liverpool and Manchester Railway.

After such experience under a man whose name was on everyone's lips his future was assured. Daniel's second brother, John, had been a pupil under Joseph Locke for the last three years. Locke had started as a junior engineer with George Stephenson when Tom Gooch was working at Newcastle and the two had become friends. He was about to emerge as a brilliant railway engineer in his own right and young John was certain to be swept into a splendid career in his wake. Surely Daniel also would be apprenticed to one of Stephenson's rising young men, perhaps even to Robert himself? Astonishingly, however, his career began in a remote, grim and less advanced environment — a South Wales ironworks.

This came about because John Gooch fell on bad times. Once again there was a severe slump which hit the iron trade hard. Two years later he wrote that 'the hand which sent chastisement always did it in mercy,' and that he and Anna, 'under the temporal difficulties which have been our lot have . . . ever been able to bear . . . the trials with which we have been assailed,' but exactly what had gone wrong is not known. He parted from Longridge and moved to become the book-keeper at Tredegar Iron Works, twenty miles inland from Newport. The Monmouthshire works had always weathered storms well and Samuel Homfray, the managing partner at Tredegar, was especially successful. Daniel was to start his training there.

CHAPTER

3

February 1831, the month of the removal, began with a severe storm and deep snowfalls. John Gooch was at Manchester where he collected young John, who was going home to help. They travelled to Bedlington and then, after a few hectic days, all was ready for the sad leavetaking. A special cart, 'a kind of omnibus, with curtains round', had been built for the journey, a flat wagon with seats bolted down crosswise at the front. The eleven Gooches took their places and the three hundred mile trek began. At length they reached the Midlands, crossed the hills to Abergavenny and took the high road over the Heads of the Valleys to Tredegar. 'I do not know how many days it took us,' wrote Gooch, 'but I well remember it, and the beautiful view as we crossed the Malvern Hills.' They must have marvelled at their luck, as the bad weather had blown itself out, and Gooch thoroughly enjoyed the trip.

Tredegar was one of a crescent of iron works which stretched across Glamorgan and Monmouthshire. Where the long river valleys merged into the high hillsides iron ore, coal and limestone outcropped and a vast industry had developed. At the beginning of the century Samuel Homfray's father, who was a partner in the great Penydarren works at Merthyr Tydfil, became involved in the building of a new factory at Tredegar. It grew rapidly, owing its success to the Sirhowy Tramroad, a public railway which Homfray and his associates laid to Newport, 23 miles away. Homfray took over as the managing partner in 1818, when he was 23, and by the time of the Gooches' arrival he was smelting more iron than Penydarren.

Daniel Gooch started in the huge factory as soon as they had settled into their new home. 'A large works of this kind is by far the best school for a young engineer,' he wrote. 'He gets so general a knowledge of what he needs in after life.' There had been an adventurous engineering tradition in the area since the turn of the century. Homfray's father had become a partner in Richard Trevithick's patent for the high pressure steam engine. In 1804 he and his artisans, including a man called Thomas Ellis, built one of the first of the new engines. Then he made a famous bet, wagering 500 guineas that ten tons of iron would be hauled by steam power along a tramroad from Penydarren to Abercynon Wharf. Trevithick built the world's first railway locomotive for the purpose and Homfray won. No doubt young Samuel, then a nine year old, watched the huge Cornishman at work.

Trevithick's promising development was dropped and it was a quarter of a century before Wales saw another steam locomotive. Once again a Homfray was involved. Late in 1828 Samuel sent Thomas Ellis and his mineral agent to the North-East to see Stephenson's engines at work. They were given the red carpet treatment, being looked after by Robert Stephenson himself. Their report was favourable and Homfray bought two engines, one for Penydarren and the other for Tredegar.

Before he parted from Robert Stephenson, Ellis was given a letter of introduction to one of the engineers on the Liverpool and Manchester Railway – Tom Gooch. He was asked to show them the tunnel and the other works at his end of the line, and

Tredegar Iron Works, 1844

perhaps this was the seed from which John Gooch's move to Monmouthshire grew.

Ellis' son, Thomas Ellis Junior, the works engineer at Tredegar, was present on 15 September 1830 when the Liverpool and Manchester Railway was opened. Tom Gooch played an important part in the ceremonies and it would be surprising if Ellis did not seek him out. John Gooch was also there. Only a few months later he left

Pouring pig iron from a blast furnace, 1844

Bedlington and, interestingly enough, his predecessor at Tredegar was a man called Ellis. The seed had perhaps flowered.

Tom Gooch soon paid his first visit to the family's new home. On Saturday 19 March he was at Tredegar all day: 'Went through the works. Walked to Ebor Vale with Mama and the sisterhood and returned to Sirhowy House.' His words are the only indication of where the Gooches lived at Tredegar. The house stood at the foot of the bleak hillside at the north end of the township, fronting onto the road to Ebbw Vale and Abergavenny. It was long and two storied with thick stone walls and heavy chimneys, its size reflecting the importance of the book-keeper in the community. It still exists, the southern half now the Railway Hotel.

A quarter of a mile down the riverside was the ironworks, with the workmen's dwellings clustered around. 'Their houses are ranged round the works in rows, sometimes two to five deep, sometimes three stories high', a general description of the valley towns said. 'The surface of the soil is frequently blackened with coal, or

covered with high mounds of refuse . . . .
The road between the rows is so imperfectly
made as to be often . . . ankle deep in black
mud. Flat pavement is rarely seen . . .
Volumes of smoke from the furnaces, the
rolling mills, and the coke hearths are
driven past . . . Gardens are few, and
almost entirely neglected . . . The house of
the master or resident director stands
conspicuous amidst a small group of stun-
ted and blackened trees.'

Gooch began work in the foundry under
the foreman moulder, Ben Williams. His
first job was core-making, in which he
learned how to handle sand, the moulders'
basic material. He started at 6 a.m., stopped for breakfast at nine and had an hour for
mid-day dinner. Fourteen weeks went by
before he received his first pay, 'this
important question' taking some time to
settle: 'The amount per week being 9s., I
was indeed a proud boy as I walked away
from the pay table with upwards of £6 in
my hand. I did not think there was so rich a
person in the whole world.'

Gooch's pay was considerably higher
than apprentices earned. Michael Longridge's lads had 4s. a week at fourteen, increasing by a shilling each year. Even the
young labourers at Tredegar earned only 5s.
to 6s. 6d. Nowhere does Gooch say that he
was indentured to Homfray but he notes
that the mineral agents were very kind to
him: 'Altho' only a boy' – that is, though
not an apprentice, – 'they always gladly
told me anything I wished to know.' He
was a privileged worker, with no entitlement to be taught, rather than a pupil, it
would seem. Perhaps John Gooch could not
afford a premium.

After the first few months Gooch moved
on to the more responsible job of moulding
tram wheels. The foundry was close to the
huge blast furnaces. Much of the work was
done by lads on low wages. Each, according
to a description of a Scottish factory, had
ground charcoal and sand on the floor
beside him and a few simple tools. 'A space
is allotted . . . where he places his moulds
when made . . . The smaller boys doing the
lighter articles are at one end of the
building, and they rise in size and strength
progressively. At the time of casting, two
boys . . . convey the molten metal in a pot

Casting pipes in a foundry, 1844

. . . A third boy, or a man on purpose,
ladles out the metal . . . and pours it into
the moulds . . . When sufficiently cool the
. . . castings are then dressed with
sandstone and water to take off the rough
parts.'

Gooch's target was nine moulds before
breakfast and nine afterwards. The work
was hard, as the pattern alone weighed
52 lb. He had to set a heavy moulding-box
around it and shovel in sand, ramming it to
firmness. Then the pattern was rapped to
loosen it and drawn out, leaving the shape
of the casting behind. Whilst he was at
home having breakfast the metal was
poured into his work. Then he returned to
make the second set, generally finishing at
between four and five o'clock. Nine shillings a week and eighteen moulds a day,
Monday to Saturday, was a penny a casting,
so Samuel Homfray was getting a bargain.

Homfray was highly thought of at
Tredegar. 'His efficiency as a manager was
unquestionable,' the local historian said.
'His endeavour to promote the success and
prosperity of the town and its inhabitants in
every sense was proverbial. Being of a hot
temperament his actions often-times were
eccentric, but in an instant the storm was
over, and those who had been the victims of
a most violent reproach were more warmly
beloved than before.' He was a benevolent
despot. His workers were paid at least
partly in truck tokens, exchangeable only at
the company's shop. Piecework was

competed for on the contract system, the men bidding against one another for their livelihood. As employer, magistrate and master of his own mint Homfray's power was virtually absolute, but he had earned the loyalty of his workpeople, as events were soon to show.

In 1801 the population of Bedwellty Parish, of which Tredegar formed the major part, had only been 619, but by 1831 there were almost eleven thousand inhabitants.

Loading ore into a blast furnace, 1844

'The workmen's houses are generally good, but there are exceptions', it was said. 'Some places are very bad, I may say filthy . . . They have also pig sties and privies in some few cases, but they are very badly off in this respect. On holidays such as Christmas Day and Good Friday, their pastimes are very various, but the men spend their time generally in drunkenness.' Sanitation was

Puddling furnace and hammer, 1844

probably little better than Merthyr Tydfil's, over the hill. 'Scores, I dare say hundreds, of houses', it was reported, 'have no such convenience as a "necessary". I am assured also by people whose houses look into open spaces or fields . . . that persons of every age and sex are constantly seen exposing themselves. It is difficult to estimate how brutalising an effect such circumstances produce.' Other conditions at Tredegar were primitive. Water came from four springs, the better-off buying theirs at a ha'penny a pitcherful from donkey carts. All lighting was by candles and oil lamps. For those who could read, and the still fewer who could write, there was a daily postal service. There was also a coach down the turnpike road to Newport, but not many could afford to use it.

Whilst Gooch was working in the foundry the atrocious living conditions provoked an upheaval in which he found himself amongst the ranks of the oppressed. In 1831 Britain came close to revolution. Parliamentary Reform was the cry, but there were also the deeper social issues, which were inflamed by the depression in trade. In South Wales the men were incited by the ironmasters, who wanted seats in Parliament to balance the power of the landowners. They managed to persuade their workers that reform was the answer to all their problems. There were minor riots in a rising election fever.

On 30 May 1831, soon after the election, there was a mass meeting outside Merthyr Tydfil. Red flags and banners proclaiming reform were waved, but soon the mood of the men swung to their own troubles – the misuse of Poor Law funds, the brutality of parish officials, and truck. They decided to strike. Over the next few days large bands of men pillaged company stores and wrecked the court of Merthyr where records of their debts were kept. The magistrates sent to Brecon for the 93rd. Highlanders.

On Friday 3 June men from Ebbw Vale and Nant-y-glo paraded through Tredegar. Samuel Homfray's men refused to join them. At Merthyr a day of open warfare followed. The magistrates marched at the head of the troops to the Castle Inn for a meeting with the High Sheriff. The strikers, armed with clubs and pickaxes, fought with the soldiers. The Highlanders fired on them from the windows of the inn, killing at least fifteen and wounding about sixty others.

The next day the strikers laid ambushes against the troops of cavalry who were arriving as reinforcements. One detachment was forced to retreat and another surrendered, but the soldiers steadily increased in number so the men retired to gather their own strength.

Early on the Monday morning a large force of Ebbw Vale and Nant-y-glo men came pouring down the hill past Sirhowy House and into Tredegar, going into the houses to force all the men they could find to accompany them. Gooch, he said, 'was amongst the unwilling ones, and with the others was placed in front, the men behind having sticks with spikes in the end to poke us on. There were 8 or 10,000 altogether. When we got to Rhymney we saw a lot of soldiers, drawn up on Dowlais Hill. A considerable amount of bluster took place as we ascended the hill, we in front not liking the look of things at all. When we reached the soldiers some of the magistrates came forward to advise the men to disperse and return home. This could not be listened to . . . The magistrates then retired and the soldiers were ordered to present arms, no pleasant sound to us in front, as one word of command more and who could say how many of us would roll in the dust?'

'A panic certainly took possession of us in the front and was quickly communicated to those behind, and a general scramble took place, so that in a very few minutes the word "Fire" would have done us no harm. We Tredegar people were right glad to get back, and we had some revenge on our oppressors as they, in parties of two or three, passed through Tredegar on their way home.'

Gooch's attendance had hardly been as unwilling as he pretended. His group had marched behind a bayonet with a small flag tied to it, a trophy from Friday's battle, and no doubt he, and many others, were incensed at Friday's massacre. 'I have often asked myself whether I was really frightened at the position I was in, but I think not,' he wrote. 'I seemed to enter into the spirit of the march and the excitement of

the shouting and the noise, and I had no real occasion to get into the mess. Had I stayed at home I would not have done so, as they only went into the workmen's houses.'

After Monday's rout there was no further rioting. Gooch returned to his labours in the foundry, where the atmosphere of the furnace house and the hard work began to affect his health. In the hope that sea air would do him good he was sent to Bristol and took a ship to Liverpool. He then went to Warrington to spend a few days with his brother John before sailing home again.

On his return he moved to the carpenters shop, a cleaner and quieter place than the foundry where all kinds of woodwork were done, from patternmaking to the building of large timber roofs. The foreman was Thomas Ellis. 'Old Ellis, as we used to call him,' wrote Gooch, 'was somewhat of a character, but he was always a kind friend to me and gave me any information he could'. He was a Shropshire man, just coming up to his fiftieth birthday. He recorded that 'Mr Daniel Gouch began to work with Thomas Ellis Senior Feb 6th 1832'.

Many of the castings produced at Tredegar were complex and the craftsmen often had to work out a design before they could make the pattern. Gooch was allowed to browse through Ellis's notebooks, which included his rough schemes for large water wheels, rolling mill gears, cast iron bridges, locomotive safety valves, parts for steam engines and so on. His usual workmate was Jonathon Miles, who went to great pains to help him. In his two years in the shop he had many adventures, some of which came close to costing him his life.

A regular job was the repairing of the wooden flap-valves of the three blowers which supplied air to the blast furnaces. The carpenters had to crawl into the cylinders, the work being done on a Saturday, when an engine could be stopped. Gooch enjoyed the task and usually took part. On one occasion the engineer who was responsible for the blowers nearly killed him: 'We were in the bottom of the cylinder and had just finished work. One of the men had gone out and we were just about to follow when we were much astonished to see the engine start.' Fortunately it was on the up stroke, or they would have been crushed. As it was they were able to crouch in the valve boxes before the piston descended, coming to within an inch or so of their heads. The man who had just left realised what was happening and shouted to the engineer, who was able to stop the engine before it made another stroke.

His second escape came after dangerous horseplay. The three blowers discharged into a large vessel, sealed by powdered lime, which evened-out the air flow to the furnaces. One day Gooch and his friend Isaac Jenkins were inside a blower whilst the other two were running. The furnaceman opened a valve a little, allowing air and lime dust to rush back into their cylinder, choking them and closing the flap-valves, preventing their escape. Luckily there was a valve open elsewhere and the white powder swirled into the engine house, warning the engineer that something was amiss. He closed the valve and then returned to find the two youngsters nearly suffocated: 'A very little more and it would have been all over with us'.

The third fright came when Gooch was helping with the erection of a roof over the rolling mill. One morning, shortly after he had clambered down for breakfast, the flywheel broke and flew through the roof. Half an hour later and he would have gone with it.

Gooch was given the opportunity to learn all that he could about the great works. He studied the refining processes in which pig iron from the blast furnaces was turned into tough, wrought iron by the puddlers. Once in a while he went underground with the mineral agents to see how coal and iron ore were mined. He kept careful notes of all that he saw.

Both the ironworks and the town were dominated by the five great blast furnaces. Tredegar was illuminated at night by the lurid glow of their flames. Only the slender chimney of the engine house rose higher, its plume way above the billowing, sulphurous smoke which rose from the very ground. The coke which was used in enormous quantities was made in large clamps, where coal was heaped up, covered with earth and ashes and ignited. As at Bedlington there

were terrible dangers. Records of a few years later show that no less than thirteen of the young people working for Homfray had been crippled or maimed. Many of the boys and girls, including eight year olds, were on an 84 hr week. Once a fortnight they had from 6 a.m. on Sunday until 6 a.m. on Monday to themselves, but in return they had to work a twenty-four hour shift the following weekend.

As part of Tredegar's upper class Gooch kept aloof from his workmates and had few companions of his own age. Alfred Homfray, Samuel's nephew, and another young man, who were pupils of Jackson, the surgeon, taught him how to make "plaisters" and draw teeth. He used to go with them on visits to patients and shooting expeditions on the mountainside. Jackson in later years complacently told a Parliamentary Commission that the physical condition of the children and young persons of the district was generally good and not in any degree affected by their employment. One of his lay acquaintances, however, thought that not many of them lived to be old men.

Jackson and his sister – a very pretty girl, according to Gooch – were family friends. The Gooches also grew to know the Homfray's well, often dining at Bedwellty House, a graceful, two-storied building a little way up the hillside from the works. Daniel's lathe was put to good service by Mrs Homfray and her sister. He enjoyed the little tasks which they gave him, as they were a rest from the hard work of the shop. Samuel Homfray's mother-in-law, Mrs. Staples, who was a most formidable person, also kept him busy. He had to make her a back-scratcher, a device new to him: 'This I learned was employed to do a little bit of scratching where her own hand could not reach. She was a very fat woman, and I daresay could not reach a great deal of her body.'

Gooch was surprised to find that the final care for Jackson's patients lay with Thomas Ellis, as he was the undertaker for Tredegar Ironworks. He kept a shop in which he sold carpenters' tools and trimmings for coffins: 'These coffins were made in our shop by overtime. Jonathon Miles was the chief man interested in them, and as we got paid extra for the work, I was glad to be allowed to assist'. Many were elaborately carved and it is an indication of Gooch's skill that he was allowed to help. Their busiest time was during Britain's first cholera epidemic, in which 18,000 died. Tredegar was ripe for the disease, which is spread by bad sanitation, contaminated water and poor hygiene. It made its appearance in October 1832 and continued until the following March. A special cemetery was opened for the victims, whose bodies were not allowed into church. Prayer meetings were held at the works, the whole populace being in a state of terror.

Some forty people lost their lives at Tredegar. Gooch's grim story was that one of his shop-mates was the first: 'He and I had been making a coffin, and I remember the side boards had been cut too short and were laid aside. Two nights afterwards I used the boards for his own coffin. Poor fellow, he little thought he was preparing part of his own coffin.'

In mid-1833, when Gooch was almost seventeen, his father's health began to fail. In the July, when the better-off at the ironworks took a holiday, he went to London for medical advice. On the way back he made the long detour to Worcester to spend Race Week with his sister and brother-in-law, the Robinsons. In the meantime Daniel again made a sea voyage to Liverpool. There he met Tom Gooch, who had come up from Birmingham. The brothers stayed at Windsor, on the outskirts of the town, at the home of Ruthanna Scaife, who was to become Daniel's sister-in-law – she and Tom had been engaged for three months.

On 26 July Tom took Daniel to the Zoological Gardens and then treated him to dinner before seeing him to his ship for the sail home. A few days later he returned to his office at Birmingham, where he found a letter to say that his father had been taken seriously ill. He hurried to Worcester but by the time he arrived John had rallied. Tom was able to spend a day at the races and John Gooch managed to walk to a place where he could see the course. The next day young John Gooch also arrived to see his father, but he was well enough for the two young men to feel able to go to Malvern and the races before leaving together for Birmingham.

The *St. David*, one of the Tredegar locomotives. The figure in the foreground is Thomas Ellis, Junior

Anna Gooch travelled to Worcester to be with her husband, finding him weak but cheerful. On 27 August he sat up until his usual time, then went to bed and fell asleep, dying peacefully a few hours afterwards. As soon as the news reached Tredegar, Daniel hurried over the hills for the funeral but he was too late. His father had already been buried, 'for ever removed', Tom wrote, 'from a world in which there is reason to believe he had more than his share of trouble and anxiety, all of which were born by him with the greatest courage and firmness'.

After a few days Anna and her sons returned to Tredegar. On the next two evenings they dined with Samuel Homfray, who was kindness itself, but Sirhowy House belonged to the company and would be wanted for John Gooch's successor, so that soon they would have to move. Daniel no doubt could have stayed on in lodgings but there were other and better ideas.

Thomas Ellis was proud that Gooch had worked under him. An entry in his notebook, carefully witnessed by both Jonathon Miles and Isaac Jenkins, records that 'Mr Daniel Gouch . . . laft January Pay 1834'. Anna and eight of her children took the high road to Abergavenny in the same wagon as they had used for the journey from Bedlington three years before. They travelled to Coventry, close to where Robert Stephenson's immense new project,

the London to Birmingham Railway, was to pass. Work had just begun and the resident engineer on the northernmost stretch, from Kilsby Tunnel to Birmingham, was Tom Gooch. His headquarters were at Coventry, so no doubt Anna was to keep house for him.

Gooch looked back on his time at Tredegar as 'by far the most important years of my life', a characteristic exaggeration, but he had gained down-to-earth experience and learned to stand on his own feet. He left with a heavy heart, sorry to lose all his friends, but especially sad over one in particular.

On his last night an un-named but very dear friend gave him a bible and prayer book 'which I have deeply valued and ever will do as long as life lasts, telling me ever to seek in it comfort and support in all my trials through life. I have never forgotten those kind words, and I pray God they may not have been used in vain'. There was, he wrote elsewhere, a family with two young ladies whom he used to visit at Tredegar: 'They are gone. The youngest rests in peace in a pretty little churchyard called Llanelwedd, close to Builth in South Wales, where a stone marks the spot'. It was no doubt the younger sister whose gift moved him so. Perhaps she was the reason why the formidable Mrs Stephens had sharpened her interest in him, which, he said, 'shortly before I left . . . was much more than I liked'.

CHAPTER
4

Barely a fortnight after the family had arrived at Coventry, Gooch left home. He went with great regret: 'I was going out into an unknown world amongst strangers, and I quite remember that I did not feel very happy'. His new job, doubtless arranged by Tom Gooch, was under Robert Stephenson at the Vulcan Foundry near Newton, five miles north of Warrington. It was an excellent opportunity, as Stephenson and his partner, Charles Tayleur, were to concentrate on the building of railway locomotives. 'My dear mother gave me much good advice,' wrote Gooch. 'I remember well her telling me always to keep my thoughts fixed upon obtaining for myself a good position in life, never to be satisfied to stand still, and altho' I was going to the Vulcan as a boy and a pupil, to strive to one day become the manager,'

Gooch caught the coach to Lancashire on Friday 28 January 1834. He then took the train to Newton Junction, where the Liverpool and Manchester Railway met the short branch from Warrington. There he found Charles Tayleur, the managing partner, and gave him his letter of introduction with great awe. Tayleur put him at his ease and he was taken to his lodgings at The Moss, a farmhouse just along the road.

The Moss was the home of two elderly spinsters, "the Miss Houghtons". The railway passed through their fields and whilst it was being built the navvies became a great nuisance. The ladies complained to George Stephenson, who solved their problem by suggesting that some of his "lads" – his young engineers – should move in as boarders to keep an eye on things. Tom Gooch was one of the first.

The Houghtons found the company so pleasant that long after the line was finished their spare room was still occupied. Daniel's father had stayed with them whenever he was in the neighbourhood, so that his rather forlorn son was given an especially warm welcome. He was introduced to the two other boarders and taken upstairs to the big bedroom which they shared.

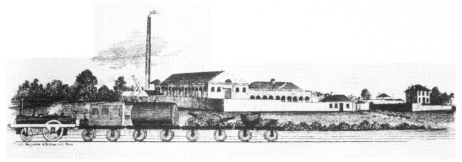

The Vulcan Foundry in the 1830's

The factory, which was a mile or so south of The Moss, was still not quite finished. Tayleur was one of the founders of the Grand Junction Railway Company, who were planning to link the North-West to Birmingham. This was sure to lead to an immense traffic and so he began to build a locomotive works. He interested Robert Stephenson in his project, to the consternation of some of his Newcastle partners, Robert managed to persuade them to let him go ahead, but he had to agree to devote equal attention to Newcastle and to share orders. The new business, Tayleur and Company, soon became known as the Vulcan Foundry, a name which survived until 1955.

Construction progressed until, in November 1832, a twenty horsepower steam engine was ordered from Forth Street to drive the machinery. During 1833 seven locomotives were built, most, if not all, being made from drawings sent down from Newcastle. By the beginning of 1834 Tayleur had about a hundred employees.

Gooch had to pick his way to the works along a muddy lane with ruts a foot deep. He carried his breakfast with him, a can of new milk and some bread and butter, returning to the Houghtons' for a hurried mid-day dinner. The factory was close to the Warrington and Newton line. The shops, which were served by turntables and spur lines, were brick built, with arched windows set high in their walls. Tallest was the turnery, where the machines were driven by clacking belts from shafts in the rafters.

Tayleur and Stephenson had planned well. The site has withstood a century and a half of continuous development and is still associated with traction, now being a part of the diesel engine division of the vast GEC organisation. Some of the original fabric still stands.

Gooch appears to have worked in the fitting shop, helping to put the locomotives together. This was an obvious gap in his experience and he tells us that he went out onto the line with the engines, a natural extension of erection work. He was again learning by doing a job, he and a man called Ireland taking piecework contracts together.

The Vulcan was no doubt similar to Stephensons' at Newcastle. Much reliance still had to be placed on hand work. One of Robert's pupils said that there 'good workmen could chip and file . . . almost as true as a machine . . . There were no small planing or shaping machines . . . There was only one slotting machine, the use of which was very restricted. Wheels were driven onto their axles by sledgehammers, wielded by strong arms alone . . . Only hand labour was available for the ordinary work of the smiths' shop and boiler yard, with the exception of the punching and shearing machines . . . There was not a single crane . . . There were shear legs in the yard, by which a boiler could be lifted onto a truck, and there were portable shear legs in the shop . . . At no little risk of life and limb, wonders were done'.

Gooch became friendly with the two locomotive foremen of the Liverpool and Manchester Railway, Melling and Fyfe, who allowed him to go out on the locomotives. He usually accompanied Jim Hurst, a devil-may-care engineman.

Seven locomotives, all of Stephensons' *Planet* class, had been built at Newton in the year before Gooch's arrival. In 1834, whilst he was in the shops, only two were turned out – *Titan* and *Orion*, both for the Liverpool and Manchester Railway. Tayleur was evidently having trouble.

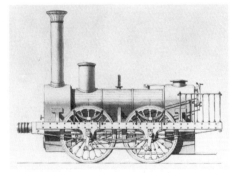

Titan and *Orion* of Stephensons' *Planet* Class, built in 1834

The *Planets* were four-wheeled engines which had developed from the *Rocket* and her immediate successors. The larger ones were proving too heavy for four wheels and so, on 7 October 1833, Robert Stephenson took out a patent for a new class with six wheels and other improvements. The prototype, *Patentee*, had been delivered to the Vulcan for trials on the Liverpool and Manchester a few months before Gooch's arrival. When she was first tried her wheels rubbed against the rails and switches. She was modified but there were still problems. In the April after Gooch's arrival the company offered Stephenson £1,000 for her, £50 less than he was asking, provided he strengthened the frames, fitted new cylinders and turned the flanges off the driving wheels. Gooch in all probability did some of the work, and he certainly learned a great deal that was to be of value by seeing her in the works.

He was happy during his brief period at Newton. His social life proved enjoyable. The Houghtons had three nieces who lived close by, a well balanced arrangement for the gentlemen of The Moss, who were frequently invited to their home for supper. 'Ellen, the youngest, died the year after I left,' wrote Gooch. 'She was my favourite, but all were as kind as sisters to me,' He also spent occasional Saturdays with the Stubs, the Warrington steelmakers, and with other local folk, some of whom were to become important associates a few years later.

George Stephenson was at his busiest and often had to weekend at the farm. He enjoyed a hand of whist with the Houghtons, one of the boarders being expected to make up the foursome. Gooch, who was never fond of cards, hated his turn. Stephenson used to sleep in the lads' room and on at least one occasion they treated him with less than due deference. They fastened a string to his bedclothes and drew them down once he had dropped off. After he had wakened and pulled them up again the dose was repeated. This went on until they were too tired to continue. The next morning their victim described the restless night he had spent.

Towards the middle of the summer, after he had been in the shops for about six months, Gooch fell ill. A doctor at Warrington treated him for a while but eventually he had to go home. Under his mother's care he soon improved and was able to spend his days on the drawing board at Tom Gooch's office or out on the line with his assistants. When he had fully recovered, however, he did not return to Newton. Instead he asked Robert Stephenson to allow him to go to James Stirling at the Dundee Foundry to learn about steam-boat engines. Work in the shops was regarded as too much for his strength and so he was to take a job as a draughtsman. It was his first professional post.

Early in January 1835 Gooch again took the coach north. He was eighteen, his wage was to be a pound a week, and he was independent: 'I made this keep me, and then ceased to be any burden upon my mother, a matter that gave me great pleasure, as she could ill afford to help me'. He went first to Bedlington to stay with George Marshall and then on to Edinburgh. After a few days in the grey city he took the ferry across the Forth, the coach through Fife to Newport and the little paddle steamer over the Tay.

Dundee, with its 50,000 inhabitants, was a place of great contrasts. "The view from the middle of the river", the local directory declared proudly, "is most magnificent and striking, the noble bulk of the town skirted on the south by its extensive docks and harbours . . . The towering Law, the romantic Hill of Balgay . . . combine to beautify the scene to the westward". There were eighty schools, two theatres and two newspapers, as well as the Watt Institute, with its library, museum and lecture hall. The main streets, however, were furrowed and the pavements uneven. The narrow alleys, walled by tall tenements and blocks of flats, were lit only by oil lamps. Cholera had carried off 512 during 1832 and more the next autumn.

Dundee was so remote that even the most important news took five days to arrive from London. It had to be both self-reliant and self-supporting. Its prosperity was based on the spinning and weaving of Baltic flax. During the thirties the population doubled as the industry was mechanised. The thriving businesses needed textile machinery, docks, ships and power plant.

Dundee Foundry, on the Cowgate, was one of the oldest of the Tayside engineering works. Iron founding had started there in 1790. They began building steam engines in 1820 and in 1829 made their first engines for a paddle-steamer. In 1834 they built their first locomotive and cast the huge gates for the Earl Gray Dock. The workmen and draughtsmen had to be versatile and Gooch was delighted at the range of experience which he obtained. He must have worked on one order which was exactly in line with his hopes. On 19 June 1835 the Dundee Advertiser reported an impudent demonstration: "A small but very powerful steamer, built by Messrs. Garland and Horsburgh, with engines by the Dundee Foundry Company, to be employed as a steam-tug on a Swedish river, has just been finished and put upon her trials. She appears very fast and was observed to come rapidly up with, pass, and cross in front of the river steam packets".

The foundry was run by James Stirling, the managing partner, and Leslie Meldrum, the works manager. Gooch found their workmen rather a change from Ireland and Jonathon Miles. 'The habits of the people,' he complained, 'were somewhat different from what I had been accustomed to, and I cannot say I liked them.' Another engineer who had worked there was equally critical. 'The character of mechanics . . . had greatly improved since the beginning of the century', he said. 'The opinion that it was necessary to acquire some scientific knowledge . . . was beginning to spread . . . Still, I must say that among the men at the Dundee Foundry there was a good deal of drinking after leaving the work . . . I reasoned quietly with some of them in the shops on the folly of the custom.'

Gooch lived well on his pound a week. He took lodgings with Mrs Stephens, a thrifty old Scotswoman. For 7s. a week he had a good sized room in her flat. He needed another 6s. or so for his food, leaving him with 7 or 8s. for clothes and pocket money – more than many a Dundee family had to live on.

In the crowded town the poorer families were crammed into tenements of one or two rooms clustered around a common stairway. Most of the better-off lived in flats, larger and more comfortable but similar in layout. Gooch found the way of life unpleasant after country quiet: 'The people who lived . . . above me were a continual nuisance . . . Their sleeping room and, I suppose, nursery, was over mine, and they must have had a very cross child as no sooner did I get to bed than it was found necessary above to rock a cradle . . . I stood it as long as I could but then became desperate'.

After standing on a chair and knocking on the ceiling with a poker, Gooch, he said, 'was at last driven to the use of the key bugle, an instrument I at that time pretended to play upon'. This roused the entire neighbourhood: 'A general explanation ensued and I got rid of the rocking, but it took a couple of months to get this grave question settled. My good old landlady took my part; after this there was peace between the flats'.

Gooch's social life was as enjoyable as at Newton. He made a life-long friend in Archibald Sturrock, a lad of his own age who was serving his time at the foundry. He also became a member of the Watt Institute and went regularly to the lectures, the only form of technical education which he ever had, apart from his books. The talks were of a high standard. He almost certainly attended the last of the session which, the local newspaper reported, "was upon that new and interesting branch of natural philosophy, electro-magnetism . . . From a magnet of great size and power was elicited the electric spark in the clearest and most palpable manner".

A good deal of Gooch's spare time was spent with an old friend from Bedlington, Tom Nicholson, who had become manager of the curious little Dundee and Newtyle Railway. He had married a local girl who was related to some of the best-known townsfolk. Gooch dined at their flat on most Sundays and often had supper with them during the week. He had an added reason for calling: 'A Miss Christy, who was a very pretty and nice girl, used often to stay with them', he wrote, leaving us to draw our own conclusions.

The Dundee and Newtyle was a frequent topic of conversation at Tom Nicholson's and there is some evidence that Gooch took more than a passing interest in it. It only had three locomotives. Two had been supplied by J. and C. Carmichael, the

Dundee engineers. The third, which was smaller but of similar layout, had been built by the Dundee Foundry in 1834. They were an extraordinary design, having vertical cylinders which worked the axles via bell-crank levers. Their most interesting feature, however, was their valve gear, the mechanism which operated the slide valves and was used to put them into reverse. This had been invented by one of the Carmichaels. Other valve gears were clumsy, requiring great dexterity and careful timing, but his was worked by a single lever. In the autumn that Gooch was at Dundee, Robert Stephenson and Company adopted it briefly and one wonders if he drew their attention to it. He certainly saw it: 'a curious sort of thing'. Another interesting coincidence is that the Dundee and Newtyle ordered their first respectable engine during his time there, and from Stephensons'.

The Dundee and Newtyle was never a financial success. Gooch appears to have played a small part in attempts to improve its fortunes. During 1835 the shareholders met to discuss a proposal "that coaches for the conveyance of passengers be drawn . . . on Sundays". The spread of intemperence, the chairman said, would be halted if the operative classes could spend a few hours each week-end in the open air: 'He could here quote the testimony of a highly respectable gentleman whom he had met lately, and who was intimately acquainted with the practical results of the Liverpool and Manchester Railway in respect of Sunday trains; and who stated that . . . the greater portion of passengers on that railway were artisans and their families, who, but for the opportunity thus offered them . . . would, in all probability, have been tempted to spend much of their earnings in gin shops'. In spite of Gooch's ingenious argument, for surely he was the "highly respectable gentleman", the motion was defeated.

Whilst he had a good deal to say about his social life in Dundee he made little mention of his work. He was far from happy at the foundry, though he always found James Stirling kind. He had come under the influence of a most distinguished engineer who, only a few months earlier, had been elected a Member of the Institution of Civil Engineers – no small honour for a man working in far-off Dundee.

In 1816 his older brother, Robert, a minister, who was an engineer at heart, took out a patent for an engine worked by heating and cooling pressurised air, rather than by steam. His prototype failed when the air-heater was burned through. In 1828 James built an improved version and later developed an even better one which drove the machinery at the foundry. The brothers' ideas made their name immortal, but nineteenth century materials were not up to the temperatures required and their engine never went into production. Stirling's stature is nevertheless clear. As managing partner, however, he was probably rather remote from the draughtsmen, who saw more of Leslie Meldrum, the works manager. 'I cannot say I ever liked him much' wrote Gooch, and this is not surprising; Meldrum, as the following story shows, detested him.

On a Saturday evening at the end of October a warehouse caught fire next to Borrie's foundry. As there had been several serious outbreaks in recent months a brigade had been formed and this was their first chance to show what they could do. Spectators were asked to help, but refused unless they were paid. In the meantime the less mercenary entered too enthusiastically into the proceedings, working away at the pumps before they were ready. Somewhere in this chaotic scene was Gooch, whose curiosity nearly cost him his life.

Soon after midnight the fire was under control and he set off for home across Borrie's yard. As he scrambled over a heap of rope he suddenly fell into deep water. Finding walls all around him he realised that he had tumbled into a well. Fortunately the firemen were using it and soon a large bucket landed beside him, just missing him: 'This was too good a friend to part with, so I got hold . . . and then began to call out'. He was soon hauled up, losing his stick and being dropped onto his hat, which, to his annoyance, was ruined. The sleeves of his coat, a smart green one only a few days old, were nearly torn off and his elbows had been scraped badly. He had been most fortunate, however. Later that night another passer-by fell into the same well, struck his head on the walls and drowned.

The next day, wrote Gooch, 'I . . . learned, much to my disgust, that Mr Meldrum of the Dundee Foundry saw me pulled on the bank at the top, but did not condescend to ask me if I was any the worse or take the slightest notice of me'. Meldrum's hatred is plain, and we may wonder why a lofty manager felt so about a mere draughtsman of nineteen. The clues lie in the later history of the Devon Iron Works, forty miles away, and reveal Gooch's real reason for going to Scotland.

Gooch's grandfather's share in the iron-works had passed to George Henry Longridge. Whilst Gooch was at Dundee the manager of the Devon was Alexander Meldrum – Leslie Meldrum's father. By 1837 he had been replaced by his son, by 1838 Longridge had retired from the business and by 1842 Leslie Meldrum had become the sole owner. His ascendency was then complete, but in 1835 the young draughtsman with the long-standing family connections was a rival.

If there was a struggle for power the younger man soon gave up. 'As it was not my intention when I went to Dundee to stay more than the year I finished with the Foundry Company on 31 December', he wrote. He went to Robert Stephenson's at Newcastle, as a draughtsman, and still on a pound a week. Fine steam-boat engines had been made there for many years, so why did he not go there in the first place? The answer, clearly, is that he went to Dundee in the hope of a career from family interests.

CHAPTER

5

On 6 January 1836 Gooch left Dundee. He travelled to Edinburgh and, after a few days, to Bedlington. It was Tuesday 26 January when he finally reached Newcastle, ready to start work the next day. He took lodgings in Blackett Street with a Mrs St. George. Her twelve year old daughter, who had a fine voice, was allowed to go along to his room to sing for him: 'This child has since been famous on the stage. I since heard her in London, but as a child she sang very sweetly and promised to be good looking'.

Gooch's private performances from the notable Julia St. George lasted only three weeks. He then moved to Carliol Street to share rooms with Harry Birkinshaw. 'I like Newcastle better than any place I was ever in', he wrote shortly afterwards. 'I had plenty of friends . . . and scarcely ever spent an evening at home.' He was probably back at his lodgings quite early,

Robert Stephenson and Company's factory, 1844

however, as from Monday to Saturday he had to be at his drawing board by 7 a.m. He had a half mile walk to the works. Even between the fine new façades of the town centre the roadways were filthy and dangerous, but closer to the factory he had to take to the narrow, stinking alleyways of the old town.

Though Robert Stephenson had moved from Newcastle to build the London and Birmingham Railway he was still the managing partner at Forth Street. 'Because I am absent from the place,' he told one of his partners, 'you appear to conclude that the works never obtains any of my attention, whereas I am satisfied if it had not been for exertions made away from home the establishment would scarcely have been in existence at this moment. I cannot, therefore, avoid feeling hurt at the comparative nonsuccess being entirely imputed to my absence. . . The business is now I believe doing tolerably well.'

Whilst Stephenson was away Michael Longridge ran the commercial side, dividing his time between Forth Street and Bedlington. Manufacture and design were left to William Hutchinson, the works manager. The 'comparative non-success' was confined to the accounts, the factory still being the finest locomotive shop in the world. Gooch was lucky to be there when important technical changes were being introduced and the way was being paved to great profitability. During 1836 eighteen engines were produced, a good total, but in the next year no less than twenty-nine were turned out and the profits exceeded £11,000.

Gooch was one of only five or six draughtsmen. He worked away at a large wooden drawing board with a tee-square in the manner customary until a decade or so ago. The most important drawings, the layouts of complete engines, showed only the main outlines, a few dimensions at most being added. The smiths and fitters scaled many of the sizes from the layouts, the rest being left to their discretion.

The most interesting development in hand during Gooch's first months concerned the valve gear, an aspect of locomotive design which became very important in his career. So far a crude arrangement had been used which required the engineman to slide the eccentrics along the crank axle until they engaged with driving lugs timed for the engine to run in reverse. This had been replaced on some of the Stephenson engines by the Carmichael gear, but this too was superseded soon after his arrival. The "gab", or four-fixed-eccentrics type, which became the standard for several years, was introduced. In the atmosphere of rapid innovation Gooch was able to show what he could do and soon his pay was increased to 30s. Newcastle offered plenty to keep Gooch occupied. After his rise he usually went to the Theatre Royal twice a week. There were also the Academy of Arts, the Philharmonic Society, concerts, exhibitions and so on. At the Literary and Philosophical Society in the autumn Dr. Dionysius Lardner, soon to become an adversary, gave a course which included talks on steam engines and railways. He particularly enjoyed visiting his friends and relations. Every other Sunday he went to Bedlington, where he was made very welcome. 'I was out to a very splash party at Mrs Marshall's,' he said in a letter to his sister. 'There were about 31 there, and I can assure you we danced in fine style.' He also saw a good deal of his cousin, George Hawks. George's mother was Anna Gooch's sister, Jane, who had married John Hawks in 1798. In 1818 her husband had retired and George had taken his place in the family business. He had just been made Gateshead's first mayor. He was a dandy, with a fondness for high life and the ladies, it was rumoured.

Gooch also dined with Sir Robert Shafto Hawks. As a brother-in-law of Daniel's aunt his connections with the Gooches were tenuous, but John Gooch appears to have known him well. He had been knighted by the Prince Regent in 1816 after playing a prominent part in the supression of riots in the North-East. He had a very good opinion of Gooch, who said that Sir Robert took great notice of him, 'both while at Newcastle and when I lived at Bedlington (he used to be pleased at my skill at turning)'. This was soon to lead to a splendid opportunity, but in the meantime Gooch continued his work in the drawing office, where he was given a most interesting job to do.

During April an energetic Czech, Franz Anton von Gerstner, paid a flying visit and ordered two most unusual locomotives. Gooch was chosen to make the drawings. Von Gerstner was a man of Brunel's stamp. He had started the Linz to Budweiss Railway, the first public line to be authorised on the continent. As he insisted on having nothing but the best costs soared and the directors forced his resignation. He was then invited to Russia to report on the mineral and metal-smelting potential of that vast, somnolent country.

Russia's main problem was her primitive and virtually non-existent transport system. Von Gerstner saw railways as the answer and prepared a memorandum for the Tsar proposing the building of a four-hundred mile line from Moscow to St. Petersburg. Not surprisingly this was thought too ambitious, but after a struggle with bureaucracy he obtained permission to build an experimental line, seventeen miles long, from St. Petersburg to Pavlovsk Park, one of the Tsar's country palaces.

The concession was signed on 1 April 1836. Von Gerstner had committed himself to running trains within six months and so he set off immediately on a lightning tour of Western Europe, visiting Belgium, Ireland, Wales and England to buy equipment. He placed orders for seven locomotives, including two from Robert Stephensons' and two from Timothy Hackworth of New Shildon, County Durham. One of Forth Street's and one of Hackworth's were required by the late summer so that Gooch had a rush job on his hands. It was especially interesting as von Gerstner, like Brunel, was not prepared to be shackled by George Stephenson's 'coal wagon gauge' – a distance of 4ft. 8½in. between the rails – and had decided on 6ft.

So far locomotives had been designed for gauges of from 4ft. 3in. to 5ft. Brunel was building the Great Western Railway to the immense gauge of 7 ft., though as yet he had not ordered any engines. Forth Street had an order for two for an American line of 5ft. 6in. gauge but design work had yet to start. Gooch's task was therefore a most original one. 'I was much delighted to have so much room to arrange the engine,' he wrote. 'I was very much impressed in making these drawings with the importance of a wider gauge, and no doubt thus early became an advocate for the broad gauge system, altho' at the time Mr Brunel had not propounded his views . . . and I did not foresee how important a matter it was to be in my future life.'

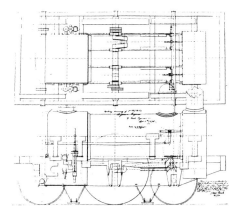

Drawing of the locomotives for the first Russian railway. Signed by Gooch in 1880 and 1886

Two drawings of the Russian engines exist. One, dated 29 July 1836, appears in James Warren's wonderful history of Robert Stephenson and Company. It bears the note, "from the original drawing", and was presumably based on a photograph of Gooch's layout. The second, a more complete elevation, appeared in *The Engineer* of 27 May 1892, which stated that "through the kindness of Mr Dean, the Locomotive Superintendent of the Great Western Railway, we are able to give engravings, which are copies of photographs taken with some trouble from original drawings". Gooch had signed the original in two places over forty years after he had left Forth Street.

Under the supervision of Hutchinson and the chief draughtsman he had made the most of the extra width. He set out the most powerful passenger locomotive built up to that time. Her driving wheels were 6 ft. in diameter, an unheard of size. Her cylinders, of 14in. bore and 18in. stroke, were as large as those of Stephenson's recent heavy goods engines. The boiler, 3ft. 6in. in diameter by 8ft. 6in. long, was bigger than any previously built at Forth Street apart from one used on an early *Patentee*. The firebox also was unusually large, being intended for burning timber.

The shops were already busy when work began on the first of the two engines. An urgent job for the Newcastle and Carlisle Railway was being rushed through but von Gerstner's was given even greater priority. Within four and a half months of the placing of the order it was complete. Gooch's layout drawing was finished only seven weeks before the engine itself, manufacture racing along neck-and-neck with design.

As there was no 6 ft. track available to test the engine it was jacked clear of the ground onto blocks for the boiler to be steamed and the wheels spun. The press were kept in the dark about the limitations of the trial, the *Mechanics Magazine* of 17 September 1836 reporting that "a locomotive of a most superior workmanship has just been constructed for the Petersburg and Pavlovsk Railway, at the manufactory of Messrs. R. Stephenson and Co., Newcastle. It was tried recently and exceeded the extraordinary speed of 65½ miles an hour". Hackworth had managed to ship his first engine on 15 September, her trial being reported as achieving 72 mph, again with the wheels whizzing in fresh air.

Both Stephensons' and Hackworth's engines proved most successful. Gooch's was tried for the first time in December when there was heavy snow. The next day it hauled eight carriages and 256 passengers 5 mls in 17 min., a good start. At the official opening on 17 December 1837 one of the Stephenson engines drew the first train, speeds of up to 40 mph being reached.

The locomotives which Gooch had set out on his drawing board gave twenty-five years of satisfactory service, besides showing that railways were feasible in Eastern Europe. They were also the prototypes of every engine of Brunel's broad gauge. Stephensons' developed the design one stage further, as we shall see, but then Gooch took over, basing his own peerless engines on ideas which he had first worked on in the quiet of the Forth Street drawing office.

During the spring, not long after he had moved to Forth Street, Gooch sat up late at his lodgings to write home. His letter, the earliest of his papers to have come down to us, is the only one to his family which has survived.

> Newcastle
>
> My Dearly Beloved Sister Barbara,
>
> I have the honour and felicity of once more spending my precious time in composing nonsense to please you and satisfy my own very troublesome conscience, as I think I am behind in answering your favours . . . I suppose I must begin with love of some sort, or it will not satisfy your love-sick mind . . .
>
> Well, to begin about Tom Marshall and Emily Wright. I think it all a fudge, although she seems to make herself very conspicuous upon certain occasions, such as crossing with her sister to Bedlington Church and going to his pew . . . But perhaps there is nothing particular in this – what do you think? And during a party, if he and she were seen sitting upon the window seat with their faces rather closer than I would like to be with anyone who had been making a hearty dinner of beefsteak and onions? Now do not take any foolish ideas in your head about love, for I daresay they were only discussing political economy . . .
>
> I was over at Sunderland . . . the other Sunday and . . . called at Miss Hubbard's. Elizabeth M. is still there and has been laid up with a bad cold but is better. They gave me a very pressing invitation to come and stay with them one Sunday which I will do some day soon. Mr W. is quite well . . .
>
> Now, Babs, I am quite tired of writing for tonight. Harry has been in bed and asleep these two hours. So you must excuse me composing more nonsense and believe me to be,
>
> Your very affectionate brother
> Daniel Gooch

It was on one of his visits to Sunderland to see Miss Hubbard and "Mr W" – John Wilkinson – that a most important encounter took place. At a party on 25 July 1836 Gooch met a young lady called Margaret Tanner: 'Why I should have mentioned this in my journal I cannot tell. I had met her sister before, but made no note of it.

Providence had, I suppose, arranged the future. I find the entry now, and also when I met her on different occasions afterwards, but have no recollection that I had any particular fancy for her. Indeed as far as recollection serves me I thought I liked Mary best'.

It was clearly not her beauty which caused Gooch to record their first meeting. The reason is, however, obvious – in the small world of Sunderland she was a person of importance. Her father, Henry Tanner, was one of the town's wealthiest men. The shipping business in which he was a partner owned eleven brigs. Most of their cargoes were of coal for London, shipped for his other firm, Tanner and Beckwith, of Noble's Quay, who were middlemen in the coal trade.

Tanner eventually left a fortune of £35,000 – well over a million at present day values – and his stature on Wearside reflected this. He became a River Commissioner and Chairman of the Marine Board. 'The mild and gentlemanly demeanour which never forsook him lent fourfold weight to his words', we are told, and clearly he was no man to be trifled with.

Tanner had four daughters. Jane, the eldest, had married a wealthy Cornish banker, William Tweedy, but the others were still single. Margaret was two and a half years older than Gooch. With such prospects it is surprising that she was still unattached at nearly twenty-three. He wrote of her sweet face and bright, loving face, and we can infer that she was choosy rather than plain. As the summer wore on their casual meetings continued. Gooch's thoughts, however, were on his career, marriage being too remote a possibility for a hard-up draughtsman, and in the early autumn his hopes of a future with the Hawks crystallised.

By 1836 no one could doubt that railways were becoming a major industry and a powerful social force. Forth Street and the Vulcan Foundry had supplied locomotives to fourteen British, nine North American and four pioneer European lines. The market was doubling every year and had increased twenty-fold since 1831. Robert Stephenson and Company were so busy that an attractive enquiry from Brunel had been declined. There were opportunities for new businesses, it was clear.

To Robert Stephenson's concern Michael Longridge withdrew from his involvement at Forth Street to start a locomotive works at Bedlington. There was no opening for Gooch with him, as he had five sons of his own, but when, at the same time, the Hawks found themselves involved with railways his opportunity came.

During the summer of 1836 the Newcastle and Carlisle Railway were so short of engines that they had to borrow some to assist at their opening ceremonies. They placed urgent orders for two locomotives, one with Stephensons' and the other with the Hawks, who had never built one before. An engine called *Lightning* was put in hand, and as a result they decided to set up in business as locomotive manufacturers. George Ansley Thompson, who had made the drawings of *Lightning*, was to be a partner. They also approached Gooch. 'Sir Robert Hawks asked me to go to their works at Gateshead', he wrote. 'He proposed they should build a locomotive engine works and take me in as a partner in this department'.

He immediately gave notice at Forth Street, leaving on Saturday 8 October. Robert Stephenson was furious that his protégé was taking hard-won expertise to yet another competitor, grumbling darkly that very month that 'rivals are coming into the field who have not had to begin by expensive experiments'.

On 12 October Gooch signed the agreement which made him a partner in the new business, Hawks and Thompson. Thompson was to be the managing partner at a salary of £200 a year and Gooch the managing engineer at £150 – twice his pay at Forth Street. The share capital was £10,000. Joseph Hawks, George Hawks' cousin, took a £3,000 share. George Hawks also took a £3,000 share, £2,000 in his own name and £1,000 in Gooch's, 'Mr Gooch not to draw any share of profits until they have amounted to his 1/3 of shares held by Mr George Hawks'. George Thompson held £2,000-worth and the remainder was in the joint names of another Hawks and a Mr Stanley, a relative of Joseph Hawks.

Gooch does not appear to have been

George Hawks

By the end of October all was going well enough for Thompson and Gooch to set off for Leeds and Manchester to buy equipment and drum up orders. At Manchester Gooch went to Joseph Whitworth's to order machine tools. The great engineer had started his own firm barely three years before and his fame was only beginning to spread. The two became life-long friends.

Thompson soon returned to Gateshead but Gooch went on to Tredegar, arriving on 17 November. He then travelled to Bristol in the hope of an order from Brunel. Unfortunately he was away, but as it was a board day Gooch was able to see the directors instead, though without any success. This fruitless visit was the start of one of the most depressing periods of Gooch's life. He next went to Warwick, where his mother was living. There he was taken ill and it was the middle of January before he was well enough to think of returning to the North-East. At last he was able to travel but instead of going to Gateshead he went to Bedlington, where George Marshall's sister, Elizabeth, was dangerously ill with consumption. Two or three days after he visited her she died and on 24 January he attended her funeral: 'Poor girl, she had been my playmate in early life and was a sweet girl'. The only consolation in the grim month was that *Lightning* had been completed and was being tested on the line.

It was in late February or early March that Gooch suffered one of the greatest setbacks of his life. 'A difference of opinion occurred between Joseph Hawks and the other members of the firm,' he wrote, 'and it ended in the scheme being given up. The machinery ordered, as far as it could be, was countermanded and I left there on 15 March.' He gives no hint as to the cause of the dispute, but a principal reason must have been that not a single order had been obtained since the partnership agreement had been signed. Nothing had come of his time in Lancashire and the West Country. It seems more than probable that he had been a main instigator of the venture, promising great things which had not yet come to pass.

Thompson stayed on at Gateshead to finish the two outstanding orders. For Gooch, however, there was no palliative

welcomed with open arms by all the partners. The agreement stipulated that he was "entering upon duty 1 January 1837. To get £20 towards the expenses he may incur improving himself in the locomotive art by visiting the Liverpool and Manchester Railway. Mr Gooch not to be paid any salary during the foregoing travels". This supercilious restriction ensured that he was out of pocket over the first few months. It was quite different treatment from George Hawks' generosity, which gave him a tenth share in the business without his laying out a penny.

The Hawks' ironworks were the largest on Tyneside. In addition to anchors, chains and other gear for the Royal Dockyards and the East India Company they manufactured all kinds of articles in iron and steel. Gooch's first job was to look after the two or three Newcastle and Carlisle engines which were going through the shops and to draw up plans for additional facilities.

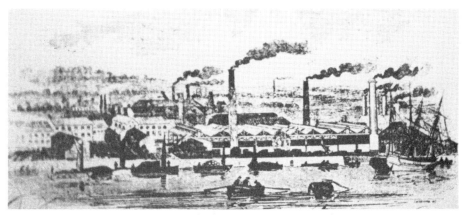

The Hawks' works at New Greenwich, Gateshead

and, to put it bluntly, he had been sacked: 'This was a great discouragement to me as I had given up my connexion with Robert Stephenson to go into this, and could not seek to return to him . . . I was therefore left without anything to do, and not a very bright prospect before me'.

Gooch's hopes of a career from family interests were now dashed. The Scottish

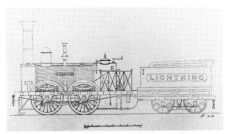

Lightning, built by Hawks and Thompson for the Newcastle and Carlisle Railway, 1836–7

connection, his kinship with the Hawks and the long-standing friendship with the Stephensons had all led to nothing. Nepotism and patronage could do no more for him, so what was he to try next? In his despair he turned to another potential route to success – marriage.

On 10 April, less than four weeks after he had left the Hawks, Margaret Tanner came to Gateshead to stay with her aunt. He saw her nearly every day and it was no doubt at this time that he gave her a touching gift. He bought some white cards with delicately fluted edges, ruled neat staves across them and, with exquisite penmanship, copied out some piano music, including a French song, Celui Qui Sut Toucher Mon Coeur, which he signed "Un Ami": 'I well remember the evening she accepted it and the pleasure it gave me to find she did so – she always valued it very much'. Then, on Monday 17 April, Margaret went unchaperoned with him to the museum at Newcastle. Amongst the glass cases of fossils, stuffed birds and relics of the Roman Wall they became engaged.

Gooch did not have Henry Tanner's permission to court his daughter, and would have been unlikely to have obtained it. Nor did he immediately dash to Sunderland to ask his blessing. The penniless draughtsman and the wealthy shipowner's daughter decided to keep their promises secret, but too much was said, the aunt was perceptive or their outing had been observed. A few days afterwards, in a final reversal of protocol, Tanner called on Gooch at his lodgings and, as he put it, "the matter was settled". 'Thus the most important step in my life was taken,' he wrote, 'probably with little thought and no consideration as to the future, for I had only a poor prospect before me, and with nothing at the time to do . . . I was, however, very anxious and unhappy at my position; there were many things to make me so. I had felt I had been too hasty, but was firmly resolved to do all I could to redeem my pledge and thus to provide a suitable home for her.'

Gooch's words make it plain that, for him at least, theirs was no love match. Margaret Tanner, however, must have faced her parents with courage and determination, or he would have been sent packing. The depths of her feelings and her confidence and trust in him had been enough to persuade them.

Margaret soon returned to her home at Bishop Wearmouth and Gooch frequently travelled over to see her. Nearby was the soaring arch of Sunderland Bridge, beneath which ships of up to 300 tons could pass with only their top-gallant masts lowered. As a final plea to the suicidal the words "*Nil Desperandum Auspice Deo*" were emblazoned on either side. The couple often walked over: 'I well recollect one day bemoaning my fate . . . She pointed to the motto cast on the bridge, "*Nil Desperandum*", and told me to make that my motto in life and all would come right. I felt the truth of it and determined to banish despair and start with renewed hopes'. So he wrote to his brother Tom to ask him for a temporary post and was soon off to Lancashire and the Manchester and Leeds Railway.

CHAPTER

6

In the spring of 1837 Tom Gooch was appointed Joint Principal Engineer with George Stephenson for the building of the Manchester and Leeds Railway, the first line in the world to tackle difficult country. His most pressing task was the placing of the contracts for the 13½ miles of line from Manchester to Rochdale. John Brunton, his resident engineer, and his team moved into the Roebuck Hotel at Rochdale and set to work. On 25 May Gooch joined them. Although he had no wish to make a career building railways he found the life enjoyable: 'We were a large party . . . and had some good fun. It was a pleasant time.'

Besides working Gooch went to the opening of the Grand Junction Railway. He also had an exhausting day out when he and a colleague hired horses with the intention of riding to Halifax. Having crossed the worst of the hills they felt fresh enough to go on to Leeds to see Margaret Tanner's uncle. On the return journey, however, Gooch thought he would never make Rochdale: 'I had not been on horseback for years, and was so fatigued I could hardly sit, feeling also very sick. The distance we rode was seventy-five miles, and this on hack horses . . . I was surprised to feel how little it affected me next day'.

Soon events began to move towards the most crucial moments of his life. On 9 July 1837 George Henry Gibbs, one of the directors of the Great Western Railway, wrote to the secretary of their London Committee to say that 'we shall very soon require also an intelligent man to take charge of our engines . . . There is no time to be lost, I should think, in securing such a person'. This was just the kind of post

that Gooch was looking for. Someone told him about it and only nine days later he wrote to Brunel.

> I.K. Brunel, Esq. Manchester & Leeds
> Railway Office
> Rochdale, July 18th 1837
>
> *Dear Sir,*
> *I have just been informed it is your intention to erect an engine manufactory at or near Bristol and that you wish to engage a person as manager . . .*
> *I have until the last two months been constantly engaged in engine building . . . The first three years of my time I was with Mr Homphry at the Tredegar Iron Works, Monmouthshire. I left him to go to Mr R. Stephenson and was at the Vulcan Foundry 12 months when I obtained leave from Mr Stephenson to go down to Mr Stirling of the Dundee Foundry Co., Dundee, to get a knowledge of steam boat work. I remained with him 12 months and returned to Mr Stephenson's works at Newcastle where I remained until last October when I left, having had an offer from a party in Newcastle to take the management of a locomotive manufactory which they intended erecting, but which owing to some unavoidable circumstances they have now given up the intention of proceeding with, and we have countermanded the orders for machinery. This has left me without a situation . . . At present I am with my brother on the Manchester and Leeds line, where I have employment*

31

*until I meet with something more suitable
. . .*

*Should you approve of my application
I shall be glad to hear from you stating
the salary and any other information you
may think necessary.*

I am, Sir, yours obl^t,
Danl. Gooch

He was fortunate that Brunel was not under
pressure to appoint someone with influence.
His surname was far from unfamiliar to
Brunel, who must have known a good deal
of Tom and perhaps something of John V.
Gooch as well. Within a fortnight he had
replied, promising to call on him.

At the end of July, Brunton and his staff
moved from Rochdale to Manchester and it
was at their new offices on 9 August 1837
that Isambard Kingdom Brunel and Daniel
Gooch met for the first time.

Brunel was thirty-one, a tiny man of
great charm and dazzling intellect with a
unique blend of artistic, engineering and
architectural flair. After assisting his father
to build the world's first underwater tunnel
he had struggled to establish his own
career. His chance came when he won a
competition to design a bridge to cross the
Avon Gorge at Bristol. The grace and
boldness of his design and the skill with
which he handled the Bridge Committee
impressed   local   people   who   were
considering how to launch a project for a
railway between London and Bristol. They
invited him to make the preliminary survey
and, armed with the plans and facts which
he gathered together, were able to marshall
public support. On 27 August 1833 the
prospectus for a Great Western Railway
Company was approved and Brunel was
appointed as the engineer. The first Bill was
opposed fiercely. Brunel put up a valiant
fight and, though defeated, his reputation
was made. The following year, after forty
days of expensive warfare, a second Bill was
passed, receiving the Royal Assent on 31
August 1835. Soon thousands of navvies
were unleashed to press the immense
project forward.

Brunel had arranged that the Act made

no reference to the gauge and as soon as it
was passed he sprang a surprise. He had
selected a route which was brilliantly engineered with speed and economy in mind.
As a further improvement he proposed a
gauge of 7ft., half as broad again as the
so-called "narrow gauge" of George Stephenson and his followers. He believed that
it would be safer, swifter, cheaper to run,
more comfortable for passengers and more
commodious for goods. He expected it to
prove so much better than the narrow
gauges that they would be superseded. To
get the best from it he needed a first class
locomotive superintendent, so his interview
with Gooch was fateful for both. He did not
hesitate. Gooch was offered the post and
was delighted to accept. 'I was very glad of
this appointment,' he wrote, 'as I felt it was
a permanent thing in which, by dint of
attention and perseverence, I might hope to
get on. I was also very glad to manage the
broad gauge, which filled my mind as the
great advance of the age, and in the
soundness of which I was a great believer'.
His salary was to be £300 a year increasing
to £550 when the line opened, far better
than his highest hopes at Gateshead.

On Monday 14 August 1837*, ten days
before his twenty-first birthday, Gooch
began his many years of service to the Great
Western Railway. All had not been plain
sailing. Many years later Mr F.W. Gower,
who was a director when his application was
put to the board for approval, told him that
he had objected because he was so young.
'Mr Brunel said I would mend of this',
wrote Gooch, who had no such doubts
himself: 'I was very young to be entrusted
with the management of the locomotive
department of so large a railway; but I felt
no fear.' He had a right to his confidence,
as, for his years, he could not have been
better trained.

Gooch lost no time in giving up his
temporary job. Within five days of his
interview he was in London and hard at
work, as Brunel was striving to open the
first part of the Great Western by the end of
the year. Though this was hopelessly
optimistic he had to work to the deadline.

After a few days preparing plans for the

*   Not Friday 18 August, as is usually stated – see p. 193

engine houses he set off north to recruit staff, buy equipment and urge the completion of the first engines. He called at Warwick on Thursday 24 August to spend his twenty-first birthday with his mother but then went to Newcastle, where three of the seventeen engines were being built.

His most reassuring call was at Forth Street. Robert Stephensons' were building a single engine, which was nearly finished. At the time she was known only by her Works Number, No. 150, but soon Brunel was to have her named *North Star*. Gooch was probably surprised to see her in the shops because she had been started a year before whilst he was working there. In fact he came to believe that he had designed her himself. He said years later that 'some drawings I made for locomotive engines for Russia were, oddly enough, afterwards two engines for the Great Western . . . the *North Star* and the *Morning Star*'. In his later years he endorsed an original drawing of Nos. 163 and 164, the Russian engines, "D. Gooch Engineer" and with the note that "these engines were built for a Russian order . . . but were not delivered. The Great Western bought them . . . the *North Star* in 1837, the *Morning Star* later". He was wrong, as there is no doubt that Nos. 163 and 164 went into service on the St. Petersburg and Pavlovsk Railway, but his confusion is understandable as *North Star's* origins were complicated.

North Star. Robert Stephenson and Company Works No. 150

Brunel's first enquiries for broad gauge engines were sent out to eight firms in June 1836. Stephensons' declined to tender,

being too busy. One of their orders was for two locomotives, Nos. 149 and 150, for the New Orleans and Carrollton Railroad, which had been opened on 25 September 1835. It was only $4\frac{1}{2}$ mls long and its gauge was 4ft. $8\frac{1}{2}$in. Its charter had been extended to allow a line to be built to Bayou Sara – St. Francisville on the Mississippi, for which Nos. 149 and 150 were intended. They were to be of 5ft. 6in. gauge, the broadest ordered at Stephensons' apart from the two Russian six footers. Because the works were so busy they went back in the queue and the layout drawing was not dated until 13 December 1836, nine weeks after Gooch had left. It is quite possible that he did some work on them, though what is as relevant is that they were very similar in layout to the Russian locomotives.

There is some evidence that one or both of the engines reached New York but neither got as far as New Orleans. The cotton planters opposed the new line and then a financial panic hit the United States. The project was stopped and on 14 November 1837 a report to the New Orleans and Carrollton directors stated that 'it will scarcely be deemed necessary . . . to recommend an early disposal of the locomotives ordered from England, not even as a matter of record, as this has been done on a previous occasion'. So Robert Stephenson found himself with two engines on his hands which were too wide to be adapted to the commoner gauges. He must have heaved a sigh of relief when Brunel placed an urgent order for a broad gauge engine on 4 July 1837. Work began immediately to convert No. 150.

The drawing showing the alterations was dated 20 August, a week or so before Gooch paid his visit. Her driving wheels were changed from 6ft. 6in. diameter to 7 ft.

and the steam dome was moved from just behind the chimney to the mid-point of the boiler barrel. To accommodate the larger driving wheels the frames were replaced by a much stiffer arrangement with an arched top and generously curved horn-guides. This novel shape was only used by Stephensons' for their first twelve engines for the Great Western, the *Star* Class, but it became Gooch's trademark, embodied in virtually all his own designs (including those with inside frames). He was no copyist and as he stuck so firmly to this feature and several other *North Star* characteristics one feels that he had at least some say in her final layout.

Gooch was no doubt pleased with what he found at Stephensons'. *North Star* was a passenger engine at least the equal of any yet built and her similarity to the Russian engines was comforting. But at Hawthorns', only a stone's throw away, he found a quite different state of affairs. They had two engines in hand based on a patent of T.E. Harrison's. *Thunderer*, which was well towards completion, had her cylinders and crank axle mounted on one truck and her boiler on another. The steam was transmitted between them by ball and socket pipes. This 'sort of procession', as it was described, was completed by the tender. Harrison's idea was that a broken-down engine or boiler would not put the whole locomotive out of action. The ball and socket pipes, however, added a new unreliability, as did the step-up gears which drove the 6 ft. driving wheels. *Thunderer* also lacked power – her draw-bar pull was only 1,000 lb, less than half that of the Russian engines.

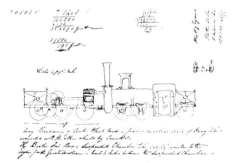

T.E. Harrison's sketch of one of his patent locomotives

The second Hawthorn engine, *Hurricane*, though more powerful, was to have wheels of the enormous diameter of 10 ft. The men

of the Great Western, when they eventually saw her vast wheels whirring and the connecting rods bounding rhythmically above her frames, dubbed her *The Grasshopper*.

Gooch went on from Newcastle to Lancashire, where he visited four other firms. They too had unusual locomotives under construction, though fortunately none so outlandish as Hawthorns'. The Vulcan Foundry were building six, all with wheels 8 ft. in diameter. *Vulcan, Aeolus* and *Bacchus*, which were nearly ready, had boilers of a respectable size but their cylinders were too small to match their huge wheels and they were underpowered. The remainder of the batch, *Apollo, Neptune* and *Venus*, were even feebler, as their cylinders were smaller still.

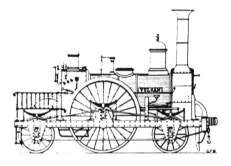

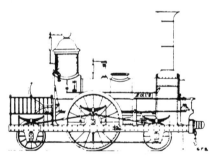

Vulcan and *Aeolus*, Tayleur and Company, 1837

Two of the remaining engines, *Snake* and *Viper*, were being built at the Haigh Foundry, Wigan. They were to prove especially troublesome as they too had step-up gearing and the detailing and workmanship were poor. Gooch nevertheless became great friends with Edward Evans, the managing partner, and was soon to use the foundry in an important venture.

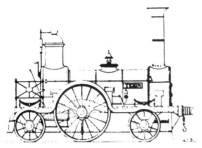

Teign, originally *Viper*, Haigh Foundry, Wigan

Lion, Sharp, Roberts and Company, 1838

The fifth contractors were Mather, Dixon of Liverpool, who had nearly completed two engines, *Premier* and *Ariel*. Like *North Star* they had driving wheels 7 ft. in diameter, but there the resemblance ended, as their boilers were small and their valve gearing, though sophisticated, was far too feeble. Their third order, *Ajax*, was another freak. Her driving wheels were immensely heavy, being no less than 10 ft. in diameter and made from solid iron plates. Sharp, Roberts, the famous Manchester firm, were making the remaining three engines, *Lion, Atlas* and *Eagle*. They had sensibly proportioned wheels and cylinders but nevertheless lacked power, as their boilers were the smallest of all.

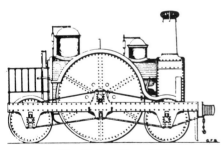

Ajax, Mather, Dixon, 1838

Gooch was appalled at what he had found. 'I felt very uneasy about the working of these machines,' he wrote, 'feeling sure they would have enough to do to drive themselves along the road.' Fortunately *North Star* was an exception, because Brunel had not been able to influence her design, whereas the blame for the rest lay with him.

The trouble began in June 1836 when the Great Western's Railroad Committee agreed that the first orders for engines should be placed. Brunel then wrote to the prospective manufacturers, laying down the following conditions:

A velocity of 30 miles an hour to be considered as the standard velocity, and this is to be attained without requiring the piston to travel at a greater rate than 280 feet per minute.

The engine to exert . . . with the pressure of steam . . . not exceeding 50 lb. upon the square inch . . . a force of traction equal to 800 lb. upon a level . . .

The weight . . . exclusive of the tender, but in other respects supplied with water and fuel for work, not to exceed 10½ tons, and if above 8 tons, to be carried on six wheels'.

Later, when Brunel came under severe criticism because of the poor performance of the engines, he claimed that he had left their form of construction and proportions entirely to the manufacturers, merely stipulating that they submitted their drawings to him for approval. This was not correct, as his conditions placed severe restrictions on the designers.

Brunel's most surprising limitation was to the "force of traction", the pulling power of the engines. His figure of 800 lb. was very low. Even in 1830 Stephensons' *Northumbrian* had developed 1,300 lb. and Gooch's Russian locomotives could manage a ton. The piston speed of 280 ft./min. also implying a feeble locomotive, was well below normal practice, 400 ft./min. at 30 mph being common. Fixing the piston speed also fixed the size of the driving wheels – a simple formula gives the wheel diameter as six times the stroke of the cylinder for Brunel's requirement to be met. An eighteen inch stroke was customary at the time, requiring either 9 ft. wheels or the novelty of step-up gearing.

A more complicated formula relates "force of traction", piston speed, boiler pressure and cylinder bore. Brunel had fixed the first three of these and so the fourth, the bore, followed from simple arithmetic. Finally his weight restrictions had serious effects on the size of the boilers, unless strange expedients such as Harrison's were used. Brunel had set his conditions because his calculations suggested that the broad gauge would not need such large locomotives as the narrow. In principle he was correct but later events will show that he seriously underestimated the power requirements of his trains. More importantly, however, he had ignored the safety and reliability which sheer size could bring. If the manufacturers had applied his conditions strictly all the engines would have developed a mere 64 hp at 30 mph. Fortunately they ignored them at least to some extent, but Brunel's influence on the design of all except *North Star* was considerable. Four of the first seventeen developed less than 100 hp at 30 mph whereas *North Star* could manage 150 hp. Another eight were no more powerful than the long outmoded *Northumbrian*. The remainder were the extraordinary *Hurricane* and the Sharp, Roberts engines, with their small boilers.

Whilst he was in Lancashire Gooch began buying tools and other equipment. At Manchester he called on Richard Dawes, who became a troublesome supplier of all sorts of stores and small items. He ordered machine tools, millwork and taps and dies from Joseph Whitworth, being amongst the first to adopt his standardised screw threads.

To start building up his staff Gooch went to Salford to see Sandy Fyfe, the locomotive foreman at that end of the Liverpool and Manchester Railway. In his spare time Fyfe ran a recruiting agency. His first capture for Gooch was Jim Hurst, the engineman he had met when he was at the Vulcan Foundry. Hurst had recently lost his job after causing a derailment. Fyfe offered him posts abroad, as well as on the Great Western: 'My mind leaned on the last, on account of it being in England', he said. 'Mr Gooch . . . stopped for a while at Sandy's house and there I met him. He at once recognised me, gave me a warm greeting and spoke of the old days, and our interview ended in him engaging me as an engine driver at 6s. 8d. per day'. Hurst was sent to Charles Tayleur's to work as a labourer until *Vulcan*, which was to be his engine, was finished.

With his department beginning to gain momentum Gooch returned to London. He had much to think about. 'The designs of the engines then contracted for were as bad as they could be,' he wrote. 'I, however, had made up my mind to do my best to aid Mr Brunel in carrying out his views, and therefore said nothing, but certainly dreaded the result.'

CHAPTER

7

Brunel was striving to complete the 22½ mile stretch of the Great Western between Paddington and Maidenhead. Gooch set up his base at West Drayton, half way between the two, as this was where the first long length of broad gauge rails was to be laid. It was also on the canal, which was convenient for the delivery of the locomotives. He moved into lodgings, set up his office in a wooden hut and began a voluminous correspondence. His letters were astonishingly mature and often blunt, as he was allowing no-one to stand in his way as he launched his division. Besides gathering his staff together and buying tools and stores he had to build repair shops and a running shed at Paddington, together with a smaller depot at Maidenhead and accomodation at West Drayton for the first few engines.

Brunel had sent him a draughtsman to help with the design of the buildings but he soon found that he needed another. He moved quickly, as by the end of October the shed at West Drayton was nearly ready and he was anxiously awaiting rollers for the doors. Early in November he was enquiring for cast iron columns for his biggest building, the Paddington engine house. This took shape rapidly, an octagonal, mainly wooden building with a turntable at the centre serving seven short radial tracks with inspection pits, where the major repairs were to be carried out. At one end he was building a long shed where the locomotives would be prepared for service, and at the other an annexe for the fitters' benches and machine tools. Early in November he needed the window frames and by the end of the month he was preparing to instal plant. 'I now write at once,' he told Dawes, 'that you may have no excuse for not completing my order as soon as possible . . . We are nearly ready to open and I have no smiths' tools yet, and if you do not let me have them at Paddington within the next fortnight I must of necessity get them in London . . . You must charge me as low as you can for the forty-inch bellows or you will be cut out of the trade by the London houses.' He was being

The octagonal engine house at Paddington

less than honest with Dawes. The line was still a long way from completion and he had only just sent Brunel the drawings for the roof of his smithy.

The coke to fuel the locomotives was to be made at West Drayton, using coal brought by canal from the Midlands. Fox, of the London and Birmingham Railway, helped by sending him drawings of their coke ovens. Within five months they were virtually complete and he was ready to start cutting a branch canal to serve them. 'I think you preferred that plan to a lay-by,' he reminded Brunel. 'I wish to have it begun as soon as you shall fix upon it . . . I have not been able to get a good coke burner for a less wage than £2 a week . . . It is time I had one to try the ovens.' Sandy Fyfe had found him an experienced man but he wanted too high a wage. 'I think the coke burners in London are not getting near so much as he wants,' Gooch wrote, 'and he will also have to live in the country, which will be much cheaper'.

To cut down the time he spent travelling he persuaded Brunel to let him have a horse and gig. 'At present I am obliged to hire one,' he complained, 'which is not only very expensive but it often happens that I am unable to get one at any price . . . I tryed the coaches on the Bath Road but found I had to wait so long before I could get a seat that I lost more time than would have taken me to do my business, and now winter is coming on even walking through the fields to the Bath Road will be impossible.'

His biggest worry was the transportation of the engines. Some were to come by sea to London but most were to be brought by rail to Birmingham and then by wagon and horse teams to Braunston on the canal. He checked drawings of the openings in the bridges to make sure that the boilers would pass through.

Sandy Fyfe had been busy recruiting enginemen and was supposed to keep them stood by in the north until they could come with their engines. He annoyed Gooch by sending some too soon. 'I shall be glad to hear from you stating whether the men . . . have had any money from you, also what time they have been kept out of work upon my account,' he was told stiffly. It was

presumably Fyfe's poaching activities which led to Gooch receiving a spate of anonymous letters. He asked one acquaintance if he had written them and received a strong reply. Unabashed, he told him that his letter was 'a pretty hot one, but that I can easily excuse knowing the circumstances under which it was written . . . I must confess I was in a very bad humour when I received that letter without any name to it . . . I have been favoured with so many, some wanting the foreman turned off and some one thing and some another . . . Not one of the parties can I find . . . or I would make them pay for their fun'.

To make sure that he was not overpaying his men Gooch wrote to Fox and his brother John to find out what their rates were. He complained to his foreman at Paddington that some were earning too much: 'Millwood and Chaplin whom I have engaged as firemen are getting 20s. per week. This is more than I had bargained for as I agreed with them for 2s. 6d. per day and they must not have more as it makes those here discontented'. He wrote to his friends for other information. One of Tom Gooch's staff, a 'd'm'd good natured fellow', was asked where the Liverpool and Manchester bought their stores. He was sent a box of samples, for which he said he was much obliged, 'particularly to the kind friend who went without his dinner that he might send me a little bread — it is very useful for us hard working fellows on the Great Western'. He fought hard for a bargain. 'I think 3d. per lb far too much for waste — this is the price of hemp,' he complained to Dawes. 'You can send me 2 cwt at 2d. and 2 cwt at 1d. . . . and do not forget what I have said concerning the completion of the order as I am bound to have the things in the course of a fortnight.'

In the meantime the shipping of the first engines began. Jim Hurst was still at the Vulcan Foundry and told Gooch that his orders were not being followed. Charles Tayleur was immediately sent a terse note by his former boy and pupil: 'I had a letter from Hurst this morning saying you would not allow him to go to Town with the engine. I should like to know what objection you had to his doing so, also whether you have sent anyone else . . . When you told me the engines were to be ready in a fortnight I did not think it would be two months, or I would never have thought of engaging Hurst upon the terms I did'. By the time Gooch's letter reached Newton the problem had solved itself and Hurst was on his way. 'I left the works taking two engines with me, the *Vulcan* and the *Premier*,' he wrote. 'They were brought from Liverpool to London by sea, and took six days from port to port. At the London docks Mr Gooch met me and by his directions the engines were taken by barge to West Drayton . . . and it was only last year . . . that I saw the old elm standing which supported the gearing which lifted the engines from the barge. Mr Gooch met me at Drayton, received me very kindly and took

me down the village to his own lodgings.'

Gooch had arranged with one of Brunel's assistants for tackle to be sent down for unloading the engines but was furious when it arrived: 'I never saw such trash sent for the job it was put to . . . but having the barge there and the men all collected . . . I was anxious not to delay'. This led to a row with Brunel.

He began the tricky operation by setting up a pair of shear legs. A strong chain was used as the back guy and the luffing gear was anchored to the trunk of Hurst's old elm. He added extra tackle to take the strain from the main blocks and also set up a safety rope, which stretched across the canal from the top of the shear legs to prevent them from toppling backwards.

North Star, delivered to the Great Western in 1837

His plan worked well and he soon had the job done, the only hitch being the failure of the hook of one of the smaller blocks.

When Brunel realised that the engines had been unloaded in his absence he was furious. He had seen the gear beforehand and been critical but, Gooch said, 'I certainly did not understand you as decidedly condemning using the tackle . . . or I would not have proceeded with it . . . I got one of the boilers out the day you were here and the other the following day, and everything stood well and appeared to be sufficiently strong'. Hammond, Brunel's resident engineer, was drawn into the affair, complaining that Gooch had not used blocks which he had sent. Gooch grumbled that he could not possibly have known this and asked Brunel testily 'whether you look to Mr Hammond or I as the responsible party for the unloading . . . For if I am responsible it is hardly fair that I should be obliged to take his opinion'. He ended the argument diplomatically by telling Brunel that he 'was sorry to find I have done aught contrary to your wish, as it is my greatest pleasure to work so that you may approve of it'.

Gooch was upset at being rapped over the knuckles and the quarrel rankled with him. 'One feature of Mr Brunel's character,' he wrote long after his old chief had died, 'and it was one that gave him a great deal of extra and unnecessary work, was that he fancied no one could do anything but himself, and I remember him giving me a scolding for unloading these engines . . . without consulting him . . . There was a carriage sent from London which had to be got down the side of the cutting from the bridge, and he sent elaborate instructions how this was to be done. These . . . of course were of no use in reality, as there was no kind of difficulty in the work . . . As a rule he did not get experienced and qualified people about him, and with them it was perhaps necessary, but the work in consequence was often badly done and always expensively.'

Within a few weeks Gooch's story had a terrible sequel. *North Star* was taken by river to Maidenhead. Brunel went to unload her himself and it nearly cost him his life. A similar arrangement of lifting tackle was used as at West Drayton and again there was a safety rope to prevent the shear-legs from toppling backwards. Unfortunately this was let go when there was no load suspended from the main blocks. The weight of the back guy then brought the legs over with a crash, killing one man and just missing Brunel. 'But for the loss of the man's life I rather rejoiced, after the scolding I had . . . but of course said nothing,' wrote Gooch.

As winter came on Brunel began to lay the first broad gauge rails at West Drayton. He was so determined to have a perfect permanent way that he was experimenting with grinding their surfaces after they were in position. A truck was equipped with two horizontal grindstones for the purpose. Brunel sometimes came down before daylight to supervise the work: 'A person of the name of Murphey had prophesied that one particular night would be the coldest for many years', Gooch wrote. 'As luck, for him, would have it, it came true and made him for the time famous, and then there was a grand rush for his almanack; but it was anything but good for us, as Mr Brunel kept us out all night and it was certainly awfully cold. We suffered dreadfully, but nothing seemed to check the zeal of Mr Brunel'. He was unsuccessful, however, as the flatness was lost as soon as any settlement of the rails occurred.

Towards the end of December Gooch was able to try *North Star* on the rails. Unfortunately he struck a snag. 'I find the wheels . . . are too large in the flanch,' he told Brunel, 'and I have written to Reading to see if they can put them as they are, on the axle, in the lathe and take ¼ inch off them.' It seems unlikely that a firm of Stephensons' standing had made *North Star's* axles to the wrong size. A more probable explanation is that Brunel had specified too narrow a gap between the wheel flanges and the rails. With only a short stretch of line laid it would be easier to move all the rails apart by ¼ in. rather than machine every axle, and perhaps this is the reason why the broad gauge was 7ft. 0¼in. wide, rather than an exact 7 ft. The odd fraction in George Stephenson's 4ft. 8½in. gauge has been said to have occurred in the same way.

When Christmas arrived Gooch took a few day's break, but he spent much of his holiday in coaches. 'I am going to Acton today,' he told Brunel on 22 December. 'I go into town at night and start for New-castle sometime tomorrow . . . Any letter will find me directed to the care of Henry Tanner, Esq., Wearmouth Walk, Sunder-land.' He had a great deal to discuss with Margaret. Now that he had a good job behind him he felt confident enough to marry and Tuesday 20 March was chosen for the wedding. They only had a short time together, however, as he was anxious to be back at West Drayton by New Year's Day. The first few miles of line were ready at last and the engine trials were about to start.

According to Jim Hurst the first run took place on 28 December 1837: 'It was a trial trip from the 14th to the 15½ mile post close to Langley and for three and a half months I daily made short trips with Mr Brunel and Mr Gooch'. Gooch rode a broad gauge footplate for the first time on 9 January 1838, when *Vulcan* and *Premier* were tried out. George Henry Gibbs, an indefatigably active director, happened to be present. 'We were much pleased to find that the two engines were about to be tried,' he wrote. 'The engines, after some delay in getting up the steam, sallied forth, but the curve in the turn-out proving too sharp for them they got off the rails two or three times and it was an hour before they could be got onto the main line. When there, however, they performed beautifully and we had a very interesting drive.'

The testing continued and on 5 February a euphoric newspaper report announced that 'a full trial was made . . . on two or three miles of the line . . . An engine with eight feet driving wheels, made by Messrs. Tayleur . . . and another by Messrs. Mather, Dixon . . . ran the whole day without producing the slightest vibration either in the rails or the wood under them. The rails are, in fact, so beautifully firm, smooth and true, that the engines glided over them more like a shuttle through a loom or an arrow out of a bow than like the effect on any previous railway . . . A speed of forty-five to fifty miles an hour was attained'.

By 15 January enough track had been laid for *North Star* to be steamed. Six locomotives were then in operation, which was a good excuse for a celebration and so a dinner was organised. Gooch acted as one of the stewards. 'Some Irish gentlemen took more wine than was good for them,' he complained, 'and amused themselves by dancing an Irish war dance on our hats, which happened to be piled up in a corner of the room. I was rather disgusted with the termination of our dinner and resolved never to have anything to do with another.'

The guests were more refined at a much grander social occasion to which he was invited a fortnight later. This took place at 1, High Row, Kensington Gravel Pits, the home of Brunel's in-laws, the Horsleys. 'I believe I did succeed in getting as far as the staircase,' Gooch wrote, 'and left disgusted with London parties, making a note in my mem. book never to go to another.'

Gooch's comment on his first, but far from last, such affair caused other writers to dub him 'a supreme example of the dour north country puritan', and to suggest that 'a vertiginous evening party given by Brunel's mother-in-law, the tremendous dinners . . . gay routs . . . and colossal balls, shocked his North Country puritan soul to its very depths'. Gooch, as we have seen, enjoyed lively company as much as most. It was then the height of fashion for a London party to be crammed to the doors. The affair which followed Brunel's wedding, according to the Horsleys' daughters, would have been like the Black Hole of Calcutta if some of the guests had not been able to go out into the garden. On a less auspicious occasion they invited seventy-six to supper at their relatively modest house and danced until two o'clock. 'There were two waltzes and seven sets of quadrilles,' wrote one of the girls, 'I wish you could have seen the countenances of the old Kensington ladies singing the choruses . . . the delight that played on their several fat, jolly or wizened visages'. This was the sort of evening which Gooch usually enjoyed, but at the Horsleys he did not care for the crush.

Out on the line the testing continued. Gooch set to work to improve the per-formance of his locomotives, adjusting the

timing of the slide valves of the Tayleur
engines so as to give some expansion of the
steam. He was also urging the completion
of the line-shafting in the shops at Paddington and telling Whitworth to provide
neat keys for the stationary engines. Much
was, as yet, makeshift: 'We are at a great
expense daily in having water carried in
buckets some distance for . . . the engines',
he complained, 'and it is of great
importance to us that we should . . . have a
pump upon the spot'. Dawes was still
upsetting him. 'I wish you would be more
careful in making the goods and account
agree as without this you will never get
your money', he was told. Despite all these
pressures he found time to look ahead. On
16 March he sent Bramahs' a pattern for a
feed pump, warning them that he would
require a great number, 'but the pattern
will have to be fit separately to each
engine'. He was taking the first of a series of
steps towards standardisation by changing
the hotch-potch of feed pumps to one
common type.

Bramahs' were sent the pattern on the
day that Gooch left for Sunderland and his
wedding. The London and Birmingham
Railway had yet to open so once again he
had to make the whole journey by coach –
270 mls. in 36 hrs. Through two long
nights he dozed fitfully as the mail rattled
northwards. Then at last he was disgorged
at Sunderland, but at Wearmouth Walk all
was hushed and dreary. That very morning,
Gooch wrote, 'Mrs Tanner had had a par-
aletic seisure, and was then hanging
between life and death. This, of necessity,
put the marriage off . . . and made the
time of its taking place uncertain. George
Marshall, who was to be my bridegroom's
man, came over on the Monday afternoon
and staid over Tuesday when the wedding
should have taken place, and then returned
home'.

By Wednesday afternoon Margaret's
mother was out of danger. Gooch was
anxious to return to West Drayton and
perhaps then put his foot down, as it was
decided that the marriage should take place
next morning: 'I went late at night to
arrange the matter with the church
authorities, and on March 22nd 1838 I was
married at Bishop Wearmouth church . . .
in a very quiet manner. A post chaise . . .
was brought to the back door . . . and
Margt. and I accompanied by a Mr
Scurfield, an old friend of Mr Tanner's,
went in it to church. The day was quietly
spent at Mr Tanner's house'.

The wedding would have been a modest
affair in any event – even Gooch's mother
did not travel north. Mrs. Tanner had
perhaps been unhappy about the match,
but whether it was worry over her daughter
marrying a man of little means which
brought on her stroke can only be conjectured. It is, however, an extraordinary
coincidence that it occurred just at that
time. Gooch was eager to return south as
soon as possible. At first it seemed likely
that he would have to go on his own but
Mrs. Tanner's condition improved steadily
and on the Sunday the couple were able to
leave by post chaise for Durham and the
London coach. They arrived two evenings
later at the furnished rooms which Gooch
had taken at West Drayton. Anna Gooch
was there to welcome her new daughter-in-
law and the next day her son was once again
hard at work.

There had been no grand wedding or
honeymoon for Margaret Tanner. Her duty
to her husband had torn her from her sick
mother and now she was in a tiny village
where she knew no-one. 'My married life
had thus a somewhat sad beginning,'
Gooch wrote, but hers was sadder still.

CHAPTER

8

Completion of the first stretch of line by the beginning of June was essential, as Queen Victoria's coronation, the Eton Montem and the races at Ascot were all to take place during the month and enormous business was anticipated. Whilst order was being created out of the chaos of partially completed lines, stations and sidings Gooch's locomotive trials continued. 'Hammond came for me at Salt Hill with Harrison's engine', Gibbs wrote. 'The engine ran beautifully smooth and for some way we cleared sixty miles an hour.'

On Thursday 31 May 1838 all was ready for the opening ceremony, a trip from Paddington to Maidenhead for the directors and their guests. *North Star* drew out of the partially completed terminus with two hundred passengers at about eleven o'clock. To hearty cheers and at least one salute of guns she made good speed to Maidenhead, averaging nearly 28 mph. After a sumptuous luncheon a cheerful party boarded for the return journey. Gooch gave *North Star* her head, averaging 33½ mph. Brunel's friend Thomas Guppy distinguished himself by clambering onto the roof of his carriage and walking the length of the train whilst it bounded along at full speed.

Normal passenger services commenced on Monday 4 June 1838 – Whit Monday. Every bridge was thronged with spectators, who were astonished at the speed of the trains as they shot through the arches. On the line, however, all was not going well. Gooch had Jim Hurst and *Vulcan* as a relief, which proved a wise precaution. George Gibbs, who was on the first train, was disappointed that the down journey took 80 min. (16.9 mph) and the up 65 min. He

was luckier than later folk, who took well over 2½ hrs. to reach Maidenhead after a tube burst in *Aeolus's* boiler.

Tuesday was an especially busy day as the Eton Montem, a traditional festival at the school, took place. Nicholas Wood, an eminent engineer, was one of the many passengers. His train, with nearly two hundred on board, averaged 25 mph. 'It appears quite certain that with such powerful engines, a much higher rate of speed will be accomplished, than has hitherto been attained,' he wrote. The locomotive was, of course, *North Star*. Gibbs went to Paddington to meet evening trains drawn by lesser engines, but they were very late, two arriving together.

Though nearly 30,000 passengers were carried during June the Great Western's share prices dropped alarmingly. 'Numerous reports have been spread injurious to the railway,' Gibbs wrote, 'and they appear to have originated partly in the vile manoeuvres of the Stock Exchange . . . and partly in the ill-will of those connected with the old system.' These were the opening shots of the Gauge War, a bitter conflict which was to rage for over a decade.

During July the troubles grew worse. On the most disastrous day Gibbs was at Paddington. News came that *Vulcan* was off the line and had sunk into the ballast up to her axles. Trains and people accumulated and, to make matters worse, a second engine was de-railed. The four o'clock did not arrive until after ten. 'I was so sick of the scene that I made off, finding that I could not be of any use,' he said.

Because the engines were so unreliable time-table working was stopped. Gooch spent most nights at Paddington, snatching some sleep in a carriage at the engine house, as he had to be on hand to supervise over-night repairs. Eventually even his fortitude began to wear thin. One Sunday *North Star* ran off the rails at Bull's Bridge. He spent the night re-railing her and then signalled the early morning train to stop so that he could send a note to Maidenhead. As it was braking a boiler tube burst, scalding the driver and fireman. It was six in the evening before he reached Paddington, and there he saw a porter fall under the wheels of a train: 'I heard his legs crack. This made me almost ill, and very little would at that moment have tempted me to give up railways.'

Soon a pattern began to emerge. *North Star* and the six Vulcan Foundry engines were the only ones that he could trust. The valve gearing of the Mather, Dixon locomotives was so weak that they broke down every few miles. *Thunderer, Ajax* and the Haigh Foundry engines were too feeble to work the trains and the slide valves of the Sharp, Roberts engines either stuck or leaked steam furiously. 'The result,' Gooch complained, 'was I had to begin to rebuild . . . one half of the stock.'

West Drayton was now too far from the focus of Gooch's work so he moved to Paddington. He had difficulty finding somewhere suitable to live, as the town was packed. After a short time in furnished accommodation in the Harrow Road he took rooms at 9 Paddington Green, close to St. Mary's Church. Margaret was pregnant, and they were relieved to find a more comfortable place.

Day by day the situation on the Great Western grew worse. 'There has been some little disappointment as to our speed and the smoothness of our line,' wrote Gibbs. 'Brunel's character and reputation . . . as well as our own peace and comfort, demand our best attention at this moment . . . Our difficulties are increased by the fact that the road is evidently deteriorating under the pressure of the trains, that the engines are getting out of order from too much use, and that our carriages are far from easy.'

Brunel's worst critics were from the North-West, the 'Liverpool Party'. 'Our Northern proprietors, who are bent upon crushing Brunel, . . . are availing themselves of the fall in shares brought about by the Stock Jobbers to accomplish their object,' wrote Gibbs. 'Brunel is showing great feeling with regard to the loss of confidence which, he believes, he has seen on the part of the directors and even of Saunders.'

To see if Robert Stephenson had been more successful the directors took a trip on the London and Birmingham Railway, which had just opened. 'We were two hours going', Gibbs recorded, 'being at the rate of $23\frac{1}{2}$ miles per hour and $2\frac{1}{2}$ hours in returning . . . The bumps and jolts are very frequent indeed, and . . . in some places very uncomfortable . . . The road is under repair in many places . . . and they still have an immense expense to incur.' This restored their confidence in Brunel but the Liverpool Party were relentless. To appease them the directors asked Nicholas Wood and John Hawkshaw to prepare reports on the broad gauge for presentation at the next shareholders' meeting. Wood was a most respected figure but Hawkshaw, who was 27, had no significant achievements to his name. He had been approached only after Stephenson and the President of the Institution of Civil Engineers had declined, not wishing to become involved in a professional controversy.

Wood began on an elaborate study which he did not expect to complete until the end of the year. Hawkshaw, however, had his full report ready before the October meeting. He went to the heart of the matter, attacking Brunel's principles rather than the teething troubles, using arguments which were to become depressingly familiar in the years ahead. 'The main reason . . . for abiding by the 4ft. $8\frac{1}{2}$in. gauge in this country,' he said, 'is that it has been generally adopted and there are no very substantial grounds for altering it. I have never heard anyone, whose opinion I should esteem . . . wish for more than a few inches of additional width . . . Perhaps if railways were just commencing in this country an addition of a few inches . . . might be made; but the advantage to be gained by making it now . . . would in no manner compensate the evil that will arise from a variety of gauges.'

The Liverpool Party found Hawkshaw's arguments so convincing that they were in favour of scrapping the broad gauge immediately. To their fury, however, Brunel's supporters decided not to put the report to the meeting but to wait until Wood's was ready as well. This enabled Brunel to mount an effective defence and a critical motion was withdrawn. The first crisis had passed.

Brunel was valiantly supported by Charles Babbage, the brilliant mathematician and philosopher, who was a shareholder. The board asked him to set his views down on paper and he too set to work on engine trials. 'I felt that I could not speak with confidence without making certain experiments,' he wrote. 'The directors therefore lent me steam-power, and a second class carriage to fit . . . with machinery of my own contrivance.' He proceeded to build the world's first dynamometer car*. It was equipped with instruments for measuring the drawbar pull and the vibrations of the carriages. He coupled his equipment to moving arms which carried pencils, so as to produce traces on lengths of wallpaper which were unrolled at a speed proportional to the train's.

Nicholas Wood was too busy to carry out his experiments in person so the directors agreed that he could engage Dr Dionysius Lardner to act on his behalf. Lardner had crossed swords with Brunel before. In 1836 he had advanced a theory that a ship could not carry enough coal to cross the Atlantic under steam alone. The arrival of the *Great Western*, Brunel's superb paddle steamer, at New York on 23 April 1838 with fuel to spare had exploded his fallacy. It is surprising that the directors were prepared to tolerate him after this debâcle.

Babbage's results were to prove invaluable to the broad gauge. Lardner's, however, were most worrying. *Premier, Lion* and four of the Vulcan Foundry engines showed up badly in his tests. *Aeolus*, which proved the most successful, only reached 37 mph with a 24 ton load. *North Star*, Gooch's best hope, managed 23.3 mph

with 166 tons, a fair performance, but only reached 41.1 mph with 15 tons, a miserable effort.

Gooch was horrified by Lardner's results, being in no doubt that his engines could do much better. He repeated some of the work himself, soon finding that there had been poor driving and firing. He had no difficulty in reaching 45 with *North Star* when drawing 50 tons. His results were reported to the directors, who included them in the statement which they eventually put before the shareholders. He then set to work to improve *North Star* still further. When she arrived from Newcastle she had a 3¼in. blast pipe, but at some stage a 2⅝in. pipe had been fitted, though whether by Brunel or Gooch is not known. He now tried a 3 in. version, which proved a great improvement. He also realised that the original one had not been mounted centrally in the chimney. 'It was wonderful how much the larger size freed the cylinders and the care in discharging it still enabled us to get plenty of steam,' he wrote. Brunel and Gooch worked most of Christmas Day on a nozzle of cruciform shape, but this gave no further improvement. They kept their results quiet, waiting to spring them on the narrow gauge once they had committed themselves.

Before the vital meeting Gooch had a crisis of his own to face. His standing with the directors had become dangerously low. On 26 December Gibbs wrote that 'our engines are in a very bad state and Gooch seems to be very unfit for the superintendence of that department'. Two days later he complained that 'the total unfitness of Gooch for his situation . . . the fall of a bridge during the night . . . and many other unpleasant things annoyed and worried me very much and I longed to have done with the whole concern'.

The inevitable confrontation took place on 2 January 1839. Charles Saunders and other board members went to Paddington for what Gibbs described as 'a very useful talk with Gooch'. Brunel, it will be noted, was not present. The most crucial moment

---

* This distinction has usually been accorded to Gooch. His contribution to this important aspect of locomotive development is discussed on page 87

of Gooch's career had arrived. He had no option but to attack the design of the locomotives for whose performance he was being blamed. He did this with coolness and skill, the outcome being that he was ordered to prepare a report on the state of the engines for direct submission to the board, by-passing Brunel. He sat down that very afternoon to write a long "Locomotive Special Report to Directors".

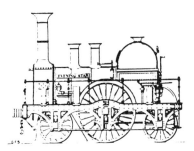

Evening Star, Robert Stephenson and Company, 1839

The directors had put Gooch into a most awkward position: 'I could only tell what I believed to be the facts, and . . . such facts would be displeasing to Mr Brunel', he wrote. 'I, however, had no choice, and had to make this report in which I condemned the construction of the engines'. Brunel was most annoyed and sent him a sharp note. From that time Gooch seems to have reported directly to Charles Saunders on most matters. He had not only weathered the storm but turned it to his advantage.

His report went into the difficulties engine by engine, cataloguing bad joint faces, leaking tubes, small fireboxes and so on. He said that the Haigh Foundry engines were not sufficiently to be depended upon to run the trains and Mather, Dixon's were not adapted to fast services. 'The whole of Tayleur's . . . have been badly constructed,' he complained. All the problems stemmed from poor design or manufacture and, though he did not mention his name, there can have been no doubt in the director's minds that the blame lay with Brunel.

Gooch's report formed part of the preparations for the crucial half-yearly meeting

on 9 January 1839. He was already a shareholder and so was certainly amongst the throng which assembled at the London Tavern to consider the various reports. Hawkshaw's concluded that it would be cheaper to convert the completed lengths of lin. scrap the existing rolling stock and go over to the narrow gauge right away. Fortunately Nicholas Wood's was less extreme, Gibbs regarding it as 'founded on hasty experiments, not absolutely opposing our gauge but tending to show that we would be better without it'.

Wood, as Gooch and Brunel had expected, made much of the poor showing of the engines in Lardner's tests. His view was that this was caused by the greater resistance offered by the atmosphere to the broad gauge carriages. The directors demolished his arguments using the later results with *North Star*. Her poor performance, they said, had been caused by a 'mere mechanical defect in the engine'. Babbage also discredited some of his work by showing that experimental data which Lardner had displayed around the walls of the meeting room had been obtained with an instrument which was quite useless.

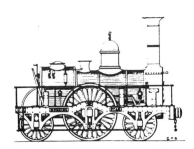

Morning Star, Robert Stephenson and Company, Works No. 149

After the reports had been presented there was a long discussion in which Brunel's opponents made a poor showing. They eventually proposed that 'the Reports of Messrs Wood and Hawkshaw contain sufficient evidence that the plans . . . pursued by Mr Brunel are injudicious, expensive and ineffectual . . . and therefore ought not to be proceeded with', and a poll was demanded. Voting was 6,145 for the motion and 7,792 against, the broad gauge surviving by a mere 1,647 votes in nearly 14,000. *North Star's* contribution had been crucial.

Out on the line Gooch's struggles continued. *North Star* had to be rescued after striking a riderless horse and finishing up in a ditch. *Vulcan's* driving wheel broke, *Hurricane* and *Eagle* were derailed by incorrectly set points and an eccentric on *Bacchus* failed. *Viper* ran into the engine house after a points error, breaking *Morning Star's* cylinder covers and frame. The joint of *Atlas's* steam pipe failed, which cost the engineman a week's pay as Gooch thought him to blame. Between the breakdowns he pushed on with a long list of modifications. He fitted "sugar loaf" tops to *Premier's* and *Ariel's* fireboxes and persuaded the Haigh Foundry to pay for extensive alterations to *Snake* and *Viper*. Hawthorns' were pressed to re-tube their boilers, samples of bursts from *Hurricane* being sent to show them what he was up against. More locomotives arrived from Stephensons' and Mather, Dixon's. Steadily the services improved.

more definite size and shape with our engines'. Next day he wrote to Fenton, Murray and Jackson of Leeds, saying that he would 'furnish the whole of the drawings for the sake of getting all our engines into some fixed plan or system'. He was taking complete responsibility for the designs so as to have full control over every detail. He was also ensuring interchangeability between the main components, enabling him to hold spare parts or borrow from one broken-down engine to return another to service.

Gooch designed two classes of six-wheeled engines, the *Fire Flies*, which had the 7ft. driving wheels, and the *Suns*, which were slightly smaller, with 6ft. wheels. He took the greatest of pains with all the parts, being assisted by his chief draughtsman, Thomas Russell Crampton, who later became a locomotive designer of great originality.

No less than eighty-three *Suns* and *Fire Flies* were eventually ordered, so that any mistakes in his moves towards standardisation would have been disastrous. To minimise the risks he based them on *North Star*, the most successful of his engines and the descendant of the *Patentees* and the Russian engines. He gave the *Fire Flies* driving and carrying wheels the same size as

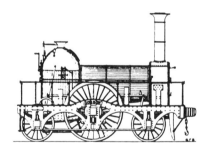

Gorgon, a Fenton, Murray and Jackson *Fire Fly*

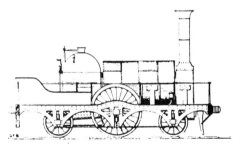

One of the *Suns*, rebuilt as a tank engine, 1849–50

Further stretches of the Great Western were soon to be opened so the directors instructed Gooch to prepare designs for new locomotives. He moved with typical speed and by 28 January 1839 was writing to the manufacturers. He told Hawthorns' that he was just about to send out specifications for twenty engines, ten of which were to have 7ft. wheels and cylinders of 15in. bore by 18in. stroke: 'I am making out the drawings complete, my wish being to get into

North Star's. Their boilers were to be the same length and diameter. He used the same kind of slotted and curved outside frames and similar brass splashers. In the proportioning and construction of many of the items – the bearings, valve gear, axles and so on – he incorporated his own ideas and experience, developing methods of giving the driving wheels a steel surface, for example. The one obvious difference was that he gave their fireboxes' high, copper-clad crowns – "sugar loaf" tops – instead of steam domes. He also changed the cylinders to 15in. × 18in. instead of 16in. × 16in. The *Suns* were similar in layout, both classes being beautifully proportioned, with fitness-for-purpose in every line.

When his design work was complete Gooch had comprehensive specifications and drawings printed and when the orders were placed iron templates were sent out for the parts which he wished to be identical in every engine. E.T. MacDermot had access to a *Fire Fly* specification in 1927 when he wrote his superb *History of the Great Western Railway*. 'Some of the details are of considerable interest,' he commented, 'and not only exhibit the great care taken over every part . . . but also the deep insight already possessed by Gooch.' With the lapse of a further sixty years a copy can no longer be found but fortunately MacDermot quoted the section on valve gear in full. Gooch required the eccentrics to be of cast iron and fastened by two steel set bolts. 'There shall also be a tightening strap, as shown in Drawing No. 12. The eccentric straps . . . shall be of best wrought iron . . . The valves shall be reversed by fork ends, . . . the face of the fork being well steeled, and the hollow to be bushed with steel and hardened, . . . the bearings being turned to templates in order that they may all fit each other . . . All the pins to be steel and the eyes well steeled and hardened. Drawings Nos. 14 and 15 shew the particular shape or strength of the different parts.'

The approach adopted by Gooch set him well ahead of his contemporaries. Almost a year later Joseph Locke was considering problems with the locomotives on the Grand Junction Railway. 'It would be well also to have in view the advantages of making as many parts of the different engines as similar to each other as possible,' he wrote. 'There is sometimes a want of tenders arising from the connecting pipes being of different sizes. I lately found an engine standing idle for want of a valve in the pump . . . and although there are ten engines of the same class on the line there was not one duplicate valve in the establishment.' Gooch had commenced the standardisation of his pumps in 1838 and was now dealing with complete engines.

Just how far he was taking things is clear from the Sketch Book which his draughtsmen prepared for him some years later. It includes 28 drawings of the 'Old Passenger Engines, 7ft. Wheel' – the *Fire Flies*. For the *Suns*, however, only the 6ft. driving wheel is shown, together with the note, 'Details, see *Fire Fly* Class'. His third design, for the *Leo* goods engines, was covered by thirteen sketches, the rest of the details again being as for the *Fire Flies*, and it is evident that Gooch was ensuring interchangeability of many parts between classes, as well as between engines. This enabled him to economise on patterns, spares and manufacturing costs, as well as to develop his later designs quickly and cheaply using well-tried components. His approach came from his traumatic experiences with the hotch-potch of engines which Brunel had ordered and perhaps from his friendship with Joseph Whitworth, the pioneer of standardisation.

CHAPTER

9

On 1 June 1839 the first of the Gooches six children arrived. Six months later Henry Tanner wrote to say that 'we are glad to hear good accounts of you all. We hope Miss Anna may soon be relieved of her toothache and not trouble you so much at night'.

For the rest of his life Gooch's home was in Paddington. At the turn of the century it had been a quiet country parish. During the twenties and thirties the population rose by nearly 20,000 but there were still green fields and woodlands all around. Frederic Harrison, born there in 1831, remembered it as 'fragrant with the quiet, sleepy strolls of babies and nurses, happily innocent of perambulators and modern toys, through flowery meadows and shady copses . . . Though it was distinctly a carriage journey to get . . . to London, my father and mother would go up occasionally to a picture gallery, or an opera or dinner party. We did not live in a pall of smoke and yellow fog . . . and up to my eleventh year I used to watch the climbing boys – little children who were sent up the chimneys to sweep them and rattle outside the pots'.

The post boy was a regular caller at 9 Paddington Green, bringing news of scattered relatives. In 1839 there was a flurry of correspondence when George Henry Longridge died. 'I hope your uncle has left your mother a good thumping sum,' George Stephenson said.

After the funeral Tom and his cousin Charles Leaviss examined Longridge's will. 'All I can say,' Tom told Daniel, 'is that it is very unsatisfactory . . . I certainly did expect that he would have died with generous feelings towards mother and the girls, notwithstanding his disgraceful conduct in withholding . . . the yearly allowance of £100 which he promised her on our poor father's death.'

George Henry had left £2,000 and the family plate to Anna Gooch, plus £700 in bequests to four of her children. The rest – £7–8,000 – was to go to Charles Leaviss. Tom and Daniel were furious that their uncle had done so much more for him than for their mother and even considered contesting the will. 'I hope,' Tom said, 'as mother is said to be a favourite with Chas, she will be able to put him in the way he should . . . for I am done with him for ever.'

Tom was looking to Daniel to sort the quarrel out. He was 'very sorry to find my mother has found so erroneous an opinion of Chas's character as to be in any way led by him. This must not be allowed . . . I am sorry to be obliged to turn over to you the task of guiding my mother . . . Chas will try to make it straight with her as cheaply as he can'.

There is no indication that the attempts to persuade Leaviss to part with some of his windfall had any effect. Anna Gooch's fortunes were greatly improved by the substantial sum which she received and she was able to move to a large terraced house in Birmingham. When she died she left £5,000, equivalent to perhaps a quarter of a million today, and we can be sure that her sons had helped her to husband her capital.

Gooch himself had little cause for concern over his finances. Besides his salary there was £100 a year coming in from Margaret's father as her 'pin money'. He lived well within his means and from the outset invested as much as he could. In the days before pensions and the Welfare State this was essential for any breadwinner who could find the wherewithal, as otherwise he and his family had no protection against the threat of the workhouse. 'If I only saved a pound . . . I was sure I could not get into debt,' Gooch wrote. 'I advise all young people to do this. Nothing is so destructive to the mind as the feeling of being in debt . . . it should be avoided as you would poison.' He involved his father-in-law in his ventures and on 5 December 1839 Tanner sent him £350: 'I hope this investment in your railway shares will ultimately turn out to your expectations, but I certainly would not recommend you to lay out more than £500 in this way'. Margaret's dowry had perhaps given him his first opportunities and already he was investing amounts beyond a year's salary.

His attempts to make the *Fire Flies* as reliable as possible had given him another hope of making a fortune. On 28 May 1840 he took out a patent for "Certain Improvements in Wheels and Locomotive Engines to be Used on Railways". It was for two methods of giving his driving wheels steel rims. Unfortunately his ideas were not entirely novel and he was disappointed at the eventual outcome: 'I found so much trouble connected with it, and the false position I felt it placed me in with our own company, that I never took out another'.

Locomotive wheels were then made of wrought iron, which was tougher but far less resistant to wear than cast iron. Steel was the most suitable material but it was extremely expensive. Gooch had evolved ways of giving just the rims of his wheels a steel surface. His experiments had been carried out at the Haigh Foundry, Wigan, in collaboration with Edward Evans, the managing partner, and Stubs, the Warrington steelmaker. In the better of the two methods a thin steel bar and a length of wrought iron were passed through a rolling mill to fuse them together. The smiths hammered the composite bar around a mandrel and made it into a rough tyre which was machined and shrunk onto the wheel. Whilst still hot the wheel was thrown into a bosh of water to harden the rim. The alternative method used the cementation process, in which charcoal was packed

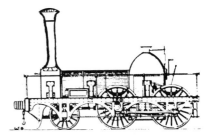

One of the *Leo* Class, 1841–42

against the rim of a wrought iron tyre, which was then heated in a furnace for a week, forming an outer steel layer.

Even before the patent had been granted tyres were being made for the *Suns* and *Fire Flies*. Gooch also mounted a vigorous sales campaign. He had some success but as a rule they were thought to be too expensive. From the outset, however, he had problems with the enforcement of his patent. Stubs, who became a partner in it, warned him that Hargreaves of Bolton had a pair of tyres in service and they must challenge him. This was the first of a series of such problems.

On the Great Western Gooch was still having to battle to keep the services going. As the year progressed the situation became desperate. In February half of his twenty engines were out of action and then *North Star's* crank axle broke: 'If I cannot get an engine which is in repair today ready by six o'clock I will not be able to take out one of the trains. Now is this not a pretty predicament to be in?'.

In March the Great Western was to open as far as Reading and an enormous increase in traffic was anticipated. Fortunately the new engines were on programme. At Hawthorns', where eight *Suns* were in hand, only the aesthetics remained to be settled. 'I should like the other brass plates made as invisible as possible,' Gooch told them, 'having rather an objection to too much brass about an engine.' By 28 February they had the first on test and he was waiting anxiously to hear how she had worked. In the meantime even more were being ordered. He had just finished designing his first goods engines, the 2-4-0 *Leos*. He wrote again to Hawthorns' to say that he

Centaur, a *Fire Fly*, built by Nasmyth and Gaskell, 1841

had persuaded the directors to offer £2450 for each locomotive: 'Should you agree . . . consider this as an order for three.' Hawthorns' accepted this topsy-turvey way of agreeing a contract price.

As the spring approached Gooch's main concern was with Jones, Turner and Evans at Newton, who were building *Fire Fly*. At last she was delivered and on Monday 16 March she was ready, boiler and tender filled with water, bearings oiled, fire glowing and pressure raised. Gooch took the regulator and the splendid engine moved over the points and onto the main line. 'She went pretty well but had far too much steam,' he wrote. 'Will you therefore open your blast pipes to four inches full.' *Fire Fly* was steaming even more freely than he had hoped and he could ease the flow of steam from her cylinders, increasing the power.

His new locomotive was ready just in time. Whilst she was on her first trial a Mr Alexander Meek was travelling in a train drawn by *Morning Star*. They were late and it was obvious from 'a creaking sound' that something was amiss. At Twyford she came off the rails, fortunately running into the side of a cutting. 'The axle of the engine had broken,' Meek complained, 'and the cause of it doing so was the improper state of the engine. It is clear that the neglect extends to the directing engineer and the responsible officers at Paddington.'

The extension to Reading was to open on Monday 30 March 1840. On the preceding Saturday *Fire Fly* made a trial trip with a truck, two carriages and forty distinguished passengers. The down journey was covered at 46.2 mph, even though a spring on the tender broke. On the way back 56 mph was reached and the average from Twyford was over 50 mph. Gooch's delight can be imagined.

On the opening day *Fire Fly* worked the first train. Thousands congregated along the line and large numbers of passengers were carried. All went well, the trains averaging 75 mins for the 35¼ mls (28.2 mph), including four or five stops.

Two more of the 7ft. singles arrived in early April. One completed a trip to Reading in 65 min. – 32.5 mph, a promising performance. Within two weeks the traffic had built up encouragingly, 4,000 embarking at Paddington in a single day. A few months later there were seventeen *Fire Flies* and seven *Suns* in service. Gooch was more than happy with them: 'They all gave everyone general satisfaction. We could now calculate with some certainty not only upon the speed they could run, but upon their not breaking down upon the journey. We had no difficulty in running at sixty miles per hour with good loads'. His only problems had been with Hawthorns'. *Sun*, he complained, 'had none of the pins and eyes of the valve gear of steel'. Some of the sizes

Acheron, a Fenton, Murray and Jackson *Fire Fly*, at speed

were also incorrect, 'thereby totally defeating our main object in furnishing drawings and templates, viz., to get our engines so that one part of any engine will fit another'.

By the end of 1840 the Great Western extended for 80¼ mls towards Bristol. The eastern end of the line had been relatively easy to build. The stretch from Bristol to Bath, however, was far more difficult, each of the 11½ mls bringing new obstacles. Brunel had made a good start in 1835 but after about a year appalling problems had developed. The contractor went bankrupt and his own staff had to take over. It was only in the August of 1840 that the line was finished. The immense Box Tunnel was still a year from completion, so the western end was cut off and Gooch had to operate the service with an isolated group of men and engines.

One of the enginemen he sent down to Bristol was Cuthbert Davison, who had just arrived from Newcastle. Two engines, *Fire Ball*, a *Fire Fly*, and *Meridian*, a *Sun*, were despatched for assembly in the shelter of Saltford Tunnel. Something of a race developed as originally *Meridian*, Davison's engine, was to have taken the first train but the other was ready first and the honour fell to her. The new service started on Monday 31 August 1840 with little fuss. The last rail had only been in position for half an hour when *Fire Ball*, bedecked with flags, left the unfinished station at Bristol Templemeads. Davison took the next train and never forgot the thousands of enthusiastic people he saw along the route and the immense crowds gathered at Bath.

Davison became a greatly respected employee but not all of Gooch's men were so easy to handle, as his "Black Book" shows. Hurst said that Gooch was rather stern and a bad servant stood no chance with him. He was fairness itself, however, only fining Hurst for a series of offences and even taking him on again after a brief period of dismissal. His first punishment was a fine of 10s. for colliding with *Wild Fire* whilst travelling in reverse. A much

A *Fire Fly* at Bristol Templemeads, 1845

heavier penalty was imposed on an engineman who was found in possession of a flute which had been missing over the Christmas holiday period: 'The gentleman who lost it was put to the expense of £4 4s. in sending for it, which he has been ordered to pay'.

Gooch usually gave his men at least a second chance. One was suspended when a piston failed on the up mail and he was stupid enough to disconnect the good one, instead of limping home on the sound side. He was in trouble again within a fortnight, however, because he had neglected his feed pumps. This time he was shown no mercy: 'He has also become generally careless and I fear is getting into drunken habits – discharged'. The drivers were sometimes let off lightly after most serious offences, perhaps because suitable men were hard to come by. A passenger reported one who walked along the steps of the carriages whilst they were in motion and joined a cheerful crowd drinking in the guard's van. The guard was sacked but the engineman was only fined £1.

In spite of his sternness Gooch enjoyed a joke once in a while. Jim Hurst recalled the time when they saw Harry Appleby coming towards them on *North Star*. 'Now, Jim,'

Gooch said, stooping behind the firebox, 'give him a little steam as he passes.' 'I obeyed my superintendent's instructions to the best of my ability,' wrote Hurst, 'and in the evening Appleby met Mr Gooch at Taplow and, making a strong complaint against me, wound up by saying that either he or I should go. He did not know who put me up to the use of the valve. "Well, Appleby," answered Mr Gooch, "All I can say is this, that the man who gives a joke must be prepared to take one". This remark closed Appleby up.'

Gooch often shared the discomforts and dangers faced by his men. With no absolute block system to guard their route and no cabs to protect them their calling was hard and hazardous. As one writer noted, 'even in bright sunshine to stand . . . foremost on a train of enormous weight . . . rushing forward faster than any racehorse can gallop, requires a cool head and a calm heart; but to proceed at this pace in dark or foggy weather . . . is an amount of responsibility which scarcely any other situation in life can exceed. The greatest hardship is from the cold, especially that produced in winter by evaporation from . . . drenched clothes'.

Gooch regarded the discomforts as

necessary to make sure that his men did not
fall asleep. He never shirked them himself
and when he travelled on the footplate it
was not as an onlooker. Francis Trevithick,
the great engineer's son, told of returning
with him after a day of ceremonies. 'On
rushing towards the West Drayton station,
through blinding darkness, the broad-
gauge superintendent hurriedly said,
"What's that?", and closed the steam
regulator. A brief reply caused it to be
again opened, and a sound, as from
compressed space, together with a
momentary glimpse of lights, indicated
that a station had been passed. On inquiry
the next day, it appeared that on the
approach of the special train, a truck was
being removed from the line to a siding; as
it cleared the points, the red signal was
turned off . . . The flying engine . . . in
another thirty seconds of time, thundered
by within an inch of the truck . . . Many
such hair-breadth escapes could be told . . .
and their narration might have checked the
headlong race for speed.'

Before long Gooch's locomotives would
be travelling to Bristol and beyond. The
Paddington engine house would then be too
small and remote to cope with the
workload. It was essential for large
workshops to be built in a central position.
The problem was first considered in June
1839, when Reading and Didcot were suggested. In 1840 Brunel asked Gooch for his
views and on 13 September he wrote recommending a point a mile or so from Swindon
where the Great Western and the Cheltenham and Great Western Union Railways
met. Brunel agreed and on 6 October 1840
the proposal was accepted by the board.
The developments which transformed the
little town into one of the most important
industrial centres in Britain had begun.

Richard Jefferies, the Wiltshire writer,
noted in 1875 that the land selected by
Gooch 'was the poorest in the neighbourhood . . . So much so that when a certain
man with a little money purchased a good
strip of it, he was talked of as a fool . . .
How vain is human wisdom! In a few years
the railway came. Land rose in price and
this very strip brought its owner
thousands'.

Alan S. Peck, in *The Great Western at
Swindon Works* points out that Gooch had
omitted a vital fact from his report: 'The
land required was already railway owned,
albeit by the Cheltenham and Great
Western Union Company! Why this large
piece of land had been purchased by such a
financially hard-pressed undertaking is not
clear'. These two statements leave a strong
whiff of land speculation, and only Gooch
could have clinched matters. His report to
Brunel was an odd one. The only disadvantage which he mentioned was the poor
supply of water. There were, however, two
others of far greater importance – there
were no skilled workmen in the area and
few houses for newcomers. The one advantage to which he referred was that it was
served by a canal, 'by which we could get
coal and coke, I should think at a moderate
price'. He did not discuss the alternatives
and nearly a quarter of his report was taken
up by an explanation that, though Swindon
was not at the mid-point of the Great
Western, he would be using the 7ft. *Fire
Flies* on the 76½ mls to London and the
6ft. *Suns* on the 41 mls of heavier gradients
to Bristol. When the increased revolutions
per mile of the smaller engines were taken
into account the distances, he said, were
'very much equalized'. His arguments are
less convincing than his usual crisp logic,
too much being said for Swindon and
nothing either for or against other places.
Perhaps his views were not dispassionate,
but whatever his reasons, the Great
Western were never to regret his choice.

CHAPTER

10

By the early forties London had sprawled as far as Paddington Green. The old village was engulfed and the houses began to encroach on the countryside to the south and west. The Gooches – there were now four, as Emily Jane had been born on 13 July 1840 – were amongst the outermost of the million and a half inhabitants of the world's greatest city.

Gooch and the other senior staff had their offices at the terminus, a few hundred yards from his home. His assistants, draughtsmen and clerks were nearby. He had several pupils who gained experience by working in the shops, on the engines and in the drawing office. They usually made good careers as a result of his patronage and, in return, were a source of additional cash. When he took his first at the end of 1839 Tom Gooch advised him to tell Brunel: 'If it is not mentioned to him he may be annoyed . . . I think you should have £400'. His principal assistant was his old friend Archibald Sturrock, who joined him in April 1841. Since leaving Dundee Foundry he had spent six months as a fitter at William Fairbairn's at Manchester and had then studied in Paris, Brussels and Edinburgh. His background and ability were exceptional.

During 1841 Gooch became involved with Lord Willoughby de Eresby, who owned vast estates at Grimsthorpe, near Grantham, and in Wales and Scotland. He took a deep interest in his land and became a pioneer of mechanised agriculture. He had invented a method for compressing peat into briquettes using a hydraulic press powered by a steam engine and was trying to persuade the Great Western to use his new fuel. Gooch carried out tests which showed that he could only maintain full boiler pressure if it was mixed with coke. Lord Willoughby was disappointed and offered Gooch a fee to continue the work. Gooch declined: 'It is my duty, being in the pay of the company, to use every means in my power to increase the efficiency of their engines and . . . to reduce the cost of working. Should we succeed as well as I hope to do I shall be sufficiently repaid by the pleasure of having operated in its interest'. Unfortunately his further trials showed that costs were greater than with coke alone and that was the end of the idea. Gooch, however, had made a powerful ally.

In the meantime preparations were in hand for the opening of the last part of the Great Western, the Chippenham to Bath section, which included the awesome Box Tunnel. It slanted at one in a hundred for nearly 2 mls through the rock and was the steepest section of the whole line. The miners had toiled deep under the hillside since September 1836, using a ton of candles and a ton of gunpowder each week. At last all was ready – or nearly so.

The first engine to attempt the climb was *Meridian*. A ceremonial opening had been dispensed with and so there was little fuss as Cuthbert Davison set off with an anxious Brunel beside him. When they reached the tunnel they found that the rails were still not complete and had to wait for 4 hrs whilst the navvies made a crossover from the up to the down line.

Brunel was afraid that the long gradient would prove too much for the locomotives but Gooch had every confidence. To ease his mind he agreed to travel through the tunnel with each train for the first couple of days whilst single-line working was continuing. Brunel, with customary thoughtfulness, looked after him well: 'He was very kind to me in sending me plenty of good food, &c., to keep my steam up'. His long vigil was to end on the second evening after he had accompanied the last up train. Having checked that the regulation green light was burning on the smokebox he climbed onto the footplate and they were soon rumbling through the tunnel. Fortunately he was neither too bored nor too tired to keep a good look-out and suddenly saw the gleam of another green light far ahead: 'A second's reflection convinced me it was the mail coming down. I lost no time in reversing the engine I was on and running back to Box Station, when the mail came down close behind me . . . Had the tunnel not been pretty clear of steam we must have met in full career and the smash would have been fearful, cutting short my career also'. What he said to the railway policeman who had made the mistake can only be imagined.

The Great Western's full service between Paddington and Bristol consisted of eight passenger and two goods trains a day in each direction. The swiftest, the down night mail, took 4hr. 10min. for the 118¼ ml journey, an average of 28.4 mph, which was far from spectacular. The goods trains, which provided the only third class accommodation, managed only 12.4 mph, the passengers requiring great fortitude, as they were crammed onto wooden benches in open trucks whose sides were only 2ft. high.

It was one such train with *Hecla*, a *Leo*, at its head which left Paddington at 4.30 a.m. on 24 December 1841. The rain was lashing down, as it had done all night, and the two third class trucks, coupled immediately behind the tender, were full. At about half past six, long before first light, they reached Sonning Cutting, where the engine plunged into an enormous mass of earth washed onto the line by the downpour. The passengers were shot out of the low-sided vehicles or crushed by the goods wagons, eight being killed and seventeen injured in the world's first major railway disaster. At the Inquiry the Chief Inspector of Railways exonerated Brunel, who had given the cutting a one-in-two slope, but was caustic about the paltry third class accommodation.

Christmas must have been a time of work and worry for Gooch. Besides his involvement in the aftermath of the terrible accident Margaret Gooch's third confinement was imminent. All went well, however, their first son, Henry Daniel, being born on 30 December. Early in the New Year the last of the new locomotives arrived. There were then 62 *Fire Flies*, 21 *Suns*, 18 *Leos* and four of the *Hercules* class, an adequate number to cover the next few years. The *Hercules* engines were an interesting step forward as they were the Great Western's first 0-6-0's. Their six coupled wheels, *Fire Fly* boilers and greater weight gave them excellent characteristics and they were to prove a valuable acquisition.

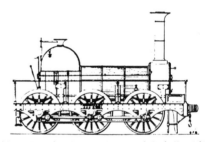

Tityos, *Hercules* Class, Nasmyth and Gaskell, 1842

During 1842 Gooch had to play an important part in a difficult family crisis. Two years previously his brother John had married Hannah Handcock, a girl a good deal younger than himself. On 2 May Anna Gooch wrote to Daniel to say that she was 'much distressed to find that you think there is no hope of poor John getting rid of that vile wife of his, without her consent to the separation. Are you sure you have taken very **good opinion** on the subject? . . . I think she sees John is frightened of her, which makes her give way so much . . . If John was more harsh, and gave her occasionally a good thrashing[*] . . . she would be more careful of irritating him'.

[*]As a less kindly husband might, Anna Gooch meant.

The law then permitted a husband to use force to prevent his wife from leaving him. Marriages were virtually indissoluble, three divorces a year being the average, and all that Daniel could do was to suggest that John had a draft deed of separation prepared. Tom Gooch thought this a good point as 'if she is really afraid of leaving him he may find it very useful'. Eventually the couple agreed to part and Gooch became an intermediary. 'I have a note from Handcock this morning,' John told him, 'but he says nothing as to what place she has chosen . . . Have you a letter this morning? If so let me know by bearer which place she has selected and I will write to them tonight . . . I am at a loss to know what to do'. Finally Gooch was asked to write to his sister-in-law to advise her and to arrange to take her to her new home. She evidently trusted him and, judging by his actions, he had some sympathy for her.

Gooch's opinions were not always so welcome within the family. In 1842 Mary Ann was working as a teacher. 'I feel sorry you do not think she is well placed,' his mother said. 'I certainly should much prefer her being in a private family . . . I wrote to her telling her my wish . . . and this morning received a letter from her saying that she would be exceedingly sorry to leave a family with whom she is so happy and comfortable . . . Mary Ann is not a giddy girl, but one of the strictest principles, prudence and discretion . . . We must let her remain a little longer.'

Anna's letter also mentioned that she had £10 for him which his brother George Henry was returning. This is the only reference in all his papers to the third of his brothers, a shadowy figure from whom he appears to have become estranged.

Gooch had another letter from his mother to say that she had seen in the papers that he had driven Queen Victoria on her first railway journey: 'Now she has once ventured you will often have . . . her company. Poor little woman, she seems to have many enemies abroad lately'.

Other royal passengers had used the Great Western to Slough, the station for Windsor, ever since the line had opened. Prince Albert had travelled even before his marriage and in 1840 had been whirled there, presumably by Gooch, at an average of 48.7 mph. Perhaps this was the occasion on which he commanded, 'not so fast next time, Mr Conductor, if you please'. Crown Prince Frederick William of Prussia had recently used it. 'When he left,' Gooch wrote, 'he gave me a silver salver, which I of course keep, not that it is a valuable one, but it is the gift of a king, and they are not common.'

The Queen's long awaited first journey by rail was triggered, all too literally, by one of the enemies of whom Anna Gooch had written. On Sunday 29 May 1842 she was returning from chapel to Buckingham Palace when Prince Albert saw a man point a pistol at them. Fortunately it mis-fired. The next day Queen Victoria bravely insisted on taking her usual drive. The parks and roads were thick with plain clothes policemen and two equerries rode close on either side to shield them. 'All was so quiet we almost thought of nothing,' she wrote, 'when, as we drove down Constitution Hill very fast, we heard the report of a pistol.' The man was caught and, like the others who made abortive attempts on her life, was found to be mad.

On Monday 13 June, two weeks later, the Queen was to return from Windsor to the Palace. It was hardly a coincidence that her advisers decided that she should then use the railways for the first time. The long awaited command was only issued on the Saturday, together with the instruction that strict secrecy was to be observed. Gooch and his colleagues must have had a busy weekend, but all went well. On the Monday morning the royal party watched their carriages loaded onto the trucks. *Phlegethon*, with Gooch driving and Brunel beside him, left at mid-day precisely. A crimson carpet had been laid along the length of the platform at Paddington and on either side an elegant throng, including the families and friends of the officers of the railway, were lined up to greet their intrepid Sovereign. Her arrival after a journey of 25 min. was greeted with deafening cheers.

Phlegethon's footplate had been rather crowded as the Queen's coachman had regarded it as his duty to travel on the engine. 'Unluckily for him,' wrote one of

Queen Victoria and Prince Albert in the Royal Saloon,
1844

the ladies-in-waiting, 'the journey had such an unfortunate effect upon his livery and shining countenance that when he descended . . . he resembled a Christy Minstrel rather than a coachman of the Royal Household.'

The Queen wrote that her journey had been free from dust and crowds and heat and that she had been quite charmed with it. It was the first of many in which she was driven by Gooch, who nearly always took over when she was travelling and never had a single delay.

In January 1841 Gooch's salary was increased to £700 a year and he decided to move house. Just north of the engine house a row of semi-detached houses had been built overlooking a pool where the Grand Union and Regent's Canals met a short branch to Paddington Dock. At its north-west corner was a particularly attractive pair of houses, No. 8 Warwick Villas, which faced southwards towards a little islet, and No. 32, which fronted onto the Regent's Canal. On 27 May 1840 Samuel Pierce leased the two and sometime during 1842 rented No. 8 to Gooch.

William Robins, Paddington's bitter historian, was critical of the speculative building going on at that time. 'Puffing advertisements for years crowded the columns of *The Times*, however, we saw no account of the contracted areas, the deep, narrow back yards, the thin and crumbling walls, the gaping doors and windows, the damp and ill-ventilated basements, the absence of drainage, the want of bathrooms, &c., &c., – all such things had to be found out by the incoming tenant.' Whatever their original condition, Warwick Villas have survived for nearly a century and a half. They still stand, pleasant in stucco and greenery, beside what became known as 'Little Venice'. All are far grander than a young engineer can hope to live in today. Gooch's house, now No 16 Warwick Avenue, has tall windows above low iron railings which form a mock balcony. The shallow roof is hidden by a neat balustrade and the imposing front door is set into a large porch flanked by imitation columns. There are two main rooms downstairs and four bedrooms above. The one which was Daniel and Margaret's had views over the tree-lined canal basin and the countryside to the west. There were servants' quarters in the attic and a kitchen and other rooms in the basement, one of which Gooch had earmarked as a workshop. On 21 September 1842 Joseph Whitworth sent him 'an order to receive a lathe from the Polytechnic Institute. I am glad to hear you say your shop shall be fit-up as perfect as you can make it. If my Godson should choose the engineering profession he will derive great benefit by being made familiar from infancy with the contents of such a workshop'.

Warwick Villas were well within earshot as the *Fire Flies* and *Suns* rumbled in and out of the terminus. In July 1842 the *Railway Magazine* noted that on one day the six o'clock to Taunton had carried 2,115 people who were going to an agricultural show. Visitors were also flocking into London in ever-increasing numbers to see the sights. Reliable services were being provided over territory stretching as far as Cirencester, Bristol and Taunton and the Great Western was beginning to live up to its name.

CHAPTER

11

In 1841 Robert Stephenson took out a patent for a new class of engines, the 'long boilers'. Amongst the improvements were boilers having up to 800 sq. ft. of heating surface, a hundred more than the *Fire Flies'*. The advantages of the broad gauge were being overtaken and Gooch kept a sharp eye on the rival camp. The prototype began its trials at York on 13 October. By January 1842 he still had not seen it but William Prime Marshall, his opposite number at Derby, was keeping him informed and sent him a sketch and description of an even more up-to-date design.

The drawing in Stephenson's patent specification showed a six-wheeled locomotive with a boiler 11in. less in diameter than *Fire Fly's* but half as long again. Because of short turntables and tight curves the wheelbase could not be increased very much to accommodate the longer boiler and so the firebox was overhung at one end and the smokebox at the other. This gave a clumsy and unstable appearance after the elegance of Gooch's designs.

One of the first was delivered to Marshall in the autumn of 1842. On 12 October he wrote to Gooch to say that it was in service: 'The new expansion gear is working very effectively, and cuts the steam off at any point between 0 and ¾ stroke'. This was the Stephenson link motion, one of the most significant inventions of the nineteenth century.

It is surprising that Gooch had not found a neat solution to the problem of reversing and controlling locomotives for himself. The gab gear could be damaged if it was operated whilst the engine was at speed, and it did not enable the expansion of the

steam to be varied. He had come across various patent gearings, such as the one which the Haigh Foundry suggested in 1840. 'Both Mr Brunel and myself have examined your proposal thoroughly,' he told them. 'It has the advantage of the engineman having the degree of expansion under his control . . . but in nine cases out of ten it would be neglected. Its greatest merit is the constant lead that is maintained, without regard to the expansion. But there are some very serious defects in the application . . . The one we have arranged ourselves is without these faults.' His own system involved the use of cams and was not a success. 'It was too heavy and clumsy,' he said. The link motion, however, was simple and elegant. The engineman could change both power and direction using a single lever with no risk of damage to the parts. It was never patented and so there was nothing to stop him from trying it out. He experimented with it in both the "ordinary" and the "crossed rods" forms, deciding within a week that the latter was best. His view was that both forms suffered from the disadvantage of not having a constant opening (or 'lead') at the start of the stroke, and he set to work to evolve a gearing of his own which did.

By 1842 a great many of Gooch's steel tyres were in service. Because of their hardness final machining could only be carried out by grinding. He built a special machine-tool for the purpose, mounting a 2ft. grindstone on the slide-rest of a large lathe and driving it at 1,000 rpm. This was not a new invention, but its size was unusual and, unlike many of the early grinders, it was a success. Enforcing the patent was, however, a different matter. His problems came to a head on Thursday 24 November 1842 when the case of Gooch versus Banks was heard in the Vice Chancellor's court.

He was seeking to prevent Banks from using steel wheels. His counsel claimed that, though their use on road vehicles was not novel, on railways it was. He produced an affidavit signed by an eminent engineer which pointed out that locomotive wheels guided the engine and provided the traction, whereas road wheels only supported the carriage. Hence the mind of someone engaged in designing railway wheels would be influenced by quite different considerations from that of a person involved with road wheels. The judge was not convinced and decided that the action should stand over, leaving both parties free to bring further litigation.

The lawyers no doubt licked their lips at the stalemate but common sense began to prevail. 'I am sorry to hear your case respecting the wheels is not decided,' Henry Tanner said. 'The suspense is almost as bad as losing . . . I hope you may ultimately succeed if you are compelled to go to trial . . . Marg^t seems to intimate there is a disposition on the part of your opponents to compromise.'

In the meantime Gooch and his partners wrote to another apparent infringer, J.C. York. He proved to be the owner of an older patent, though this used a different process from theirs. This destroyed their case against Banks and he was paid £100 towards his costs. Counsel advised them that they could either delete hardening and the exclusive use of steel from their patent or reduce their prices and command the market in that way. Characteristically they decided to stick to the higher profits and issued a 'disclaimer', restricting their patent to 'modes of forming steel tyres to be used on railways', rather than the all-embracing 'use of steel in the tyres of engine and carriage wheels'. Gooch was disappointed at the outcome of his development. 'It did not pay me during the whole of its time more than between 5 and £6,000,' he complained, though he wrote this when he could afford to turn up his nose at such a sum.

In 1843 the fastest passenger services in Britain were being run by the Northern and Eastern Railway, a narrow gauge line. Their average was only 36 mph excluding stops. Despite the vaunted advantages of the broad gauge the Great Western were a poor second with 33 mph, the rest trailing at 30 mph and less. Gooch knew that his engines were more than capable of taking the lead and before long the directors were to regret not encouraging him to try. In the meantime he made the most of every opportunity to show what he could do.

A suitable occasion presented itself on 19 July 1843 when Brunel's S.S. *Great Britain* was floated out of the dry dock at Bristol where she had been built. 'She was considered a monster ship . . .,' wrote Gooch, 'and everyone blamed Mr Brunel for building anything so large.' She combined prodigious size, an iron hull and screw propulsion. His courage and enterprise were marked by Prince Albert, who travelled down to perform the ceremony. Gooch drove, with Brunel again beside him on the footplate.

The down journey was not especially noteworthy as there was a delay at Bath for a loyal address to be presented. At Bristol the vessel was inspected. The Prince then had lunch on board with six hundred other guests before the dock was flooded. By four o'clock the ceremonies were over and he left for London. With the line clear all was set for an exceptional trip and Gooch whirled the cheerful passengers back to Paddington at a phenomenal rate. Charles Babbage was in a compartment with three other engineers. One remarked on the speed. 'My neighbour on my left,' said Babbage, 'took out his watch, and noted the time of passage of the distance posts, whence it appeared we were then proceeding at the rate of seventy-eight miles an hour. The train was evidently on an incline, and we did not long sustain that dangerous velocity.' Paddington was reached in 2hr. 40 min. – 44.3 mph, an astonishing performance.

During the spring of 1844 the last part of the Bristol and Exeter Railway was opened. As it was worked by Great Western stock Gooch's locomotives then had to provide a service extending 194 mls from

Paddington. At that time plans were being prepared for further extensions to the broad gauge system. Subsidiary companies were formed and independent groups planning railways in adjoining territories were given every assistance. The new lines were to stretch as far as Pembroke and Fishguard in Wales and Falmouth in Cornwall. Most were within the Great Western's acknowledged territory but some reached into areas which the narrow gauge companies regarded as their own. Rival schemes were put forward and opposition was marshalled. What Gooch described as 'our hardest gauge fight' began. The opening of the line to Exeter on 1 May gave a marvellous opportunity to publicise the broad gauge and Gooch organised a spectacular run.

The ordinary service was to take 7 hr. 10 min. but Gooch's special was scheduled to cover the distance in 5 hr. Most of the long stretches were timed at 50 mph and the round trip of 388 mls called for an average of 43 mph, exclusive of the stops. Gooch chose *Orion*, a two year old *Fire Fly*, for the trip. She had a variable expansion gear, this being his first recorded use of the Stephenson link, and her safety valve was set at 70 lb/sq in., twenty higher than in the original *Fire Flies*.

Orion left Paddington at 7.31 a.m., 1 min. late. Forty privileged passengers were aboard the two carriages, a load of 21 tons. Her boiler was a little too full at first, so Gooch lost a little time over the first 4 mls before settling her into her stride. He reached the fourteenth mile post on schedule, and though he had to ease off as he passed through Slough, Maidenhead and Twyford stations he drew up at Reading on time.

Orion was filled up with water in 4 min. and then set off on the easy leg to Swindon, again arriving on time. Everyone rushed into the refreshment room for a 15 min. breakfast but were not quite quick enough, as Gooch left 1 min. late. All went well through Box Tunnel and to beyond Bath, but then he had to slow down. He had caught up the 90 min. start of the six o'clock, which he then had to follow into Bristol.

Gooch held to his tight schedule all the way to Taunton, 179 mls from Paddington,

averaging 45.3 mph exclusive of the stops. He then found himself behind a long train carrying guests from Bristol, which made him 15 min. late at Exeter, though an hour and fifty-five minutes ahead of the normal timetable.

His only rest was during the banquet, as he had to spend the afternoon on railway business. Unfortunately the turntable was not complete, so that *Orion* had to be driven to Taunton to be turned, giving her an extra 60 mls to cover, tender first. 'This did more harm than the whole of the long run,' wrote Gooch, 'as she got covered with dust and there was much danger of her heating on the return trip. She ought to have had her fire pulled out . . . for it had by this time got very dirty, and little pains had been taken by the men who cleaned it.'

For some reason the special was 19 min. late leaving for Paddington. This put Gooch on his metal and the up journey was covered at an extraordinary speed. He made a good start to Bridgewater, regaining 2 min., but did even better from there to Bristol, averaging 53.5 mph. He hung on at Templemeads for an extra 2 min. to allow *Orion's* grate to be cleaned thoroughly, but even so was only 7 min. behind time when he left for Swindon, with the toughest running of the day ahead. The fire was still not as clean as he would have wished and he could not keep the pressure up, losing two minutes and arriving at Swindon with only 30 lb on the gauge. Harry Appleby, the Superintendent of the Running Department, crawled under *Orion* himself to rake the dust and clinker from the grate. This cost another 2 min. and Gooch was 11 min. behind time as he picked up speed again. The delay had been worthwhile, however, as *Orion* steamed splendidly and speeds were astonishing as he flew over the most easily graded sections of Brunel's Billiard Table. In spite of checks at signals, 8 min. were gained between Swindon and Reading. Then came the run-in to Paddington, where the fastest times of all were clocked. A 13½ ml length was covered at 57.8 mph, Gooch noting with pride that 'the engine appeared to be going through the chalk cutting I should say little short of seventy miles an hour'.

Orion came to a stand at the terminus at

Gooch with his *Fire Fly* model. Photograph of
about 1845

put on a 4½ hr service. He suggested that
this should be done by express trains for a
higher fare. Unfortunately his advice was
again ignored.

To celebrate his pride in his engines
Gooch had an accurate working model of a
Fire Fly built to one-eighth scale. 'This is a
very beautiful piece of work', he wrote.
'Many of the parts were made by Clements,
who used to be in those days the best
workman in London.' This was obviously
Joseph Clements, the great craftsman-
engineer. He died in 1844, so that at least
some of the model was made prior to that
time. It is to be seen in a photograph of
Gooch taken in about 1845, leaving its age
and authenticity beyond doubt. It is now
on loan by his descendants to the Science
Museum, South Kensington.

The locomotive caught the imagination
of its beholders in a way which no later
marvel has matched. Besides being a magnificent achievement and a shining symbol
of the future it had a comforting air of flesh
and blood.

Turner's masterpiece, *Rain, Steam and
Speed: the Great Western Railway*, painted
in 1844, however, has sinister undertones.
A dark *Fire Fly*, its blazing firebox to
the fore, bursts across an insubstantial
Maidenhead Bridge from a maelstrom
of colour. Regimented rows of passengers
are seen dimly behind, mankind being
swept from a swirling past to a dizzying
future.

Gooch had excellent taste as a connoisseur of nineteenth century art. His preference was for representational painting,
however, and he was not an admirer of the
iconoclasts. He must nevertheless have
gone to the Royal Academy to see the
controversial picture inspired by Brunel's
railway and the steam and speed of his *Fire
Flies*.

10.03 p.m., only 3 min. behind time.
Gooch had recovered 16 min. against the
tightest of schedules, averaging 46.9 mph
exclusive of the stops. Sir Thomas Acland,
the M.P. for North Devonshire,
immediately leapt out of his carriage and
dashed to the House. At ten thirty he told a
surprised Commons that he had been in
Exeter until after five o'clock. 'It was a very
hard day's work for me', Gooch wrote,
'Next day my back ached so much I could
hardly walk. Mr Brunel wrote me a very
handsome letter thanking me for what I had
done, and all were very pleased.'

In the report of the run which Gooch
presented to the board he suggested that
London to Exeter could be covered regularly
in 3 hr. 59 min. and that it would be safe to

CHAPTER

12

At the beginning of 1845 Henry Tanner was concerned about his daughter. 'I hope she will take a little moderate exercise whenever she can', he told Gooch. 'If it will at all add to her comfort to have Dear Mary with her next month I will willingly undergo the privation.' His worries were soon eased, however, as Charles Fulthorpe, Gooch's second son, arrived safely on 31 January.

His letter also raised a business matter. 'I have every reason to be satisfied with your good management of the York and London shares,' he said. 'If you have no objection I would like to keep ten of the twenty unsold. If they obtain their Act . . . there is little doubt of their running up a good premium, and if they do not . . . the risk is not very great, but I leave it to yourself to do as you think best.'

Britain had just emerged from some years of depression. Capital was available and there were no more attractive opportunities for investment than railways. The largest companies were returning good dividends, £100 shares being worth up to £229. All were expanding as towns remote from the existing 2,000 mls of lines clamoured for services. Over two hundred Bills were due to come before Parliament in the forthcoming session. The madcap Railway Mania had begun.

Investment could then involve terrible risks. George Stephenson warned of wild schemes: 'Thousands of people will be ruined, as I have learned that many have mortgaged their little properties . . . Of

course their property will be lost up to the amount of money that they have got'. Shares with a face value of £120,000,000 were sold in 1845, Parliament being so concerned that lists of subscribers were compiled. From these we learn that Gooch bought no less than £12,500-worth, an astonishing amount. He only had to make the initial payment at that stage but clearly had great confidence in both his financial position and his judgement. Tanner's letter makes it plain that he was sharing some of the risks, but the extent to which he was gambling is clear when we look at the amounts invested by some longer-established men:-

George Stephenson	£39,270
Charles Saunders	£26,500
George P. Bidder*	£17,780
William Tweedy	£13,000
Robert Stephenson	£7,500
Tom Gooch	£5,500
Leslie Meldrum	£5,000
Henry Tanner	£600
John V. Gooch	£500
Isambard K. Brunel	Nil

The multitude of new schemes introduced a bitter competitive spirit into the railway business. The Great Western came under particular pressure, the narrow gauge companies uniting against them in a conflict which surged for a decade and more – the Gauge War. In January 1845 the broad gauge lost the first round. Seven

*An associate of Stephenson who becomes important in Gooch's life shortly.

months previously the Bristol and
Gloucester Railway, a broad gauge line,
had been opened. Funds were short and so
its northern terminus was a temporary platform added alongside the much grander
station of the narrow gauge Birmingham
and Gloucester Railway. For the first time
the two gauges had met.

The most serious argument against the
broad gauge was the inconvenience at such
a 'break of gauge'. Brunel dismissed the
problem airily. The passengers, he claimed,
would merely step from one carriage to
another. Telescopic axles, container wagons
and piggy-back trucks were amongst the
schemes which he had in mind for easing
the transition of goods. At Gloucester,
however, the facilities were poor and largely
in the hands of the opposition. The result-
ant chaos became notorious.

The Bristol and Gloucester and Birmingham and Gloucester Railways decided to
amalgamate. Whilst they were preparing a
Bill, the Great Western approached them
with a proposal that all three should unite,
a potential master stroke. On 24 January
1845 the Great Western offered £60 of their
shares, then standing at £123, for each
Birmingham and Gloucester, valued at
£109. They were pressed to increase their
bid to £65 but would not, and so the
meeting was adjourned. The next day John
Ellis, the deputy chairman of the Midland
Company, stepped in and took a perpetual
lease of the two railways. So a broad gauge
line passed into enemy hands and the Great
Western were denied access to the Black
Country.

During 1845 two Bills of great
importance to the broad gauge were to
come before Parliament. Both were for
railways to Oxford, which was already
served by the Great Western's branch from
Didcot. The first of the two, the Oxford,
Worcester and Wolverhampton, was
intended to complete a broad gauge route
to the West Midlands and the second, the
Oxford and Rugby, would give access to
one of the country's most important junc-
tions. To counter these ambitious moves
the London and Birmingham put forward a
Bill for an alternative narrow gauge railway
from Wolverhampton to their main line
with branches to Rugby and Oxford. The

two gauges were competing for the same
territory.

Gladstone, who was President of the
Board of Trade, formed a Railway Board to
prepare preliminary studies of some of the
many Bills. The committee, the 'Five
Kings', were given the task of comparing
the three Oxford proposals. Their report,
published in the month of the defeat at
Gloucester, was a second blow to the Great
Western, as they recommended that Parliament should support the narrow gauge
scheme. Amongst their conclusions was the
statement that on the broad gauge 'the
actual speed . . . is not so high as on some
narrow gauge railways, . . . notwithstanding the excellence of its gradients'. This at
last spurred the Great Western board into
action and Gooch's suggestion that they
should run expresses was implemented. On
10 March a 5 hr service to Exeter was
introduced, the fastest in the world. This,
wrote Gooch 'was the beginning of that
important system of express trains which
has given so much accommodation and
comfort to the public. I may, therefore, I
think, claim to be the father of express
trains'. Phenomenal speeds were attained
and before the end of the month Samuel
Homfray was boasting in Tredegar that he
had been on a train which had covered 14
mls in 12 min. − 70 mph. The narrow
gauge fought back, starting expresses
between Euston and Liverpool, but the
Great Western then lopped off another half-
hour, 9 min. being gained by shortening
the stop at Swindon. Rigby, who held the
refreshment concession, was furious and put
the question to the Court of Chancery. His
lease laid down that all trains 'not being
goods trains or trains . . . sent express'
must stop there for about ten minutes. The
court ruled that public trains, however fast,
were not trains 'sent express' and the stop
had to be reinstated. Gooch, however,
immediately absorbed the extra time, his
engines then averaging 46.7 mph, exclusive of stops, an amazing figure.

In the meantime Parliament started work
on the Oxford Bills. The First and Second
Readings were completed without incident
but then, on 1 May, the crucial Committee
Stage began. Over the first twelve days the
case for the narrow gauge was presented by

a galaxy of witnesses led by Robert Stephenson. Their counsel urged that the gauge question was the principal point to be settled, stressing that the breaks of gauge should be at Oxford and Gloucester, rather than Rugby and Birmingham. The broad gauge then took the stand for seven days, Charles Russell, the Great Western's chairman, Saunders, Brunel and Gooch being amongst the witnesses. Gooch found the experience gruelling: 'Sitting in this heat all day and working most of the night in preparing evidence . . . all most broke me down'. His efforts were worth while, however, as the committee decided in their favour. 'I will never forget the passion poor old George Stephenson got into when the decision . . . was announced,' wrote Gooch. 'I thought he would have struck Brunel, and he also gave me his mind very freely for fighting for the broad gauge against the narrow, in which, he said, I had been reared.' The struggle, however, was far from over. In barely a fortnight the committees' views would be examined by the full House at the Report Stage of the Bill. Vigorous lobbying began immediately.

It was on 20 June 1845 that Lord Ingestre rose before a crowded Commons to move the adoption of the Committees' Report on the Oxford, Worcester and Wolverhampton Bill. The opposition was led by Richard Cobden, who proposed an amendment calling for the appointment of a Commission to consider whether all existing and future railways should be of one gauge. 'This is not merely a question of a particular line,' he said. 'It includes an important principle . . . Out of the House the proceedings of this night are looked to with great anxiety, and the crowded state of the benches within shows that the House itself looks upon it as nothing but a national question.' Other members, though, saw his suggestion as no more than a delaying tactic. 'The honourable Member is more simple than he could pretend to be,' he was told angrily, 'in supposing that the large attendance . . . present is on national grounds . . . Have a public enquiry on public grounds, if the House sees fit, but do not suffer it to be by way of obstruction to private interests.' Another speaker made it plain just what

these interests were. 'In the city,' he said, '. . . a most enormous sum of money is pending as to the broad or narrow gauge being adopted. If we do not prevent the delay upon which some parties are calculating much mischief will inevitably ensue.'

The debate was long but eventually Cobden's amendment was defeated by 247 votes to 113. This cleared the Oxford, Worcester and Wolverhampton Bill and immediately afterwards a depleted Commons accepted the Report on the Oxford and Rugby line. At the Third Readings, however, Cobden had more success. Both Bills went through without difficulty but when he again proposed the formation of a Commission the House agreed without a division. Once again the broad gauge had a battle on their hands.

On 11 July the names of the Gauge Commissioners were announced. Gooch thought them 'certainly the most incompetent tribunal'. The first, Sir Frederic Smith, had been Inspector of Railways, but Gooch thought he knew nothing about them. He was also caustic about Peter Barlow, Professor of Mathematics at the Royal Military Academy, though his involvement with railways went back to 1830. The appointment of the third, Professor G.B. Airey, the Astronomer Royal, puzzled everyone, 'the connection between the satellites of Jupiter and the motion of . . . trains being rather obscure', as one newspaper put it. They were diligent ferreters and hard workers, however, soon sending out a long questionnaire and beginning to hear the evidence on 6 August. The narrow gauge were again first to present their case and amongst the listeners was Gooch. 'The question before the Commissioners was left to me alone,' he said, 'a responsibility I did not much like, but it was to be, so I undertook the task.'

The first witness was Robert Stephenson, 'a firm and persistent hater, . . . very jealous of opposition or self assertion', according to one of his engineers. On that day he was at his grimmest. His opening blast included the comment that the original stock of broad gauge engines had been thrown away almost entirely. He then stated incorrectly that *North Star* had been designed for a 6 ft. gauge and that the width of the boiler had not been changed: 'Mr Gooch will correct me if I am wrong'. His implication that his engine had given her excellent performance without the extra foot of width being used was challenged by Gooch, who was able to remind him that the firebox had been widened from 4ft. 6in. to 4ft. 9in. He was then dishonestly finessed, Stephenson saying that even the bigger boiler was only ½in. too wide to go into the narrow gauge. The biggest firebox that Forth Street had managed to fit into a 4ft. 8½in. engine, however, was only 4ft. 3in. wide – 5½in. under the gauge. Stephenson also told the Commissioners that it was only recently that the broad gauge had managed quicker services than the narrow. 'Since they adopted express trains they have exceeded the averages on other lines because they had . . . engines built for those speeds,' he said, again unfairly, as it was six years since the *Fire Flies* had been designed.

The Commissioners then turned to the breaks of gauge. Stephenson said that where there was heavy traffic to be transferred even a canal would be preferable. He also scoffed at Brunel's proposal to use container trucks as they had been a failure on the Canterbury and Whitstable: 'Sometimes we had loose boxes and no frames and sometimes . . . underframes and . . . no boxes'. 'Suppose an importation of Irish pigs at Bristol and they had to be transferred to the Yorkshire lines?', he was asked. 'I am afraid it would be necessary to have them in loose boxes', he replied. 'You must move them en masse'.

The next to be called was Joseph Locke. He expressed a guarded preference for a wider gauge for high speeds because large wheels and a high centre of gravity were then necessary, 'but I think we have . . . obtained . . . a speed high enough and . . . I would neither increase my gauge nor my speed nor my wheels until I had more experience'. The broad gauge gave more space in which to mount the cylinders and valve gear of the engines. Locke had tried the alternative approach of using 'outside cylinders', in which the machinery was mounted outboard of the wheels, and was able to make some telling points. His engines were simpler, he said, and the

crank axle, the weakest part of the early locomotives, had been eliminated.

James McConnell, of the Bristol and Gloucester Railway, was an especially important witness as he was involved with both gauges. He claimed that there was little to choose between them on safety and that he had seen narrow gauge locomotives just as powerful as the broad. The Commissioners asked him 'would any increase or diminution of the staff of porters result from a uniform gauge at Gloucester?'. 'A very great decrease', he replied, 'with about thirty wagons we require twelve porters to tranship . . . If the gauge was uniform I should imagine we could do the whole goods trade there with . . . four.'

A long procession of distinguished engineers, managers, businessmen and hauliers hammered home the arguments. The sheer cheek of Laws, of the Manchester and Leeds Railway, must have taken Gooch's breath away. When asked if he had ever asked locomotive manufacturers about an increase in the gauge he replied that he had: 'They are very contradictory, in fact many . . . are almost as mechanical as the instruments they use. Half the operatives of locomotives are boys that are set to work to order from a drawing. They hardly know the principle on which the engine is made'.

By 4 September the narrow gauge case was complete. The Commissioners, ready for their holidays, adjourned for six weeks. Gooch summarised the arguments which had been put to them as: 'First, the broad gauge engines were too large and heavy and the large wheels . . . not necessary, as the small wheels and engines of the n-gauge Cos. were able to run at as high speeds as it was safe . . . to work. Second, . . . the carriages were too large; the public did not like to sit four abreast. Third, . . . the cost of working was greater'. 'I may also say the question of break of gauge was dwelt upon', he closed.

He regarded this latter point as their weakness, though everything they could think of was done to strengthen their position. A machine was built at Paddington for transferring the bodies of wagons from one underframe to another. At the time of the Commons' hearings Brunel had invited the whole House to come to see it. A similar scheme was in use in France for transporting the bodies of mail coaches from Paris to Orleans or Rouen, where they were replaced on wheels to continue by road. Gooch wanted to see the arrangements for himself and so spent ten days of the respite on the continent. It was the first time he had been abroad and he combined business with pleasure, taking his wife and her sister Mary with him. Margaret Gooch must have been especially glad of her company as she was again pregnant. 'I enjoyed the trip very much,' Gooch wrote. 'It was a new world to me. I landed at Dieppe and went to Paris and from there to Bruxelles and so home by Ostend.' At Orleans, where the coaches were supposed to arrive at least 20 min. before departure time, he saw one put onto a railway wagon in 2 min. and a batch of five made ready with 5 min. to spare.

After his break Gooch began final preparations for giving evidence. He drove a *Fire Fly* in some trials on 6 October. 'The up line from the west side of Maidenhead Station is very rough', he warned his staff. 'I could not keep the steam in the express engine . . . I am not quite sure whether it was safe.' Then, on Friday 17 October 1845, he at last took his place before the Commissioners.

Gooch was not fond of the limelight. He was naturally reserved, it was said, 'and this led him to shrink from obtruding his own personality upon any except those nearest to him . . . It was duty, not inclination, that placed him under the gaze of the public eye'. To railway engineers such as Stephenson, Brunel and Tom Gooch the witness box of Parliamentary Committees was a way of life. It was there that their reputations were made or broken. Gooch had no desire to make railway building his career and we can be sure that one of his reasons was a dislike of this aspect of their work. But, as events were to show, he was more than capable of holding his own under the most searching scrutiny. Brunel and Saunders had complete confidence in him, or they would hardly have left him to create the opening impression, and he was in complete command of his subject.

During the whole of Friday's session and most of the following Tuesday's more than fourteen hundred questions were put to him, over a fifth of all that were asked. Many were tortuous, but his replies were succinct and full of information. His answer to an early and prolix question as to what gauge he thought best for the design of a powerful locomotive was the pithy 'I do not think we have too much room on the wide gauge for the power we are requiring' – a nineteen-word summary of his whole case.

Gooch saw the virtues of the broad gauge as power, speed, punctuality, safety and, above all, economy. The one problem, of overriding importance to the Great Western, as they were in the minority, was the break of gauge. He spoke up firmly when the Commissioners turned to the point. The evil was very trifling, he said. Rugby, Wolverhampton and Birmingham were the right places for the breaks and for the coal trade he would recommend loose boxes.

'You see no inconvenience in the loose boxes of the Company running upon the frames and carriages of another?', he was asked in surprise.

'I do not see that there is more difficulty in carrying out that system than in carrying out many of the systems that we have upon the present railways. It is only necessary for a thing to be required, for it to be done'.

He was equally firm about the transference of passengers, seeing no problem in making a narrow platform between the two lines so that people could walk out of one carriage and into another. A train half a mile long could be dealt with in a few minutes, he said, if the traffic required it.

To his relief the Commissioners then moved on to the broad gauge locomotives. 'Your engines and tenders are of course more expensive?', they asked.

'Not in proportion to the power. We have paid on the average £1850 for our engines . . . about £9 4s. per cubic foot of water they are capable of evaporating per hour . . . The narrow gauge . . . would be about £18 per cubic foot and the Southampton engines about £12, therefore the heavier engine has the advantage.'

This was the first of a long succession of telling points. 'You have given . . . the cost of repairs per mile as 2.7 for the broad gauge and 3.46 for the narrow', he was reminded. 'Does the diminished cost . . . result from the system or from having introduced a greater number of new engines?.'

'From the system entirely. We have a smaller comparative number of engines . . . and we have not had a new engine for the last three years . . . It is a fact that we work the traffic at half the cost of the narrow gauge lines . . . .'

'Are not your workshops necessarily more expensive?'

'I heard in evidence that Wolverton had cost £200,000 and I think we have spent half that at Swindon and have a better place.'

When the Commissioners went on to the superior comfort of the broad gauge Gooch was sufficiently at ease to make a joke. They asked if he had ever tried writing in the broad and narrow gauge carriages.

'Very frequently,' he answered.

'Do you find that you can write with more facility on the broad?'.

'Very much.'

'Have you ever found any practical inconvenience in writing in the narrow gauge?'

'I have often been in narrow gauge carriages when I could not even read.'

Some of his strongest evidence was based on tests which he had carried out on locomotives of both gauges. The long boilers had a much greater area of tube surface than the broad gauge engines and yet produced far less steam, because their fireboxes were smaller. He established a 'firebox law', which showed that 2 cu. ft. of water were evaporated per hour by every square foot of firebox surface area, irrespective of the amount of tube surface. He used his 'law' to considerable effect. 'We have heard,' he reminded the Commissioners, 'that the narrow gauge engines are being constructed as powerful . . . as the Great Western's, because they make the boilers twelve, fourteen and fifteen feet long, . . . that by this enormous increase of tube surface they are getting what we are getting . . . Neither by calculation nor by experiment is that borne out in the least. The firebox is really the test of the power of the engine.'

The crucial point was that the fireboxes of the long boilers were already as large as they

could be whereas the broad gauge had ample scope for further development. The question which he had been hoping for then came.

'Is it in contemplation to construct on the Great Western Railway locomotives of greater power?'

'We are constructing engines of greater power . . . We expect to increase the weight of the trains rather than the speed'

'By what changes is it proposed to effect this?'

'By increasing the boilers and fireboxes principally and the cylinder in proportion.'

The most serious drawback of the long boilers was their instability at speed. Gooch had tested one of the worst, the *White Horse of Kent*. He found her so unsteady that before he could make measurements of the smokebox temperature he had to tie himself on. She got the name of 'Stephenson's Rocking Horse', he wrote. He told the Commissioners that she was one of the engines which the narrow gauge were expecting would compete with his own: 'The day I was on she had been running about 20,000 miles, and she was in such a state that she was not safe. She was taken off two or three days after . . . When she was examined she was worn from ½in. to ⅝in. sideways in the axleboxes and brasses.'

'Was that from the yawing motion?'

'Yes. It was created both by the outside cylinders and the enormous overhanging weight.'

A few days after the Commissioners had finished with Gooch, Charles Saunders was available to give evidence. He outlined Brunel's objectives in choosing such a wide gauge and stated that, by and large, they had been attained. Then, on 25 October, Brunel at last took the stand. After only a few preliminaries Sir Frederic and his colleagues put the fundamental question, asking if he now thought that he had been injudicious in using such a wide gauge.

'To answer that,' he replied, 'I run the risk, I am afraid, of being accused of adopting even wilder notions; I should rather be above than under seven feet now if I had to reconstruct the lines.'

This courageous statement led to a long discussion on the benefits of the broad gauge. When Brunel had given himself enough rope the Commissioners drew the noose tight. Had the gauge of his Genoa and Turin Railway been an open question, they asked innocently.

'Yes, except as far as I may have decided it'.

'How is it decided for that particular line?'

'I recommended 4ft. 8½in'.

'Is there any reason which has induced you to give that recommendation?'

'I did not think that either the quantities or the speeds likely to be demanded for many years to come in that country required the same principles . . . As a question of policy as much as engineering I advised them to adopt the gauge. I thought it wise to conciliate . . . the Milan and Venice Railway and others . . . likely to be connected with us.'

Policy and conciliation were of importance in Britain, too, and these words did much to destroy the broad gauge case. The Commissioners were particularly struck that almost all the continental railways had been built later than the British ones, yet to the 4ft. 8½in. gauge. 'Some of these railways have been constructed as well as planned by English engineers,' they said, 'and amongst that number we find Mr Brunel, the original projector of the broad gauge.'

From this point Gooch and his colleagues had their backs to the wall. Their strength was the supremacy of their engines and so, as their final hope, they issued a challenge. On 2 December 1845 Brunel proposed a contest between locomotives of the two gauges, each to haul trains of various weights at speeds of 40 and 50 mph, or faster if they could manage it. The Great Western, he taunted, would use engines which had been in service for several years and had been designed six or seven years before.

The days of the duel were not yet done and no gentleman could refuse such a suggestion. George Parker Bidder, Robert Stephenson's associate, picked up the gauntlet. The editor of the *Railway Chronicle*, however, complained that the trials were worthless and would only add confusion to a question they could not possibly clear up. He was, he said, very much mistaken over the talents of the Great Western party if they did not succeed in blowing up the entire labours of the Commission. And that, of course, was their objective.

CHAPTER

13

Even before the Gauge War, Gooch was known to have little time for George P. Bidder. John Reid wrote to him in 1844 looking for a job: 'I have been on the transfer for twelve months and am nominally engineer to a discreditable undertaking called the Northampton and Peterboro' Railway. I need only say that our works are cheap and nasty and Bidder is father of them in order to convince you that the term "discreditable" is not too strong'.

Bidder had been born in 1806. Even as a very small boy he had shown an extraordinary genius for mental arithmetic. His father arranged exhibitions of his talents and before he was nine he had appeared before Queen Charlotte. Wealthy patrons sent him to Edinburgh University, where he met Robert Stephenson. The two became life-long friends and by 1845 he was acting as a Joint Principal Engineer with Stephenson on major projects.

Bidder's closest associates knew him as a genial and warm-hearted man, not above a wrestling match with George Stephenson. With his fellow engineers, however, he could be impatient and ill-tempered. The gauge trials brought out the worst in him as he had no hope of winning. Brunel suggested tests on long, varied lengths of line but he insisted on short courses with no severe gradients. This suited the narrow gauge, as each run could be completed with one tenderful of water which could be heated up beforehand, enabling the speed to be increased by 4 or 5 mph.

The broad gauge experiments were carried out on the 53 ml stretch from Paddington to Didcot. Gooch chose *Ixion*, which had been delivered in 1841, for the passenger trials. The first runs took place on Tuesday 16 December 1845. Gooch, unlike his opponents, ran his tests to a timetable and *Ixion* pulled out of Paddington only 2½ min. behind time. She was drawing eight carriages, a load of 81 tons, and had Sir Frederic Smith, Professor Barlow, Bidder, Brunel and many other important folk on board. Gooch took her briskly to the first mile-post, where he pulled up, as the tests were to be from a standing start. In anticipation of Bidder's intentions her tender was full of hot water.

At 10.06¾ a.m. *Ixion* moved away. A little time was lost at the crossing with the West London Railway but then she began to gather speed, rattling through Acton, West Drayton and Maidenhead. A blustery south-west wind was pushing the wheel flanges hard against the rails, slowing her down, but Didcot was reached at an average of 47.5 mph. The middle 46 mls, when the train should have been at full speed, were covered at 52.8 mph, a splendid result in poor conditions.

Little time was available to turn the engine and take on coke and there were no facilities to heat up the fresh tender of water. In less than an hour *Ixion* was on the way back, setting off with a black fire and cold water. The wind was now from behind and she achieved extraordinary speeds, averaging 50 and clearing one mile at 59 mph. Later in the day two runs were carried out with 71 tons. In spite of a strong cross wind Gooch managed 54.6 mph on the eastward run, the steady-speed stretch being covered at 57.5 mph.

For the runs next morning only six carriages were attached and very high speeds were expected. Conditions were good at first, though there were ominous signs of rain. One mile was cleared in a minute and *Ixion* took only 22 min. 33 sec. from the eleventh to the thirty-third mile posts – 58.5 mph. It then started to drizzle and as they left Sonning Cutting the wheels began to slip. Gooch reduced speed but the rails were so greasy that the slipping continued over the next 12 miles. *Ixion* nevertheless averaged 52.4 mph and 56.3 mph over the middle 46 miles. On the return trip rain fell more heavily but slipping was avoided, though the rails were still dirty. Sixty-one mph, the highest speed of the whole trials, was reached at one point.

The intention was to run 50 ton trials during the afternoon but Bidder felt that this was unnecessary. 120 tons were coupled on instead, an immense load. An average of 47.5 mph was achieved for the double journey, another outstanding result.

For the broad gauge goods engine tests Gooch selected *Hercules*. She put up a first class performance, hauling 404 tons at 22.7 mph. At times the heavily laden wagons lurched along at 39 mph, an awe-inspiring sight. At some stage there was an attempt at sabotage. Craig, who became Chief Inspector at Paddington, was instructed to take an experimental train to Ealing ready for a start at five the next morning. Immediately before the test was due to begin he inspected the wagons and found that someone had taken the grease out of every axlebox during the night.

The passenger runs were completed just before Christmas. As soon as the holiday was over Gooch set off for the narrow gauge trials on the Crewe to Manchester line. He and Professor Barlow arrived early so as to see the weigh-in but nothing happened until the morning that the first test was due. To Gooch's annoyance Bidder then announced that he was postponing the start because of the probability of bad weather and that he was going to use the York to Darlington line instead.

It was not until Tuesday 30 December that the narrow gauge's experimental train stood in York station. At its head was the York and North Midland Railway's *Engine A*, a long boiler which had been built by

Stephensons' since the start of the Gauge Inquiry and was too new even to have a name. She had cost £1,925, £75 more than *Ixion,* and was 18 cwt heavier. Her boiler had 45% more tube surface but her firebox was only two-thirds the size. She had outside cylinders, inclined upwards, and stood high on wheels 6ft. 6in. in diameter. 'Every effort has been made,' wrote Gooch, 'to construct a powerful engine in as small a space with as little weight as possible . . . A couple of additional inches have even been obtained by throwing the bosses and spokes of the wheels out of the centre of the tyres . . . The cylinders were made . . . with 24in. stroke, but the boiler was found insufficient . . . and the stroke was . . . reduced to 21in. . . . . It may therefore be assumed, **that the greatest effect attainable on the narrow gauge has been arrived at in these experiments.**'

The first runs were to be with an 80 ton load but a strong wind was blowing. Bidder, to Gooch's amazement, insisted on starting with only 50 tons, the load which he had cut out of the broad gauge trials.

Engine A was severely hampered by the cross wind and only averaged 34.6 mls an hour over the 43¼ ml course. Gooch travelled on the footplate with his opposite number, J.J. Berkeley, but did not enjoy the experience. Even at these speeds she was so unsteady that he was not prepared to ride on her again and warned Brunel to do the same. At Darlington Bidder's reason for changing the course became apparent. He connected *Engine A* to an artificial blast pipe powered by a steam engine, which heated the water in the tender ready for the return journey. Gooch was not at all put out by his ingenuity, merely remarking that it would have been of great benefit at Didcot. The cross wind slowed *Engine A* even more on her way back and only 30.7 mph was averaged.

Bidder spent the next morning on another 50 ton trial. It was a fine, calm day and *Engine A* did much better, reaching a top speed of 54.5 mph. The averages were 47.1 mph for the down journey and 47.0 mph for the up. Gooch had achieved more or less the same results in similar weather with 120 tons – almost two and a half times the load.

So far Bidder had managed to avoid trials which could be compared directly with the broad gauge's and Brunel and Gooch pressed him to carry out 80 ton tests that afternoon. Conditions were so good that he could hardly refuse but he used every trick he could think of to confuse the issue. He kept everyone waiting for half an hour while the water was heated further and the last ounce of pressure was raised. Then, to Gooch's surprise, the train ran past the starting post at 15 mph instead of halting for a standing start.

The wind was in *Engine A's* favour as she clattered northwards. The Astronomer Royal, who had braved the footplate, regarded her as less steady than *Ixion*. He thought the unsteadiness unimportant, however, 'as it was not related to the strokes of the piston, but appeared to be produced by faults in the road'. At Darlington she shot past the post at 39 mph, not a lot less than her average of 43.2 mph. Even with the assistance of the flying start and finish *Engine A's* speed was 7 mph less than *Ixion's* with the same load and a favourable wind. Over the central full-speed stretch she averaged 45.4 mph, 7.4 mph less than the slower of the two broad gauge results.

To Gooch's disgust Bidder was not prepared to carry out the return run. Some excuse was offered and a different engine drew the experimental train back to York. 'No doubt they did not like to face the wind which had helped them on the down journey', Gooch wrote. Brunel had to return to London that evening but before leaving arranged with Bidder for two 80 ton tests to be performed the next day.

At nine o'clock on the Thursday morning a stiff breeze was blowing. *The Railway Chronicle* reported sarcastically that 'Mr Bidder objected to make the trial in such weather, and if the experiment were made should claim a reduction of twelve miles per hour . . . , (Shrewd, cautious Mr Bidder!) . . . Mr Gooch urged the propriety of the trip, (Knowing, clear sighted Mr Gooch!), stating that the wind was very little, if any, stronger than the one against which the broad gauge contended with its eighty tons. (Candid Mr Gooch! He weighs the wind in scales and declares there is . . . balance!). This Mr Bidder (of course) denied'.

After a long delay Bidder announced, to Gooch's amazement, that he was going to change to a different engine and wished to spend the rest of the day trying it out. Gooch, after coldly agreeing that he could do what he liked, decided to join him.

The engine was the North Midland Railway's *No. 54*, the *Stephenson*, a long boiler with inside cylinders and a central driving wheel. Bidder had tested her thoroughly some time previously, and no doubt this was why he was now going to use her. She had such a high centre of gravity, however, that Gooch regarded it as a wonder that she kept on the rails at all.

Gooch, Bidder, Seymour Clarke and J.J. Berkeley sat chatting idly together as *No. 54* rattled along with her load of only 30 tons. On the footplate was Gooch's assistant, William Martley, an Irishman noted for his happy disposition and sense of humour. He was about to need these qualities, for near Thirsk the engine jumped off the rails and rolled onto her side, taking the carriages with her. She had been travelling at 45 mph but fortunately Gooch and his colleagues were unscathed and scrambled out of the window. 'I and Clarke happened to be sitting on the side that was down,' he wrote, 'and altho' not a time to laugh, I could not help doing it afterwards at the recollection of the struggle of Bidder, who was sitting at the other side. He came tumbling down from seat to seat until he rested on me . . . I found those on the engine more or less hurt. Mr Martley . . . had his face a good deal scratched by being thrown into the hedge.' All of them had been very lucky, as the outcome would have been far more serious if they had overturned at a bridge or an embankment.

Gooch, with extraordinary aplomb after his unnerving experience, at once set off along the track to see why they had come to grief. He soon found a broken support at a place where the ends of the rails were bent. Martley had been horrified at *No. 54's* pitching and rolling, which Gooch felt had caused the accident.

Next day, whilst the narrow gauge goods trials were under way, the Commissioners held an inquiry into the crash. According to Gooch they were treated to 'as hard swearing that black was white, as I ever heard in my life', the engineman and assistant engineer telling them that *No. 54* had run very steadily. Martley, however, said that the rocking and yawing had been fearful. They concluded that the engine had been 'somewhat unsteady', with a tendency for her leading wheels to leave the rails. Like Gooch they put the main blame onto the broken support but thought that it had been in that state for some time.

Professor Barlow obtained some unexpected evidence later when he was at Derby with his son, who was chief engineer of the Midland Railway. The engineman who had extolled *No. 54's* steadiness at the inquiry buttonholed the younger Barlow. 'Did we not humbug that fat old buffer!,' he cried gleefully, not recognising the professor, who was amused enough to tell the story to Gooch.

On Saturday 3 January 1846 Gooch caught the train back to London. His report was soon in Charles Saunders' hands. 'It is . . . much to be regretted', he said, 'that notwithstanding . . . the number of days . . . devoted to the business on the narrow gauge lines, we have not yet obtained one complete experiment to match those on the Great Western.' Saunders immediately wrote to the Commissioners, enclosing a copy. In his covering letter he re-emphasised that the narrow gauge had not managed to achieve any results comparable with their own. He then turned to the argument which their opponents would use to try to turn the derailment to their advantage. The recent spate of accidents with long boiler engines, he said, might have a serious tendency 'to create apprehension of danger of speed' unless the facts were properly understood, and so the Great Western had decided to publish Gooch's account, 'having a deep sense of what was due to the public and to their proprietors'.

His report was discussed at the meeting of the Great Western board on 15 January. Brunel never forgot those who helped him in a difficulty, he said. On this occasion he spoke in glowing terms of Gooch's recent work and recommended him for a rise. The chairman, a man of great kindliness, immediately sent for Gooch to thank him

and tell him that his salary was to be increased to £1,000 a year. He was also given £500 in recognition of his efforts.

In mid-February, a month after the board meeting, the Gauge Commissioners' Report was published. It was disastrous, Gooch condensing their arguments into one terse phrase: 'The narrow gauge shall be the national gauge'. In spite of all his efforts they had come to the conclusion that there was nothing to choose between the two gauges on safety, comfort or convenience. Overall, however, they thought the narrow gauge cheaper and preferred it for goods. Whilst they were in no doubt that the broad gauge gave swifter and smoother travel they were afraid that there would be dangers in greater speed. They had crystallised their views into two main recommendations:

'That the gauge of 4ft. 8½in. be . . . the gauge to be used on all public railways now under construction or hereafter to be constructed in mainland Britain

That . . . great commercial advantage would be obtained by reducing . . . the present broad gauge lines to . . . 4ft. 8½in. . . . or of adopting such other course as would admit of the narrow gauge carriages passing . . . along the broad gauge lines'.

The report was to go to the President of the Board of Trade, who would consider what Resolutions should be put before Parliament, so once again the broad gauge began lobbying. Their strongest hopes lay with their locomotives. Even the Commissioners had admitted that they were the more powerful and economical, and Gooch, with splendid foresight, had an engine under construction capable of putting *Ixion* into the shade. Only four days after Brunel's first appearance before the Commissioners Gooch had arranged with him 'to build a **little** engine with an eight foot driving wheel . . . and a six foot firebox'. Already he had seen that it would be needed to gain publicity during the next session of Parliament. The 'little' engine was *Great Western*, the first of his magnificent 8 ft. singles and the first locomotive to be built in its entirety at Swindon.

CHAPTER

14

The old market town of Swindon stood on a hill top at the head of the Vale of the White Horse. It traded in gloves for hedging and ditching, tallow candles, leather breeches and the fine, white stone from the nearby quarries. Until the railway came the only jolt in its quiet existence had been the opening of the canal in 1818. William Morris, the writer of the town's first history, put its emergence down to the stubbornness of the Marquis of Aylesbury, who opposed the first schemes for a London to Bristol railway, as his estates lay on the most direct route. It was, however, topography which made Brunel select a huge northerly bow-curve for the Great Western between Reading and Bath. The Company's prospectus noted that the line, through Wantage, Swindon and Chippenham, had been preferred 'on account of its superiority of levels and the ultimate economy of working steam power'.

Swindon was the obvious place for a branch to Cheltenham and Gloucester. At the very least it would have become a moderately busy junction, but when Gooch chose the meadows below the town as the site of his main engine depot its destiny was transformed. 'Brunel and I went down to have a look at the ground,' he wrote. 'Our lunch was brought with us and deposited over . . . by the reservoirs.' Legend has it that after they had eaten they hurled a stone, or perhaps even a sandwich, to determine the exact spot for the workshops.

Construction began in February 1841. The engine sheds and other buildings were a major civil engineering project, so Brunel, as chief engineer, was responsible for their construction. Gooch's job was to work out the main requirements and order or design the plant and machinery. J. and C. Rigby of London were chosen as the contractors. Their navvies were soon hard at work trenching out the deep foundations. The masons then took over and before long the massive walls began to rise. By the autumn of 1842 the long engine shed and the first of the repair shops were ready for occupation. Sturrock, who was appointed works manager, was sent down to erect the plant. He made good progress and on 28 November, barely two years after the directors had voted the funds, the machines were started up, though the works did not come into regular operation until 2 January 1843.

Swindon's first task was the overhauling of locomotives. Gooch had them brought into the shops every 95,000 mls or so. The first refurbishing cost some £400 but at the second they were virtually rebuilt for £1,000. When the works opened twenty-six of the *Fire Flies* and *Suns* had been in use for three years. *North Star* and a few other engines had seen as much as six years use. A substantial workload had developed and Gooch needed to build up his staff quickly.

By August 1843 the payroll had reached four hundred. Most lived at the railway village, where there were already over six hundred inhabitants. Some were in temporary accommodation put up by Rigby, but most were in the cottages of the railway village, neat terraces of attractive houses constructed from stone excavated at Box Tunnel. In recent years they have been beautifully restored but we should not be misled by their present-day charm. At the outset New Swindon was a grim place. One

New Swindon in 1845

of the earliest arrivals, or 'settlers', as he called them, was a young engineer called Edward Snell. He came on 28 February 1843, only eight weeks after the works had opened. Next day he 'took a walk through the mud up to Swindon. Regular dull place – nothing to be seen but mud and wooden houses mounted on wheels scattered about through the fields . . . Capital shops, one of the sheds with about 100 engines in it'. A few days later he met a family of new settlers coming down to the cottages after their arrival at the station and sketched them, a doleful group. Newcomers were,

he said, 'beginning to drop in fast now but they don't much seem to like the place. For my part I hate it and haven't been well since I've been here . . . A precious place it is at present, not a knocker or a scraper in the whole place. Most of the houses very damp and containing only two rooms. Not a cupboard or a shelf . . . and the unfortunate inhabitants obliged to keep the grub in the bedrooms. Not a drop of water to be had but what comes from the tenders or out of ditches and what little we do get is as thick as mud – not fit for a jackass to drink. The Company make the men pay most

A family arriving at New Swindon. Sketch by Edward Snell, 1843

extortionate rents for these bits of huts, too
– 3s. 6d. for a single and 7s. for a double
cottage and won't allow any of the men in
their employ to sell anything whatever. We
have a couple of Doctors' Shops which are
pretty frequently visited, a Great Western
Sick Club, a school . . . and a chapel'.

Gooch, unlike his successors, never lived
at New Swindon. On 2 March 1843 Henry
Tanner wrote saying that 'Marg' has not
mentioned anything respecting your going
to Swindon to reside, but it seems a natural
conclusion . . . I shall be glad to assist you
in any way you wish'. In spite of his
father-in-law's offer Gooch remained at
Paddington. He had moved into Warwick
Villas only a few months before and clearly
intended to remain close to Saunders and
the other chief officers. It was easy enough
for him to travel down to the works and all
was organised for an overnight stay, as he
had a bedroom next to his office.

By the end of 1843 another hundred and
forty people had moved into the railway
village. The overcrowding and boredom
were having their effects. 'Some short
period afterwards,' Gooch said, 'the
complaints from the neighbouring gentry
and all the villages around . . . were in
reference to the Swindon works, which they
said were a curse. The villagers were disturbed . . . by the drunken revels.' There was
a lock-up available for the worst of the
offenders, a vault 8ft. × 7ft. × 6ft. 6in.
high, which became hopelessly inadequate.
The lawlessness was such that on one occasion a tunnel was dug and a prisoner
rescued by his mates. 'The matter,' Gooch
continued, 'of course demanded attention.'
He adopted a solution based on what he had
seen at Dundee and Newcastle: 'I got
together those of the workmen whose moral
character was superior to their fellows and
formed them into a Workmen's Institute'.
In January 1844 an office was turned into a
reading room. By the end of the year
membership had reached 129 and books
were being borrowed at the rate of eighty a
week from a library of over five hundred.
Dances and theatrical entertainments
started as soon as a workshop could be
spared. Within four years there were two
hundred and fifty members and a library of
twelve hundred books. Lectures on science

and literature were being given, each meeting being preceded by a concert by the
Institution Band. Conduct improved
steadily. 'My policy,' Gooch said, 'was to
endeavour, by moral suasion, to teach men
that the better, nobler and more agreeable
mode of spending their leisure hours was by
resorting to our Institution, . . . that this
is better than sipping and sopping in a
public house hour after hour.' He was,
however, no teetotaler. 'No one can be
more anxious than I,' he said, 'for the
improvement and moral elevation of our
working men, but . . . I believe – at least,
I may say I know – a glass of good beer is
good for a working man.'

By mid-1845 Gooch's division numbered nearly eight hundred. All were busy,
as about a tenth of the wages were for
overtime. To run the 126 locomotives there
were 72 enginemen and 73 firemen. Over a
hundred cleaners and 23 labourers were
distributed between the various depots.
Almost all of the 305 craftsmen were at
Swindon, their earnings ranging from a
guinea a week for the foundry trades to £1
14s. 6d. for the spring makers.

From the outset Gooch had intended to
go far beyond repair work. Workshops were
being added for the building of wagons,
carriages, permanent way equipment and
locomotives. He had built his first rolling
stock, a batch of goods vans, twelve months
before. On 29 October he wrote to
Hammond, Brunel's assistant, urging
completion of the new smiths' shop. He
needed it urgently, as he had an order for
forty-eight first and second class carriages to
complete by December.

By the end of the year all was ready for
the construction of Swindon's first locomotive – Premier, the prototype of the powerful

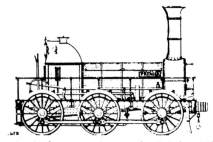

Premier, the first new engine erected at Swindon, 1846

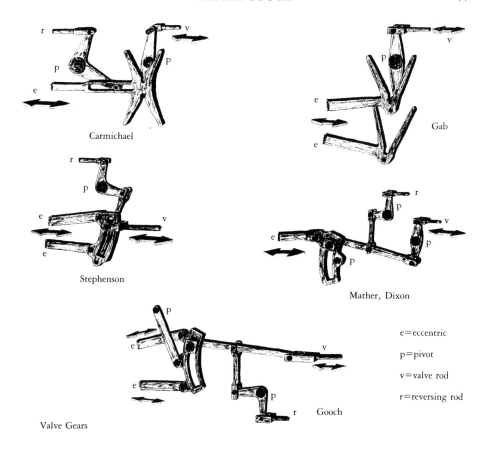

Carmichael

Gab

Stephenson

Mather, Dixon

e=eccentric

p=pivot

v=valve rod

r=reversing rod

Gooch

Valve Gears

new engines and the first of many hundreds of Swindon-built 0-6-0 goods engines. She was massive, with half as much power again as *Hercules*, which had performed so well in the gauge trials. All her parts were made on the premises apart from her boiler.

Premier appears to have been the first of Gooch's engines to be fitted with a constant lead valve motion which he had evolved, the so-called Gooch valve gear. It was similar to the Stephenson link motion in that the two eccentrics were connected to the ends of a curved link. In the Stephenson a slot in the link engaged with the slide-valve rod, the link being raised or lowered to vary the direction of motion or the degree of expansion. In the Gooch, however, the link swung on a pivoted arm and could not be moved vertically, so that it was often called the 'stationary link' motion. The slide valve was driven by a

rod, one end of which engaged with the slot in the link. It was this end of the rod, rather than the link itself, which was raised or lowered to control the engine.

Gooch has been credited with inventing the stationary link, but this he himself denied. A few years after *Premier* had been built he appeared as the principal witness for the defendants, the London and North Western Railway, in a patent case. This had been brought by John Gray, who claimed that the Stephenson link infringed a patent which he had taken out in 1839. As most railways and engine builders had adopted it Gray *v.* L&NWR was an important test case. During a long session in the witness box Gooch admitted that he had used the Stephenson valve gear, though 'only the old engines . . . were altered – on all our new engines that we build we do not vary [the lead] at all'. After he had stressed his belief in the virtue of a constant 'lead' Gray's counsel asked him if he had had some expansive gearing of his own 'in the north'. He denied this, and later Brunel said that 'an improvement still upon the link has been, I think, fixing the link vertically and moving . . . the valve rod . . . as we do on the Great Western. I do not know whether it originated with us'.

D. K. Clark, in the first exhaustive textbook on locomotive engineering, published in 1855, included a review of the development of the early valve gears. He stated that the original form of the Stephenson link was of the stationary type. He also wrote that 'the suspended link motion, with the shifting radius link, was, we believe, first matured and employed by Mr Gooch'. To him, he said, belonged 'the merit of having originally apprehended the virtue of this method of adjustment', indicating that he had developed, rather than invented, it. Gooch's link motion bears an interesting similarity to the gearing which Mather, Dixon used in their first engine for Brunel in 1838. Evidence given in the Gray case by John Dewrance, who had been one of their erectors, suggests that this had a curved link and a moveable valve-rod actuated by a single eccentric. The Gooch gear is, in fact, a cross between the Mather, Dixon and the Stephenson motions, and one wonders if he consciously combined them. Having evolved the basic layout he explored the design systematically, varying the proportions of the parts. He worked out an arrangement which gave a constant lead and equal periods of admission and exhaust at all settings of the link, precisely the characteristics he desired but could not obtain with the Stephenson.

Premier was completed in mid-February 1846. She was overshadowed already, however, as a much larger engine, bigger than any ever built before, was being rushed through the shops.

On 29 October 1845, when Gooch had written to Hammond urging the completion of the new smiths' shop, he had also mentioned the '**little** engine with an eight-foot driving wheel' which he was hoping to build: 'I can do this if I get assistance in the rapid completion of the crane in our boiler shop'. Edward Snell, who had become his chief draughtsman, started work on the drawings that very day, but before construction could start the agreement of the board had to be obtained. This took some time and it was well into January 1846, after the derailment at Thirsk, before Gooch was given the go ahead. The lateness of the decision was most awkward for him, as it was vital for her to be ready as early as possible in the Parliamentary session. There was no time to produce proper working drawings and so she was built from a few centre-line and outline drawings, pen and ink sketches being used for most of the parts. Work went on night and day, the hard-pressed workforce nicknaming her *The Lightning*, but in the company's books she became *Great Western*.

The new locomotive was an enormous stride forward. Her driving wheels were 8ft. in diameter, a foot larger than *Fire Fly's,* and her huge cylinders, 18in. bore by 24 in. stroke, were twice the volume. Her boiler had well over twice the tube surface and seventy percent more grate area. The boiler pressure of 100 lb/sq. in. was twice as high as in the original *Fire Flies*. Gooch's bold design gave her almost three and a half times the tractive effort of his first passenger engines.

He had many problems to solve as manufacture raced ahead. The boiler was the first to be built at Swindon. The corner plates of the firebox's 'sugar-loaf' top had to be beaten into shape using dies and heavy mallets, which proved an especially tricky job. The most vulnerable component was the crank axle. One of 24 in. stroke had already been made for *Premier*, but *Great Western's* had to be stouter still. In 1841 James Nasmyth had patented the steam hammer, making it possible to produce large forgings of the highest quality. In July 1844 he had written a disarming sales letter to Gooch, reminding him that he had 'been long expecting to hear from you in reference to your having one of my patent steam hammers . . . You really ought to have one . . . we are already at No. 22'. It is hard to see how he could have constructed *Great Western* without one and in April, just as she was nearing completion, Nasmyth wrote again, this time about a 25 cwt hammer, 'which I am glad you meditate ordering'.

As the days lengthened *Great Western*

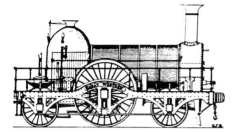

Great Western, the first engine constructed in its entirety at Swindon. As originally built with six wheels, 1846

began to take on shape. For all her size she had a reassuring familiarity. Like the *Stars*, *Suns* and *Fire Flies* she was a 2-2-2 with the driving wheels mounted under splashers of polished brass. Her outside frames were of the usual Gooch form. The massive boiler and greater amount of steam to be discharged gave her a shorter, chubbier chimney and powerful, hunched-forward lines. By late April she was ready. She had been completed in the amazing time of thirteen weeks, 'probably as quick a job as was ever done', Gooch wrote with pride. She proved no easy charge. The enginemen called her *The Russian*, as she was a voracious eater of oil

and tallow. To the platelayers, who tidied up after she had passed, she was *The Mangle*. She was, however, an immediate success. Whilst Gooch was building *Great Western* the fight to save the broad gauge began. He and Brunel went to Charles Saunders' house for a few hours each day to work on a vigorous response to the arguments of Sir Frederic Smith and his colleagues. Within a month copies of a pamphlet entitled *Observations on the Report of the Gauge Commissioners* had been sent to everyone who could influence the final decisions. In it they tore the report to shreds, closing with the triumphant statement that 'the experiments made in the presence of the Commissioners demonstrated beyond all controversy THE COMPLETE SUCCESS OF THE BROAD GAUGE SYSTEM'.

Early 1846 was one of the busiest and most worrying times in Gooch's life. Once again Margaret Gooch was pregnant, but again all went well and their fifth child, Alfred William, was born on 2 March. The ordinary work of his division had to continue. *Premier* went into service and *Avalanche*, an extremely powerful six-coupled banking engine of great tractive

A broad gauge train, 1846

effort, was delivered by Stothert and Slaughter. He set up a system of recording the usage of fuel and oil by each engineman, enabling him to detect any waste. 'As a copy is hung up at each engine station', he wrote, 'a spirit of emulation is thus produced, and is further assisted by a premium . . . A copy is sent to each foreman every month, with such remarks as I may have to make'.

The enormous amount of verbal and written evidence collected by the Gauge Commissioners was published towards the end of April. This gave the broad gauge another opportunity to challenge their views. After their public sessions Saunders had sent them two documents prepared by Gooch. The first was his report on the gauge trials and the accident at Thirsk. They refused to publish this, on the curious grounds that it was not confined to the experiments themselves, but they were prepared to include the second, which was a complete résumé of the broad gauge case. When the evidence came out, however, Gooch was annoyed to find that they had done precisely the opposite – the trials report had been included but the resumé had not. He was also enraged that a table which he had given to them had been altered prior to publication. A second pamphlet, *Supplemental Observations on the Published Evidence of the Gauge Commissioners*, was hurriedly prepared. 'When the *Observations on the Report* were published,' they complained, 'the advocates of the broad gauge were under the serious disadvantage of having only a portion of the *viva voce* evidence . . . and they were consequently ignorant of the source from which [the Commissioners] could have derived such erroneous conclusions . . . But to the unqualified surprise of the parties . . . the evidence when published failed to give the public the proper opportunity of forming a judgement.'

Besides its hints of supression and injustice the *Supplemental Observations* included the material which the Commissioners had left out, together with the results of the gauge trials and a drawing in which the stable-looking *Ixion* and *Hercules* were compared with the top-heavy long boilers. Gooch's contribution is of especial interest as he gave an account of his views and achievements as a locomotive designer. He leaves us in no doubt about the superiority of his engines. The average Great Western train, he said, weighed 67 tons and travelled at 37½ mph for a cost of 0.15d / ton mile. The narrow gauge engines, however, only managed 39.9 tons at 21.4 mph for 0.29d / ton mile – 60% of the weight, 57% of the speed and almost twice the cost. He included a fascinating list in which he compared the performances of his locomotives, maker by maker. To avoid upsetting anyone he left out the names, but it is an easy matter to work out which was which, enabling the following table to be drawn up:-

Performances of G.W.R. Engines * to 30 June 1844	Tons hauled	Pence per mile	Pence per ton mile	Miles per month
Early G.W.R. Locos	24–28	16.7–18.6	0.59–0.78	2–400
Star Class (Stephenson)	44	15.5	0.35	783
Sun Class (Hawthorn)	35	12.8	0.36	1126
Fire Fly Class				
Fenton, Murray & Jackson	62	9.9	0.16	1583
Nasmyth & Gaskell	54	9.8	0.18	1230
Longridge	54	10.3	0.19	1238
Jones, Turner & Evans	45	13.6	0.3	1310
Rennie	53	11.6	0.22	1050
Leo Class Rothwell	121	12.1	0.1	1166
Fenton, Murray & Jackson*	137	12.3	0.09	1450
Hawthorn*	95	13.3	0.14	1060
Hercules Class (Nasmyth & Gaskell)	252	12.6	0.05	1881

* Probably this firm

Gooch commented that if all his engines had been as good as the best the broad gauge would have had an even greater advantage over the narrow. Despite his efforts at standardisation there were large differences in performance, the Jones, Turner and Evans *Fire Flies*, for example, costing almost twice as much per ton mile as Fenton, Murray and Jackson's. His reasons for wishing to build his own engines at Swindon are clear, as besides having control of the costs he would then be able to ensure a complete uniformity of quality and design.

The excellence of Gooch's designs is apparent. Even Stephensons' *Stars*, made by the most experienced locomotive firm in the world, could not match the *Fire Flies*. The *Hercules* class, the latest to be listed, were hauling ten times as much as the first broad gauge engines at a twelfth the cost, a staggering change. The steady improvements in his own designs are also evident, *Hercules*, for instance, hauling more than twice as much as the earlier *Leos* at half the cost. Gooch, however, expected the running costs of his engines to be low, because the width of the gauge and comparatively low centre of gravity made them steadier: 'It requires very little consideration to arrive at the conclusion that the less a piece of machinery . . . is shaken about, the less must be the destruction of the parts'.

He enjoyed working on the two pamphlets. His contribution even included a joke. 'The fact is,' he said, 'that the process of renewal of engines is constantly going on under the head of repairs . . . and in the course of time, probably the only part of the original engine left will be her name.' He was able to announce in the *Supplemental Observations* that the first of the new, powerful broad gauge engines had been tested. Already *Great Western* had hauled a gross load of 94 tons at 67 mph. Then on 1 June she made the round trip to Exeter in 6 hr. 49 min., exclusive of stops – 388 miles at 56.9 mph. These were astonishing achievements and so a spectacular run was arranged to gain final publicity before the next battle of the Gauge War.

The Board of Trade, after spending four months considering the Commissioners'

Report, had at last published their views. To the delight of Gooch and his colleagues these were most favourable to the broad gauge. Five Resolutions embodying their recommendations were to be debated on 17 June 1846. So on Saturday 13 June, in time to catch the newspapers before the debate, *Great Western* made a sensational trip to Bristol with a load of 100 tons.

The heavy train consisted of ten of the large broad gauge carriages. Charles Russell, Brunel and the directors and guests travelled in three, the rest being ballasted with iron. *Great Western* had no difficulty as she left Paddington and ran through Kensal Green, Ealing and West Drayton but at Slough a feed pump failed, holding her back a little. Nevertheless, as she raced onwards she reached 69 mph at one point and covered a 10-mile stretch at nearly 66 mph. The 77 mls to Swindon took 78 minutes – 59.2 mph – and Bristol was reached in 2hr. 12 min., excluding the stops. This was 17 min. quicker than the lightly-loaded expresses, the average for the 118¼ mls being 53.75 mph.

Great Western's achievement was celebrated by a dinner attended by many guests at which there was a good deal of speech making. Charles Russell called the trip 'a "great feat", and it was a great feat', Gooch wrote proudly. 'Had we had this engine ready in time for the gauge experiments how different the results would have been, altho' I don't suppose it would have altered the report.'

Four days after the epic run the Resolutions came before Parliament. During the debates some amendments were made and then the way was clear for the introduction of a Regulation of Gauges Bill, which received the Royal Assent on 18 August 1846. It decreed, as the broad gauge had feared, that no further railways were to be built in Great Britain of gauges other than 4ft. 8½in, but there was a rider: All lines were to be excluded that were 'constructed or to be constructed under the provisions of any present or future Act containing any special enactment defining the gauge'. The tracts, the lobbying and the race to build *Great Western* had paid off. The broad gauge had won. Their existing lines were safe and they were free to fight to extend their territory.

CHAPTER

15

Gooch was now able to concentrate on the affairs of his division again. His first objective was to gain experience with *Great Western*. She was so novel that it is hardly surprising that he struck trouble. After she had been in service for only a few months her leading axle broke. When the material was tested with a press it flew into several pieces, one of which shot across the yard and made a dent in the wall of the drawing office. The iron was brittle, probably because the smiths had swaged it at too low a temperature. The main problem, however, was that the load on the front axle had been too high. An extra pair of wheels was needed to support the massive engine and so Gooch extended the frames forward and added a second axle under the smokebox. She was the first eight-wheeled engine since the crude Wylam Dillies of the early years of the century. He had no further difficulties with her and she remained in service until 1870, completing 370,687 mls.

Whilst Gooch was proving *Great Western* he brought out a less ambitious class, the *Princes*. These had 7ft. driving wheels but their cylinders had the 24in. stroke of his recent designs and the boilers were scaled up to match. They were highly successful, averaging 2,000 mls a month for almost twenty-five years.

As soon as he was satisfied with *Great Western* Gooch put a complete class of 8ft. singles in hand at Swindon. He intended them to be the broad gauge's crack express engines for many years. The first was tried out on 29 April 1847, which was the Duke of Wellington's seventy-eighth birthday, so she and her class were christened *Iron Duke*. During the next seven months five others were built, huge engines similar in layout to *Great Western*. The 'sugar-loaf' firebox, however, was replaced by one of simpler raised-casing form. To improve their fuel consumption he extended the smokebox to surround the cylinders, and to give even more power at high speeds he added another 200 sq. ft. of boiler tube surface. He also added a 'mid-feather' to the firebox, a transverse wall of water tubes which divided the furnace into two and gave extra area just where it was most effective. They proved brilliantly successful, setting the

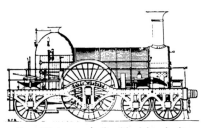

Great Western as rebuilt with eight wheels

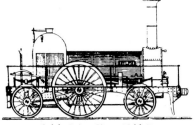

Sylph, *Prince* Class, 1846–7

pace for locomotive design for years to come. Twenty-three more were built between 1848 and 1855, all proving highly reliable as well as swift and powerful. *Lightning* averaged 2,219 mls a month for over thirty years. Three were rebuilt in 1870, one remaining in service until 1887. Gooch's successors perpetuated his design in the twenty-four engines of the *Rover* class, the *Iron Duke* 'rebuilds' or 'renewals', constructed between 1871 and 1888. They epitomised the later years of the broad gauge and ran until the last lengths of 7 ft. rails were torn up, Gooch's influence extending until after his death.

One of the men who helped to build *Iron Duke* was a Mr R. Sheward. 'I was in the works for six years under the wisest, the ablest and best gentleman it has been my lot to work with in a long life, namely . . . Daniel Gooch,' he wrote as an old man. The enginemen, he said, 'were of opinion they could maintain seventy miles an hour with an ordinary express train if 'Dan'l' would allow them; but 'Dan'l' never would, for anxiety and permanent care were ever visible on the brow of 'Dan'l' . . . I am proud . . . to bear witness of his never-ceasing care to make railway travelling perfectly safe – as far, of course, as possible for poor human nature to do so'.

On 14 May 1847 'poor human nature' let Gooch down. *Queen* was approaching Southall, running at speed. As she was crossing the Wharncliffe Viaduct, high above the River Brent, the tyre of her off-side driving wheel shattered. She did not even leave the rails, but by a sad coincidence a goods train was passing and one whizzing fragment killed two drovers

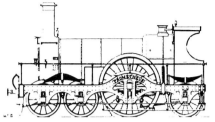

Prometheus, 1888, one of the *Iron Duke* rebuilds

who were accompanying their cattle. A second derailed the goods, though fortunately onto the side away from the express. The safety of the broad gauge was never more dramatically demonstrated than in this extraordinary accident. A defective hammer-weld had caused the failure, Gooch found.

At that time Brunel was in difficulties with a railway which was to damage his reputation and raise Gooch to riches – the South Devon. Brunel's next goal westward of Exeter was Plymouth, but Dartmoor lay in his way. An easily-graded line would have been long and expensive so he chose a shorter route which penetrated into the foothills of the moors. He laid out a tortu-ous line, with a mile-long gradient of one in forty-one between Newton and Totnes and a gruelling two-mile bank at almost one in forty-two near Plymouth. He thought that locomotives would not be able to achieve acceptable speeds on such a difficult line and at first considered using rope haulages. Soon, however, he became attracted to an entirely different form of propulsion – the Atmospheric System.

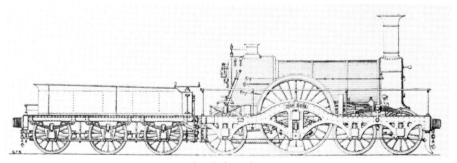

Iron Duke, 1847

In 1839 the Samuda brothers and a Mr Clegg had developed a scheme which they expected to supplant steam locomotives. By 1843 the Dublin and Kingstown Railway was in operation using their system, which involved laying a continuous length of pipe between the rails, inside which was a piston. An air pump, driven by a stationary steam engine, was used to produce a vacuum in the pipe, the piston then being pushed along, drawing the train behind it, by the pressure of the atmosphere, hence the name. The great problem was the coupling of the piston to the carriages. In their method there was a narrow slit along the top of the pipe for the whole of its length. This was closed by a leather flap, fastened to the pipe along one edge but loose at the other, being held shut by the vacuum. A bar, fixed to the piston at one end and to the leading carriage at the other, passed through the slot, pushing the leather open as it went along. A roller pressed the flap back into place after the bar had gone by.

The new idea divided the engineering profession into two camps. The Stephensons scoffed at it as 'a rope of wind', suffering from the same drawbacks as a rope haulage, but others thought it would be cheaper than locomotives. As the trains were light and could be drawn up steep slopes quickly it seemed particularly suitable for the South Devon, so as soon as the company's Act had been passed the patentees pressed the directors to use their system. Brunel prepared a report for the board, in which he said that he had 'no hesitation in taking . . . the full and entire responsibility of recommending the adoption . . . and of recommending as a consequence that the line and works should be constructed for a single line only'.

In September 1844 Gooch went with Brunel and a party of directors and engineers to see the Dublin and Kingstown in action. He was caustic, stating in his memoirs that 'from the calculations I then made . . . I found I could do the work much cheaper with locomotives. The result of our visit, however, was the determination to use the atmospheric pipes on the South Devon. I could not understand how Mr Brunel could be so misled . . . and believe

while he saw all the difficulties and expense of it on the Dalkey, he had so much faith in his being able to improve it that he shut his eyes to the consequences of failure'.

By June 1847 the easily graded parts of the line between Exeter and Newton had been opened but the atmospheric system was only in use for some experimental trains, the ordinary service being operated by engines on hire from the Great Western. The Gooches were staying at Exmouth, on the other side of the river. Margaret was in the later stages of pregnancy and presumably took quiet outings with the children, as Gooch was combining business with pleasure. The steep sections between Newton and Totnes were soon to open and there would be no alternative but to work them with locomotives, so he was keeping an eye on the preparations. He managed to take days off to go fishing, however, and on one occasion had a severe fright.

Gooch and two friends arranged to go out with a boatman at five one morning but he did not turn up. When they tracked him down they found that he was not willing to go as the sea was too rough, but they were not to be put off and pressed him until he agreed. Then, with the boatman at one oar, a strong lad at the other and Gooch steering they set off down the Exe. As they neared the narrow mouth of the estuary Gooch realised that the boatman had been right. A strong ebb tide was ripping through and the sea was very rough. The current, however, was too fierce for them to turn back so they rowed onward, but then the lad's oar broke. Fortunately the boatman managed to maintain steerage-way on his own and Gooch was able to keep them heading into the breakers. As they thumped their way through he saw a wave nearly 6ft. high coming and thought how foolish he had been, feeling certain that they would be drowned, but at last they reached calmer water. 'We had a flask of rum with us,' he wrote, 'and all seemed glad to get a glass of that.'

On 20 July the Newton to Totnes line was opened. A *Leo* and a *Fire Fly* took the first train over the inclines thought too steep for locomotives. 'I never saw Mr Brunel so anxious about anything,' Gooch said, 'but his worries disappeared with the day of opening . . . He shook hands with me in a very kind manner for my share in the day's work.'

This was by no means the end of Gooch's involvement with the South Devon Railway but for the present he was able to hurry back to Paddington, where Frank, his fourth son, had arrived on the day of the opening. Margaret, who was 33, had borne six children in the nine years of their marriage and their family was complete.

The view from the room where she lay recovering had been spoilt. On the low ground between Warwick Villas and the canal basin a pair of opulent semi-detached houses was rising. Gooch had taken a 92½ year lease on the land at a rental of £11 a year and during the latter part of 1846 and most of 1847 the builders were at work. The left-hand of the two, which was named Fulthorpe House after Gooch's most distinguished ancestors, was to be theirs. Its smaller and less imposing neighbour, Tunstall House, was to be let. Their new home had five storeys, each with two tall windows to the front and four to the side. It was light and open by comparison with the lofty terraced houses in which most of London's well-to-do lived. Most of the rooms had views over greenery and the canals. It was a commodious place, a fitting home for an important but still rising man.

All traces of the two houses have vanished as they were damaged in the blitz of 1941. The site was cleared some years later, now forming part of Rembrandt Gardens, a pleasant little park which commemorates London's association with Amsterdam. Once again their first house looks directly onto Little Venice.

At the time of their move Tom Gooch's health was giving great cause for concern. On Sunday 24 August, whilst he was at his Westminster office, he became seriously ill. Eight weeks previously the Trent Valley Railway, for which he had borne the full responsibility, had been opened. It was 50 mls long and he had built it in twenty months. This and recent sessions before Parliamentary Committees were too much for him and he hardly ever worked again. His younger brother had perhaps been wise to choose the different pressures of locomotive engineering.

CHAPTER

16

Gooch achieved eminence in practically everything to which he turned his hand. A curious exception, however, was that, though he was one of the most distinguished engineers of his generation, he never joined the Institutions of Civil or Mechanical Engineers. After 1848 he remained aloof from all the affairs of the engineering establishment. This was because he fell out with the narrow gauge faction who were predominant in the Civils.

The trouble stemmed from a paper entitled *On the Resistances of Railway Trains at Different Velocities*, which Wyndham Harding presented at the Institution of Civil Engineers on 26 May 1846. It was an important contribution to knowledge and virtually all the great men of the profession were there to hear him speak and to participate in the discussion sessions on 9 and 16 June. The dates are significant, for it was on 17 June 1846 that Parliament debated the Resolutions which followed the Gauge Commissioners' Report. Both sides were busy grinding axes.

The Institution's meetings were intended as a forum for discourses on the art and science of engineering, bickering over business rivalries being forbidden. Controversial matters were, however, aired, but subtly, and Harding's paper was intended as a blow against both the broad gauge and the atmospheric system.

Wyndham Harding had been at Rugby at the same time as Tom Hughes, the author of *Tom Brown's Schooldays*. It was unusual for a classical scholar to take up engineering, but he became a pupil under Tom Gooch. Later he was manager of the Bristol and Gloucester Railway, the thorn in the flesh of the Great Western, and then Secretary of the London and South Western, where John Gooch was locomotive superintendent. His close involvement with the Gooches did not prevent some sharp exchanges with Daniel.

At that time construction of the South Devon was advancing rapidly and on the Croydon Railway atmospheric propulsion was showing promise. Speeds as high as 61 mph were attained. The challenge to conventional 'Stephenson' railways was becoming dangerous. Harding's objective was to show that Brunel and Samuda were optimistic in their views and that some of Gooch's statements on the broad gauge were wrong.

The power required to draw a train along a level line depends on the 'resistance' offered by the atmosphere and the friction of the bearings and wheels. Harding had gathered together all the measurements of resistances which had ever been made. These suggested that figures quoted by Brunel to the Parliamentary Committees which had considered atmospheric railways were far too low. He had claimed 17 lb a ton as the resistance at 60 mph, whereas Harding's figure was, he said, 'more than twice as much as Mr Brunel, Mr Samuda and Mr D. Gooch, have assigned to it. With great deference . . . it is submitted, that the experiments of which we are in possession lead to the conclusion that their opinion on this subject is erroneous. If this be so, it will soon be made manifest, by the amount of propelling power which will be found requisite'.

With ordinary railways if more power was needed another engine was coupled on or some bigger ones were built. With the atmospheric system, however, the power to even a single train could only be increased by replacing all the pipes by larger ones and providing more stationary engines, a ruinously expensive change. Harding was going as far as he dared in a scientific paper to suggest that the new system would be a failure.

Harding's data included the results of tests which he had carried out and of experiments made by John Scott Russell, Bidder and Gooch himself. All the information tied in with his figure of over 40 lb a ton at 60 mph with one exception. This was a value of only 18 lb a ton on the broad gauge given by Gooch to the Gauge Commissioners. Harding set out to attack his result, which was vulnerable, as he had obtained it by a round-about route. 'It appears,' said Harding, 'that Mr Gooch attaches the greatest confidence to the experiment . . . as . . . upon it . . . rests a large portion of the evidence given by him to the Gauge Commissioners.'

Neither Gooch nor Brunel was present but Gooch replied to Harding's criticisms by writing a letter, parts of which were read out on 9 June. 'I regret that I am unable to attend, for the purpose of explaining the error that Mr Harding has fallen into', he began. 'I, however, think that Mr Harding's figures . . . give amounts at least one-third more than the resistances experienced on the broad gauge.' He explained that he had been well aware of the limitations in the *Ixion* results, but they were the only ones which he then had. He quoted up-to-date broad gauge data of 23–30 lb/ton at 50–60 mph, and of 34 lb/ton at 67 mph obtained from *Great Western*. These were uncomfortably high for Brunel. Gooch, however, had scored two important points. He had proclaimed the extraordinary performance of his newest engine to an eminent audience. Also his recent measurements confirmed that less power was needed to haul trains on the broad gauge than on the narrow. Robert Stephenson, Bidder and Harding therefore attacked the accuracy of his measurements. They made no reference to a statement in his letter that he was making preparations for a series of large-scale experiments on train resistances.

Harding's paper appeared in the press,

confirming that it was an attempt to gain publicity. It was undoubtedly embarrassing to the atmospheric railway faction, but with *Great Western's* achievements behind them it can have had little effect on the standing of the broad gauge.

Gooch's difference of opinion with Harding lay dormant for a while. In the meantime he carried out his promised experiments. He conducted a classical piece of engineering research, the first deep study of the science of steam locomotion. A dynamometer carriage was built for the work. He was not the first to construct one, as some writers have suggested, that honour belonging to Charles Babbage. Scott Russell had also used one in 1843 but Gooch thought his instruments had been on too small a scale to give useful results.

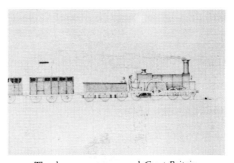

The dynamometer car and *Great Britain*

Dynamometer carriages became important items of equipment on all the major railways in years to come. Their main feature was a large spring balance, which acted as the coupling between the train and the tender. The pull which it measured was the tractive force of the locomotive, and this was equal to the resistance when the train was moving at a steady speed on a level line.

Gooch mounted his equipment in a six-wheeled third-class truck, a spartan vehicle with no ventilation apart from louvres high in the sides. One end was modified to incorporate the spring balance, whose deflections were transmitted to an arm carrying a pencil. This plotted a graph on a paper chart which was moved along at a speed proportional to the engine's by belts and bevel gears from a measuring wheel running on the rails. A clock made a mark on the paper every few seconds, so that the speed could be calculated. Gooch also fitted a weather vane which plotted the wind speed and direction on the chart.

The spring balance, the most important part of the gear, was designed with Gooch's customary care. The leaves were connected by pivots and rollers to minimise friction

A particularly useful part of his instrumentation was an 'engine indicator', which he developed to investigate what was happening inside the cylinder. This produced 'indicator cards', graphs which showed how the steam pressure varied during each stroke. These were difficult measurements, as the pressure changed so rapidly. The instruments used for stationary engines proved unsatisfactory for locomotives, so

Gooch's cylinder pressure indicator

and there were two dash-pots to prevent oscillations. The carriage proved highly satisfactory, eventually being converted to the narrow gauge and remaining in use until the turn of the century. Though not novel his was the first really practical equipment for testing locomotives under service conditions and as such represented a major step forward.

Gooch designed one for himself. It still exists and is in the Science Museum at South Kensington. It is an enormous device by present day standards but exquisitely made. The pressure was measured by a spring-loaded piston, whose movements, as in the dynamometer, were recorded by a pencil on a chart driven from the engine wheels.

D.K Clark based a substantial part of his treatise, *Railway Engineering*, of 1855, on indicator cards given to him by Gooch. 'The application of the indicator to the cylinder of the locomotive,' he wrote, ' . . . has aided essentially in giving precision to our knowledge of the behaviour of steam in the cylinder . . . Mr Gooch was the first, so far as I am aware, who applied the indicator to the locomotive; and he is the only engineer who systematically applies that instrument as a sort of stethoscope for testing their physiological condition.' Gooch obtained his records by mounting the instrument on the front of the locomotive and connecting it to the cylinder by a tube. He or one of his assistants then perched on the buffer beam to operate it as the engine lurched along. 'Only those', commented Clark, 'who have undergone the fatigue and risk . . . with occasionally a brisk side wind to make them conscious of how short a distance there is between time and eternity . . . can fully appreciate their value.'

Gooch carried out his first tests in April 1847 on the steep Brimscombe incline using *Great Western* and *Dreadnought*, a *Premier*. His main experiments, however, did not commence until September, by which time three *Iron Dukes* had been completed and he was able to use *Great Britain* for tests on a flat stretch of the Bristol and Exeter at Banwell. He made forty-one runs over a measured mile at speeds of up to 62.4 mph with trains weighing 50 to 100 tons. The resistances which he obtained were, as he had expected, considerably lower than Harding's.

Gooch's tests were carried out to provide ammunition for the next phase of the Gauge War. In the early part of 1846 the two most powerful railway companies in Britain, the Grand Junction and the London and Birmingham, had been bitter enemies. The Grand Junction decided to build an extension from Birmingham to Knightcote on the Oxford and Rugby Railway, the line won by the broad gauge in 1845–6. This would enable their traffic to travel over the broad gauge through Oxford to Paddington, providing an alternative route to the capital to the London and Birmingham's. The new line, the Birmingham and Oxford, was to be of seven foot gauge and the Grand Junction even considered adding a third rail to their main line to make it of 'mixed gauge', suitable for trains of either width. Broad gauge rails would then have reached into Lancashire and the whole future of Britain's railways might well have been changed. But the Grand Junction and the London and Birmingham patched up their quarrel and combined with the Manchester and Birmingham to form the immensely powerful London and North Western Railway.

The board of the Birmingham and Oxford were undeterred by the Grand Junction's change of heart and prepared Bills for the scheme. The L&NWR mounted fierce opposition but Parliament were glad to see competition for the country's most lucrative traffic and on 3 August 1846 their Act became law. The Great Western, who had been giving support, then stepped in and bought the company.

So far the question of the gauge had not been raised. Once the Bill had been passed there was agitation for the line to be built to the broad gauge. The outcome was that in June 1847 the House of Lords ordered the Railway Commissioners, a new government department, to consider the problem.

To the annoyance of the Great Western they decided to conduct their enquiry by seeking written evidence. Having all the Gauge Commissioners' information at their fingertips they concentrated on a detailed comparison of the locomotives and in January 1848 sent both the Great Western and the L&NWR a long questionnaire. They were sent four replies, a joint one prepared by the L&NWR's two locomotive superintendents, James McConnell and Francis Trevithick, together with individual submissions from Joseph Locke, Brunel and Gooch.

Locke's answer was brief, his response to the question of what he thought to be the best boiler pressure being the contemptuous 'the pressure shown by the indicator of the safety valve'. Trevithick and McConnell's was longer and more useful, but not to be compared with either of the two Great Western replies. Brunel's was thorough, but Gooch's was superb, being exhaustive and peppered with facts. In what amounts to a complete résumé of locomotive practice he included the results of his resistance trials, information on the back pressures in engines without the link motion, comparisons of the proportions of broad and narrow gauge engines and his opinions on many design matters. 'It is clear,' he said in a comment which summed up his whole approach, 'that the engines can be made on the broad gauge double the power of those on the narrow.'

Whilst the Commissioners were mulling over the arguments Gooch prepared a paper on his dynamometer results for the Institution of Civil Engineers. His intention, as the timing shows, was to gain publicity for the broad gauge as well as to publish important results.

He presented his paper on the evening of 18 April 1848. All the most eminent railway engineers were present, just as they had been two years previously to hear Harding's. His work provoked great, though not dispassionate, interest. 'It was . . . a simple party fight', Gooch wrote, 'Stephenson and Co. against the broad gauge, and was unworthy of the profession.' Amongst the audience were Wyndham Harding and Scott Russell, who were certain to be offended. They and the other enemies of the Great Western sat waiting their opportunity to pounce.

He began with an outspoken attack on Harding's paper. Its author and Scott Russell, he said, had given their results in a diagram into which they had introduced a red line, stating this to be a law of resistances contended for by Brunel, Samuda and himself. He for one had made no such law and Harding was mistaken. He then went on to criticise Harding's data item by item in blunt detail. By the time that he had finished with him he was a third of the way through his paper and an old score had been settled.

Gooch next went on to describe his dynamometer carriage and engine indicator before turning to his Banwell experiments. He compared his figures with a formula in Harding's paper which gave resistances 46–78 percent higher than his own results. The implication was clear. If both sets of measurements were accurate the narrow gauge trains, on which Harding's work was based, had higher resistances than the broad. Gooch suggested that the large differences had occurred because Harding had used the results of tests in which trains were allowed to run down long banks – 'inclined plane' experiments. He also referred, more provocatively, to the possibility that the narrow gauge trains had higher resistances as they were longer, weight for weight, than the broad. Stephenson and his followers could not ignore this statement but they had no opportunity to reply that evening as the meeting came to an end when Gooch had finished speaking.

On the following Saturday much of what Gooch had said appeared in print. *The Morning Herald*, which was an enthusiastic supporter of the broad gauge, set aside almost a whole page to a verbatim account, together with abridged tables of his results. Unfortunately for Gooch this left him open to an attempt by the narrow gauge to suppress both further discussion and the publication of his paper in the Institution's Proceedings. Within a few days he received a letter from Charles Manby, the secretary, asking him to explain why it had been published in the press. This took him aback and he replied enclosing extracts from a letter obtained from a Mr Brooke, presumably the editor of *The Morning Herald*. These cut little ice with Manby, who pointed out that the Laws of the Institution forbade publication elsewhere without the Council's permission. The reason for Gooch's surprise is evident from Manby's further comment that 'when I saw you about this matter I had forgotten that the same improper course had been taken by Mr Scott Russell and Mr Harding and that the Council had not followed the matter up as they ought to have done'.

Behind the scenes the attempts to suppress the paper continued but on 3 May Manby wrote saying that the Council had agreed that discussion should go ahead. Gooch had broken no formal undertaking on publication, as they had also decided that 'in future before any paper was read the Author should be engaged to abide by the rules of the Institution'. The delaying tactics continued, however, and it was 16 May before Gooch sat in front of his professional colleagues awaiting their onslaught.

Scott Russell opened the proceedings suavely, praising his equipment, but then went on to say that in his own work he had considered it desirable to study ordinary trains under ordinary circumstances, whereas Gooch had only studied variations in the working of special trains. Harding repeated his arguments and then expressed his regret that the gauge question had been introduced. He tried to hold Gooch to the old figure of 18 lb a ton and the 'red line law', but made the mistake of saying that the Banwell experiments had been made on trains much heavier than his own, accounting for the lower resistances. Brunel then rose to make short work of Harding. He also would have deprecated any introduction of the gauge question, he said, but all that had been stated was that a train of 50 tons must be longer on the narrow gauge than on the broad, a fact independent of the merits of the two systems. He dismissed Harding's point about the heavier trains with the crushing reminder that 'it would have been a perfect absurdity to have made the experiments on the Great Western Railway with a train of only fifty tons'.

Brunel was followed by Bidder who, after pious remarks on the introduction of the gauge question, poured scorn on Gooch's wind measurements, claiming that he had called a breeze of 16 mph 'a stormy wind'. Gooch admitted that his wind direction measurements ought to have been more accurate, but Bidder was remorseless. 'The only facts of importance, the direction and velocity of the wind,' he said, 'had been ascertained by an instrument admitted to be very imperfect.'

Joseph Locke became an unwitting ally when he took up the question of speeds on inclined planes. Gooch's data, he said, suggested that carriages would reach 60 mph coasting down a bank of one in a hundred, but his own experience was that only 36 mph would be reached. The results in the paper, he concluded scathingly, were 'in opposition to the laws of gravitation'. This gave Gooch a glorious opportunity. At the next session he was able to announce the results of tests which he had just carried out. Trains of carriages weighing 50 tons had been launched down the Wootton Bas-

sett bank, which had a slope of one in a hundred. Even in bad weather they reached 45.9–52.3 mph, and when he tried the ordinary expresses with the steam off they reached 60 mph. These tests showed conclusively that the broad gauge had the lesser resistance.

After the second evening of discussion *The Morning Herald* again took up the cudgels. On 25 May the editor pointed out that the narrow gauge, because of their inferior engines, had an interest in making it appear that the resistances of trains at high velocities were great and that travelling at high speeds was therefore expensive. They had been astonished, he said, by Gooch's results. 'We cannot conclude our notice of the discussion at the Institution,' he continued, 'without expressing our strong dissent from the propriety . . . of the practice . . . of permitting notes of the proceedings to find their way into the public press only through the medium of their secretary.'

As a result of these bold statements the discussion at the third and final session took an unpleasant turn. Robert Stephenson reminded the meeting that a copy of the paper had appeared in *The Morning Herald* and that this had introduced the question of the gauges. Bidder then followed his chief's lead. Since Gooch had read his paper the Report of the Railway Commissioners had appeared, containing all his results. 'Immediately afterwards', said Bidder, *'The Morning Herald* inserted the paper as conclusive of the superiority of the broad gauge.' He thought that the Institution ought not to have been used for such a purpose, and that the discussion of the paper must now be regarded as on the relative merits of the two gauges. Bidder was implying that, as such, it could not be published by the Institution. He had distorted the facts, as the newspaper account had appeared on 22 April, a month before the Commissioners had issued their report.

Neither Gooch nor Brunel made any attempt to answer these forceful attacks. The evening ended with a half-hearted suggestion from Stephenson that experiments should be made on both gauges under joint supervision. Not surprisingly, nothing came of this, as the experts on the narrow gauge side must have had enough faith in both their own results and Gooch's to know that the truth had already been established.

The narrow gauge efforts to prevent the publication of Gooch's paper met with success. Only a thousand word summary was permitted to appear in the *Proceedings*, and this contained only two numerical results, but the discussion, with all the adverse comments from the narrow gauge side, was published in full. The Institution's next annual report included the statement that the original communications of the session had possessed great merit. Ten papers were referred to, including Gooch's. Medals and premiums had been awarded for several, but his had not been considered, 'because it had been published by the Government (*vide* Minutes of Evidence taken before the Gauge Commissioners, p.135, London, 1846), and was merely brought before the Institution, under a peculiar arrangement, in order to raise a discussion on so interesting a subject'. At the conclusion of this shabby affair the Council had not even taken the trouble to get their facts right.

So Gooch and his professional Institution parted company. He never spoke again at one of their meetings, even when subjects close to his heart were discussed. Tom Gooch had been a Member since 1845 and John was elected in 1854. George Henry joined the North of England Institution of Mining Engineers and William Frederick the Institution of Mechanical Engineers. Only Daniel, the most distinguished of the five, never sought membership of a professional body, and we can understand why.

The valedictory for Gooch's research came from D.K. Clark, who combined his results into a resistance formula which stood for over forty years. 'Mr Daniel Gooch,' he said, 'is the only experimentalist whose results are worthy of implicit confidence, for he operated with the trains precisely under the conditions of ordinary practice . . . It is our conviction that they were conducted with the strictest impartiality, and . . . the apparatus was elaborated with the utmost care and consideration, worthy of the high character of Mr Gooch as an experimentalist and observer'.

The disappointment which he must have felt at the treatment of his paper was no doubt eased by the outcome of the Railway Commissioners' deliberations. They recommended that the Birmingham and Oxford should be built as a mixed gauge line. Parliament accepted their view and Birmingham was open to the broad gauge.

So ended what Gooch saw as the last of the real gauge fights. 'It may be said', he wrote nearly twenty years later, ' . . . that a difference in the gauge of railways in this country, now that they have covered its surface..is an evil and is now to be regretted, but were the whole question now open to be decided, the broad gauge is safer, cheaper, more comfortable and attains a much higher speed than the narrow, and would be the best for the national gauge, but . . . the day will come when it will cease.' The fight, he continued, 'has been of great benefit to the public; it has pricked on all parties to exertion'.

The gauge war, in fact, had swept Gooch to the head of his profession. Those best able to know were in no doubt about his pre-eminence. At Tredegar his old foreman, Thomas Ellis, was a sick man, nearing the end of his life. On 10 April 1849 he spent a nostalgic day on the old Sirhowy Tramroad and then made one of the last entries in the notebooks which Gooch had perused as a boy: 'Capt. Simmons, Gov' Inspector of Tram Roads, for the purpose of examing it from Tredegar to Pill laft Bedwelty House per St. David locomotive . . . Capt. Simmons on talking of Daniel Gouch Esq. says he is the first and Best Engineer on Locomotive Branch in Great Brytton'.

CHAPTER
17

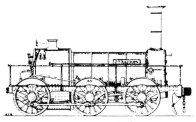

Pyracmon, 1847

By mid-1847 Swindon was well into its stride as a locomotive factory. The workforce had reached eighteen hundred, leading to severe overcrowding in the railway village and for miles around. Over seventeen hundred people were living in New Swindon, an average of over seven per house. Sturrock had applications for accomodation from well over a hundred of his men but only five cottages and two shops were being built.

The village had become a balanced community. St. Mark's Church and school, founded by subscriptions and a bequest left by George Henry Gibbs, had been open for two years. There was a park, where cricket was played, and during the summer there were lectures on The Genius of Boz, The Rise and Progress of Language and The Mineral Acids at the Mechanics' Institution. The band was rehearsing for a concert of seventeen items. The works was at its busiest. Eighteen engines had been turned out in the previous twelve months. There were five *Iron Dukes* and the first of a new class of goods engines under construction. The future looked rosy, but the bubble of the Railway Mania was about to burst.

Britain was in the midst of the Hungry Forties, the years of the potato famine in Ireland. Agriculture had been protected by the Corn Laws, harvests had failed and the price of wheat had soared. The Railway Mania, with its insatiable demand for capital, was at its height. The economy and, above all, the poor, were vulnerable.

In 1846 the Corn Laws were repealed. The harvest was a bad one and blight ruined the potato crop over the whole of Europe. The effects became dramatic in Britain in mid-1847. The highest price of wheat during the previous year was 62s. 5d. a quarter, but by the end of May a record of 102s. 5d. had been reached. The merchants scented fortunes and foreign grain began to flood into the country.

In the meantime the Bank of England had reacted to stave off the crisis threatened by the Mania. Loans were refused and the discount rate was raised. Then there was a golden autumn, an excellent harvest and the promise of a good potato crop. The grain ships, bearing cargoes ordered months before, were still arriving at the ports. Supply outstripped demand and in September the price of wheat plummetted to 49s. 6d., taking business houses with it. Capital could no longer be found for railway projects and share-prices collapsed.

The crash had immediate effects on the Great Western. Painful economies were necessary to free revenue to finance partially completed projects. Swindon bore the brunt, as locomotive overhauls and construction were obvious areas for cutting back. Perhaps Gooch had seen trouble coming, as he had been attempting to build up the load on the works. In September he

tendered for locomotives for the Bristol and
Exeter Railway, who were soon to take over
the running of their line from the Great
Western. Sadly for the railway village the
order did not materialise.

The axe fell soon and swiftly. *The Railway Times* for 27 November reported that
three to four hundred men had been
discharged at Swindon. The remaining
eight or nine hundred had agreed to give
3½ percent of their wages towards the
support of their former workmates. Brunel
donated £100 and Gooch £50 to the fund.

In the late autumn Gooch wrote a
graphic and revealing letter to Charles
Saunders about the plight of his men. It
had important and long-lasting results.

> *My Dear Sir,*
>
> *The serious distress that will be occasioned
> . . . at Swindon by discharging so many and
> putting the rest upon short time induces me to
> hope the Directors will grant a request . . .
> made to me, namely to assist the men to pay
> the Doctor for attending all the families of the
> men both in and out of   work . . . The bulk
> of those discharged have determined to remain
> in the neighbourhood . . . in hopes of better
> times, . . . and many have been very lately
> induced to come to Swindon at considerable
> expense to them in removing their families.*
>
> *Those men who are to be retained . . . have
> very generously offered to assist the unfor-
> tunate men in any way in their power . . .
> One of the plans is to arrange with Mr Rea*,
> Surgeon, to attend the whole for a small
> weekly payment by each man. The arrange-
> ment I have no doubt I will be able to bring
> about if I can get some assistance from the
> Directors. What I would beg of them to do is
> to allow Mr Rea to live in the Cottages
> house-free in consideration of his attending all
> the accidents that occur in the works.*
>
> *The attendance in these cases is at present
> on a footing . . . not . . . just either to the
> surgeon or the men. In all private establish-
> ments the Doctor's bill for attending accidents
> is paid by the Employers: up to the present time
> at Swindon this has not been done, as I have
> not felt myself authorised . . . and have only*

> *done so in one or two cases, where he has been
> money out of pocket for bandages, etc. . . .
> The result in a great many cases is that the
> Doctor is not paid at all . . . There is more
> than one accident per week . . . and many of
> them very serious ones . . . What I hope the
> Directors will allow me to do is either to give
> me authority for accidents as they occur, or
> that they will give Mr Rea £30 a year to take
> them all, or . . . give him a house free of
> rent. If this is done I feel convinced it will be
> considered a great boon by the men . . .*
>
> *It must not be forgotten that our men . . .
> are themselves only allowed to work three-
> quarters of their wages. I am sure if the
> Directors would themselves visit Swindon and
> hear the many distressing cases I heard yester-
> day they would at once grant what I so
> earnestly request and in all possibility much
> more. I believe with the good feeling now
> existing at Swindon the men will do much
> good amongst their unfortunate fellow workers
> . . . It is not a gift to the Doctor that I ask
> but that the men may be relieved of the cost of
> numerous accidents, leaving them still to
> support their own sick, which I fear will be a
> heavy matter this winter as amongst the other
> misfortunes we have some very bad cases of
> smallpox in the village. I have to meet some of
> the men Thursday evening and shall be glad
> to tell them their request and mine is agreed
> to. Your own kind assistance in this matter
> will much oblige,*
>
> *Yours very truly,*
> *Danl Gooch*

Gooch's plea was successful and the
directors agreed to the rent free house, a
concession which cost them only a few
shillings a week. Within a month a Medical
Society was formed with Sturrock as its first
president. This was the start of a scheme
which developed steadily in scope, standing
employees in excellent stead for a century
and serving as a model when the National
Health Service was set up.

The Medical Fund gave Rea a reasonable
security. Besides the rent free cottage he
received capitation fees, in return for which
he had to provide leeches, medicines, ban-

---

* Rae' in the clerk's copy of Gooch's letter at this point, which has led to confusion. The spelling is Rea elsewhere
in the letter and on other documents and his tombstone.

dages and splints, as well as his services. Gooch, besides wanting Rea to stay to look after the men, also felt a special responsibility towards him. He was an Irishman whose brother, Minard, had been one of the first of his pupils and Gooch had persuaded him to come to the village. Just over a year previously he had married a local girl, Ann Pavy, whose family Gooch knew well.

Rea died in 1848, leaving his widow far from well off. Gooch, who knew how to appeal to a penny-pinching board, then wrote to Saunders to suggest that the rent-free house should pass to the new surgeon, 'as from the number of accidents we have I think it is less expensive than it would be if we had to pay him his charge when we called him in'. He also wrote to Sturrock about a meeting which was to be held on the cricket ground. 'Will you be good enough,' he ordered, 'to let those involved know . . . no **political** or **religious** subject can be introduced . . . The Company are very desirous to give every encouragement to the Temperance Society provided no use is made of it to set up **political** or **religious** discussion, which must be injurious to the men.' This was the Year of Revolutions in Europe, the Chartists were active in Britain, and caution was to be expected.

After the initial shock of the dismissals the factory remained surprisingly busy. In the first ten months of 1848 eleven engines were built, but then the suffering in the village grew worse. Over the next two and a half years only twelve were turned out, a 60% cut in the work rate. Two hundred men were probably enough on new construction and further dismissals were inevitable. 'I see no way of reducing our men but by letting them who have come on last leave now,' Gooch wrote on 4 December. Times were also hard amongst the footplatemen. 'I have got some spare enginemen and firemen and must get rid of some,' Gooch told one of his foremen. 'Which of your firemen is the least value to the company?.'

It was a lean Christmas in the cottages, many of the families facing homelessness and impoverishment. To give some insurance against the dreaded workhouse men banded together, with the support of the better employers. At Swindon, in addition to the Medical Fund, they had the Great Western Provident Society and the Locomotive Department Sick Fund. There were also the Friendly Societies, such as the Oddfellows and Foresters. In 1849, however, the means were insufficient and Gooch played a leading part in the organisation of a relief fund.

New Swindon had more than unemployment to fear. Like all the industrial towns it was not a healthy place. The average age of death in the locality fell from 36 in the 1820s to 30 in the 1840s, no doubt because of a high birth rate and the appalling infant mortality. In 1849 there were special worries, as Britain was enduring another cholera epidemic. On 4 August Gooch instructed Sturrock to give notice in writing to each of the men whose houses he thought required cleaning: 'The drains – you had better see what can be done with them that are stopped up . . . Where you say there is a bad smell . . . one of the boards had better be taken up . . . If the pig is a nuisance it must not be allowed'. By luck and good management the village escaped the scourge and a Day of Thanksgiving was held.

The need for work remained desperate. In the autumn of 1849 Gooch pressed the directors to build locomotives in advance of their needs, arguing that during the depression men would work for low wages and materials could be bought cheaply and on long credit: 'It is very important for us to keep together the good men we now have, who are well acquainted with our work and can build the engines both cheaper and better than fresh hands'. Over thirty of the houses in the village were unoccupied as a result of the dismissals. Gooch pointed out that they were another consideration: 'The company are losing £580 per annum in rent, and this will be considerably increased when the wagons now in hand are finished and the men discharged'.

Gooch did everything that he could to obtain outside work, though not all of the directors were happy about this. His report of 22 September 1849 shows that orders for outside contracts worth £16,256 were in hand, all for Brunel. A bridge to cross the

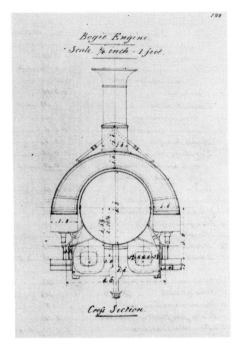

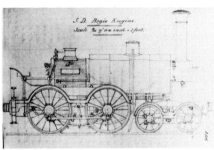

Drawings of *Corsair* from Gooch's *Sketch Book*

recently completed engine was *Corsair*, the first of two massive bogie-tanks. A second, *Brigand*, was nearly finished. They had been designed for service on the South Devon. Their 36 tons were carried on a leading four-wheeled bogie and four coupled wheels, six feet in diameter. A fat saddle tank was mounted on the boiler and the coke was carried in a chariot-shaped appendage to the footplate. They had an ugly air of purpose and proved most successful.

The bogie-tanks had been designed in the first place as tender engines, being modified whilst going through the shops. The original layout is shown on some drawings dated December 1848 which are now in the National Railway Museum at York. The standard of draughtsmanship at Swindon had reached a superb level, every component being beautifully colour-washed to make it stand out in relief. Five men worked on *Corsair*. The main drawing was made by Edward Snell, who had moved into the office in December 1844, a few months after T.R. Crampton had left. The following August he had been promoted to head draughtsman, his wages being increased from 32s. to two guineas a week. He had later been made responsible for the design and construction of an extension to the factory, probably shops for the building of carriages and wagons, which led to his promotion to General Superintendent, next under Sturrock, on a salary of £2 15s. a week. At its height Snell had two hundred workmen engaged on his project. It was important enough to survive the cuts until October 1848 but then he had to sack all his men and he himself went back to the drawing office. Though Sturrock was his immediate boss his work and all the drawings made by his draughtsmen were initialled by Gooch. Snell himself had little flair as a locomotive designer, as will emerge later, and it is evident that Gooch exercised full control over every detail.

Snell was also a fine artist. In 1849 he resigned from the Great Western because Sturrock cut his salary. Not long before he left he painted a detailed bird's eye view of the works and railway village, peopled with tiny figures. His cricketers, schoolchildren at play, haymakers, churchgoers and

Isis at Oxford had been finished and the Cardiff Canal and Bute Street bridges were well in hand for the South Wales Railway. Sixty pairs of switches, fifty crossings and a hundred rail guards were also being made.

Swindon's ordinary work included modifications to eight locomotives. The order for 150 coal and stone wagons had just been finished, swelling the ranks of the unemployed. Two 8ft. singles, *Prometheus* and *Perseus*, were under construction but progressing only slowly, the men often being diverted to breakdowns. The most

Edward Snell's painting of New Swindon, 1849

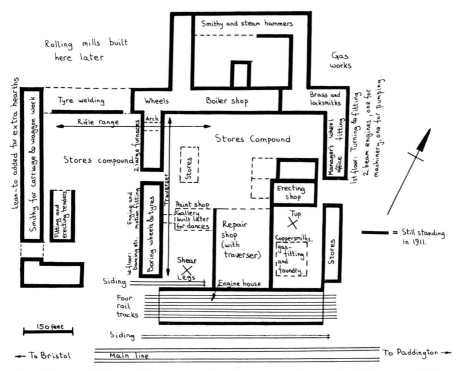

Plan of Swindon Works in 1849, based on Snell's painting and articles by A.J.L. White in the *G.W.R. Magazine*, 1911–14

A *Fire Fly* on the traverser in the Repair Shop

workmen give his spirited picture a fascinating social, as well as historical, interest. It is now in the Great Western Museum at Swindon and has been reproduced in virtually every book about the town or railway.

Snell's picture and a series of articles by A.J.L. White, written shortly before the First World War, tell us what the factory was like in the late forties. The oldest of the buildings was the long engine shed, open at both ends, where minor repairs were carried out and engines were weighed, cleaned and fired ready for running. On its north side was another large building where the major overhauls and breakdowns were dealt with. Beyond was the erecting shop, where the new engines were put together. It was served by the overhead hydraulic crane built by Napier in 1844, which the labourers worked by hand-operated pumps.

The rest of the shops were arranged around three squares, in the centre of which were the foundry and a huge pair of shear legs, capable of lifting a complete locomotive. On the eastern side of the main square was a two storey building in which were fitting shops, crammed with benches, lathes and other machine tools. The brass-fitting and locksmiths' shops, Sturrock's office and a pair of beam engines were also in that part of the factory. Not far away were the gas works and a pumping engine which supplied all the water.

The western side of the main square was bounded by a two storey building in which was the room used for dancing and theatricals. Next to this was the paint shop, later cleared to give more room for entertainments. On the ground floor the large components were machined and fitted. Close by were the furnaces for the heavier smiths' work, with their two 80ft. stacks, and the steam-hammer shop, where wheels were forged and plates flanged for the boilermakers, whose shop was next door. A large beam engine, built by Harveys', the famous Cornish firm, powered the machine tools on that side of the works and the blowers which supplied the air for the forges and smiths' hearths.

Swindon was already big enough to accomodate nearly three thousand men, but that was as nothing. Over the years factory and town grew together. Richard Jefferies, the Wiltshire writer and naturalist, wrote in the seventies that 'much, if not all, of this marvellous transformation, of this abounding life and vigorous vitality, is due to the energy and forethought, the will, of one man. It is notorious that the Swindon of today is the creation of the companion of Brunel at the lunch in the furze bushes . . . Daniel Gooch'.

Gooch was well aware of the scale of his achievement and of the social responsibilities which went with it. 'I did my best as far as I could,' he wrote, 'and, while I strove to do my duty I remembered that the moral welfare of those under me was a thing for which I would have to answer at a higher tribunal. The happiness of my men and their families depended much upon the influence I exerted over them, and I have striven to make the influence beneficial.'

CHAPTER

18

The *Iron Dukes* were Gooch's zenith as a locomotive designer. They became the pride of his enginemen and the source of many legends.

In 1848 the morning expresses were allowed 55 min. for the 52⅞ mls from Paddington to Didcot – 57.7 mph. This was not fast enough to suit the drivers, who vied with one another for the best time. According to Gooch they regularly covered the distance in 48–50 min. – 66.1 to 63.4 mph. He stated that on one occasion, when Capt. Simmons was present, an average of 67 mph was achieved with a train of 115 tons.

It was Michael Almond who laid claim to the record. He is said to have reached Didcot in 47 min.– 67.5 mph. The story was that when he arrived he had a shock, as, unknown to him, Gooch was on board. Whilst he was filling up with water his chief came up, watch in hand. 'Do you know, Michael, how long it is since you left Paddington?' Almond said that he supposed that he had not lost any time. 'Lost time!,' exclaimed Gooch. 'Why man, do you know that it was only forty-seven minutes since you left Paddington? This is all very well, just for once, to see what your engine can do, but it must not be repeated.'

There are other tales of even higher speeds. Charles Sacré said that in 1848 78 mph was reached down Wootton Bassett bank, and one man who knew Almond and his workmates well was quite sure that 90 mph was achieved at times. 'Of course, I am referring to the early days before 'coal-dodging' became chronic,' he said.

Critics of the broad gauge have regarded such stories as apocryphal, as they are not supported by detailed timings. Fortunately the pages of *The Morning Herald* include ample evidence of speeds which, though falling a little short of those quoted above, were phenomenal.

During Gooch's trials early in 1848 the shortest time to Didcot was 53 min. 34 sec. (59.1 mph). On 18 March the *Herald* reported that *Lightning*, driven by William Cowell, had improved on this by almost 2 min. He lost the record to *Emperor* on 26 April, when more than 1 min. was cut from his time and several individual miles were cleared in 49 sec. – 73.4 mph. When the *Herald* announced that the even faster time of 49 min. 19 sec. had been achieved on 14 July the narrow gauge's supporters expressed disbelief. Their report, the editor responded angrily on 20 July, was perfectly true – 'We went down with the train'. He then gave detailed timings, showing an average of 64.4 mph and a peak of 70.9 mph. Forty-eight mls had been covered at 67.6 mph.

The seventh of the *Iron Dukes*, *Courier*, which was turned out at Swindon in June, was even more powerful than the earlier ones. Her grate was larger and the boiler pressure was increased to 120 lb/sq. in. Her driver, John Heppell, made an attempt on the record on 29 August. With Gooch's permission he took Jonas Brown, one of the L&NWR's crack drivers, along as a witness. He covered 43 mls at 70.2 mph, completing the journey in 49 min. 13 sec. (64.3 mph). With such speeds on a level line we can well imagine the eighties being reached downhill. The best which the narrow gauge could do at that time was an average of 56 mph, achieved on 19 February 1848 between Normanton and Darlington by a special train drawing only a light load.

The 8ft. singles inspired affection in all who knew them. One devotee wrote that 'one only had to look at their polished brass splashers and their bright name-plates and axle-covers. When the eye, after dwelling upon narrow gauge models, catches sight of them, admiration can scarcely be withheld. It stands out from among the inferior fry with an air of grandeur and symmetry'. It took an expert like D.K. Clark to recognise any flaw in them. In his 1855 treatise he frequently praised Gooch's detailing. His one criticism was that the 8ft. singles were not efficient producers of steam. *Ixion* had raised 7 lb of steam for every pound of coke burned. The *Iron Dukes* gave an even better performance, achieving 7.67 lb of steam per pound of coke. Clark, however, had tested engines which produced as many as 10.47 lb/lb, and no less than fifteen out of twenty-two locomotives for which he had results gave better steam raising performances. Clark believed the fault lay in the close pitching of the boiler tubes. It is interesting to note that when Gooch's successors designed the 8ft. re-builds they used smaller tubes, less closely pitched, and there was evidently something in Clark's point.

Gooch was not always as kindly to his men as Almond's tale would suggest. He could be as irascible as ever, and he expected unflinching devotion to duty from his engine crews. 'I have thought over Pigeon's case,' he told one of his foremen, 'and cannot overlook the fact of his jumping off the engine after he saw it was to strike the trucks. I cannot therefore retain him in the service. The fireman may go to work again at 3s. per day, but if he ever leaves his brake again, as long as he can hold it, I will not overlook it, and only do so in this case because the engineman set him the example.' In the extreme his wrath was scathing. 'You will, I think, not be surprised at the communication I am obliged to make to you,' he told one unfortunate employee. 'I have made arrangements for altering the present system of working our ovens . . . I regret very much to tell you that you have by your total neglect of duty, after repeated promises of amendment, compelled me to

make this change, and to say that your services will not be required after Saturday.' He stood up for his men, however, if he felt that they were being treated unreasonably, showing especial concern if they had to work excessively long hours. He sent a blunt letter to Lane, Brunel's assistant, complaining that a ballast-engine man had been kept on duty for 92½ hr in one six day period.

Gooch concentrated on the operational side of his division and on the design and performance of his locomotives. None of his correspondence was about the fine detail of affairs at Swindon, which he left to Sturrock. He was never office bound. 'I went down on the *Red Star* yesterday. She has all the weight on the driving wheels and is not fit to run,' he told one of his men. 'She will destroy both the road and herself. Do not let her run again until I see you.'

His engines were still the mainstay on the South Devon, as Brunel's difficulties with the atmospheric system were continuing. During the autumn of 1847 some of the Exeter to Teignmouth services were run by 'Master Piston' but with the onset of winter his troubles grew even worse. The twenty miles to Newton were nevertheless turned over to atmospheric working on 23 February 1848. In the next two and a half months over sixteen hundred trains were run but behind the scenes there were formidable problems. The vacuum sucked the moisture from the leather valve strips, making them hard and brittle. The air and sunlight hardened the grease seal and the salt air corroded the backing plates and fixings. Even the stationary engines proved unreliable. Locomotives had to be sent out to rescue stranded atmospheric trains and the public complained bitterly.

By June 1848 nearly 2½ mls of valve had been renewed. Running costs were nine times higher than had been expected and two to three times greater than for locomotives. On 19 August Brunel submitted a report to the board on the situation. After outlining the problems with the engines and the valve he gave in, admitting that he could no longer recommend the system for the steeply graded sections, though he believed that improvements could be made on the 20 mls that were in use. This was the death knell, as there was no point in using the system to work the easily graded portion of the South Devon and the rest by locomotives. Although there were attempts by a few diehards to revive it this was the end of the atmospheric railway, but its legacies – the 40 mls of single track, the severe gradients and the tight curves – remained and the Great Western's locomotives were barely coping.

The most powerful engine which Gooch then had at work there was *Goliah*, a *Hercules*. Drastic measures were sometimes needed to enable even her to mount the steepest banks. On 27 June she was approaching the foot of the gruelling 2 mile incline near Plymouth. Suddenly, with an appalling roar, the crown of the firebox collapsed, sending a blast wave of steam into the furnace. The crew were lucky to escape with their lives.

Gooch travelled down for the inquiry. On the way he had a couple of hours to spare and got off the train at Kingsbridge Road station. It was a glorious day and two miles away the hills of Dartmoor rose invitingly to over twelve hundred feet. Gooch, who loved walking, decided to make for the top of the nearest. He found the going very wet in places. Seeing what he thought to be a sound piece of ground he took a jump onto it, but it was one of the moor's notorious bog-holes and he began to sink into the mud. He let his body fall flat and managed to drag himself to safety. Soaked and exhausted he stripped off, spread his clothes on the warm rocks and lay in the shade whilst they dried. 'How easily a man might disappear from the face of the earth in that way, leaving no trace behind', he wrote, thankful to be alive.

At the inquiry Gooch found himself on equally uncertain ground. The Inspector had taken the safety valves from the wreckage and tested them. They were supposed to operate at 70 lb/sq. in. but it was only when he applied 150 lb/sq. in. that they lifted. He was scathing, and on 5 July Gooch had to issue an edict that 'the engineman must once every week **himself** examine both safety valves and ascertain that they are in proper working order, and that the spring valve is not screwed down to beyond 75 pounds on the square inch in the

old engines and 100 pounds in the engines built at Swindon . . . Both enginemen and firemen are strictly forbidden on any account to **hold down** the . . . valve'.

After his uncomfortable experiences Gooch was no doubt glad of a holiday. In August he and Margaret went to France and Belgium for a month with their friends the Minets. Whilst he was away a most important shareholders' meeting took place.

The depression which followed the financial crisis of 1847 resulted in a sharp reduction in railway dividends. The Great Western's dropped from 8% in 1846 to only 4% three years later and the shares fell from £149 to £95. The board were anxious to placate their worried investors and readily accepted a suggestion that they should meet with a Consultative Committee to discuss economies. Gooch prepared a report for them, a typically thorough account of his stewardship in which he said that he had improved twenty-four engines by adding the link motion and another thirty-four by increasing their strokes. Amongst other economies he had converted fourteen *Suns* and *Leos* to tank engines and was tackling another thirteen. Each cost nearly £50 to alter but as there were then no tenders to clean and repair he saved £3. 15s. per week, an excellent return on the capital.

The Consultative Committee soon satisfied themselves that the company was well managed but they insisted on economies, their main proposals being cuts in staff and salaries. This led to an uproar, many of the best staff moving elsewhere. To Gooch's fury they proposed that his salary should be cut from £1,000 to £700. He made up his mind to resign rather than accept this and no doubt made his views plain, as in the event he was amongst the few whose pay was left alone. This led to ill feeling, Edward Snell, who had emigrated, noting in his diary that letters from home said that 'Sewell at the stores had got into a scrape for writing . . . to Herapath's Journal about Gooch and Sturrock's salary'.

Snell's extracts from his correspondence give a vivid picture of life at Swindon in late 1849. The news, he said, was principally bad. 'Work getting slacker and slacker . . . the men making only 4½ days per week and a great number of them sacked. The bogie engines had been tried and did not run very well at first but they did better afterwards . . . Ten fitters and erectors got notice to leave . . . A talk of two hundred hands being discharged from the factory shortly. Mrs Patterson and Warburton discovered in a delicate position in the cricket ground after dark by Mr P., who kicked his wife's stern all the way home . . . Bonnet, Howard and Stewart sent out experimenting with the indicator van and got drunk . . . The company had taken steps to force the men to live in their cottages. No new work in the shops and no new materials arriving . . . Nineteen clerks sacked from Paddn. at once. Mrs Sturrock in the family way again. The directors examining into the loco. accounts pretty severely, have overhauled the books four times.'

Snell also noted some surprising gossip. 'Mr D. Gooch,' he wrote, 'suspected of getting Mrs Rea in the family way – she was grown very stout and has gone to France.'

The lady of this intriguing rumour can only have been Ann Rea, the widow of Swindon's first surgeon. She revered her husband's memory and the thoughtful and delightful will which she prepared many years later gives an impression of great charm. Consular registrations of births yield no evidence as to whether there was any foundation to the story. Whatever the truth of the matter it is interesting that Gooch's staff thought him (and, indeed, her) capable of an affair. If he succumbed he handled the matter with enough tact to remain on the closest of terms with the Pavys, her family.

The threat of a reduction in salary, said Gooch, opened his eyes to the poor security of a railway post. Sturrock and Seymour Clark, another of his senior colleagues, were sufficiently disillusioned by the board's actions to leave, both taking up better posts on the Great Northern Railway. To gain greater independence Gooch saw Charles Russell, the chairman, and obtained his permission to do private work as long as he did not neglect the Great Western. 'Acting on this principle,' he wrote, 'I found no difficulty in making money by professional services in other ways and it is thus what

fortune I have realised has been obtained. I may therefore thank the Consultative Committee of 1849 for the view they took of railway management.'

At this time Gooch took up an interest which began to absorb a great deal of his spare time – Freemasonry. On 14 February 1850 he joined St. George's Lodge, Exeter. 'Many ridicule the society,' he wrote, '. . . saying there is no secret and the only object is good dinners . . . I look back on my connexion with Masonry as a very **useful** and very pleasant part of my life.'

Gooch tackled his new interest with his customary energy and success, learning the rites and attending all the lodge meetings during the first few years. After being 'passed' and 'raised' at Exeter he became a member of the Royal Sussex Lodge of Emulation at Swindon. Early in 1851 he also joined Middlesex Lodge. Within three years he became Master of the Lodge at Swindon and in 1853 was a founder and the first Master of Lansdowne Lodge of Unity at Calne, Wiltshire. In the same year he was appointed Deputy Provincial Grand Master of Wiltshire and a member of the Board of General Purposes.

Gooch eventually rose to the top fifty or so in a society which numbered 300,000 and was headed by the Prince of Wales. He served on national committees and became a Life Governor and Steward of the Royal Masonic Institution for Boys and the similar institution for girls, as well as a Vice-President of the Royal Masonic Benevolent Institution. An article describing his achievements as a Mason began with the quotation:

"For he is gracious . . .
He hath a tear for pity, and a hand
Open as day for melting charity."

He was, the writer said, no holiday Mason, but one of those who joined with the intention of doing whatever was required of them to the utmost of their ability. He had done his work admirably, he continued, and in a manner which had gained him the love and approbation of all who had been associated with him in the craft.

Whether Gooch's interest in Freemasonry

was wholly altruistic can only be conjectured, but as a result of the Consultative Committee's actions he had broadened his horizons to a point at which his job no longer dominated his life. He began his private work, however, even before he saw Charles Russell. On 30 November 1849 he wrote to Saunders to ask if the directors would allow him to build a small engine at Swindon for Lord Willoughby de Eresby. Lord Willoughby was then in his late sixties but still active as an agriculturist. He had asked Gooch to design him an engine to operate a steam plough. 'This I did,' Gooch wrote, 'and I went down to his place at Grimsthorpe to try the ploughing. The arrangement . . . was Lord Willoughby's own.'

Schemes for ploughing by steam power had been patented as long ago as 1810 but it was only in the late forties that reasonably successful ideas emerged. In 1849 James Usher, an Edinburgh brewer, had a rotary digger built and in East Lothian John Osborn used a two-engined system for ploughing. The engines stood on wooden rafts, drawing the plough to and fro between them by means of winches. Chains and anchors were used to enable them to haul themselves along to the start of a new furrow.

Lord Willoughby's system was not unlike Osborn's but had only one engine, mounted on a wooden raft to which guide rails were fitted. An anchor cart was used in place of the second engine. The plough was first drawn backwards in its raised position out to the anchor cart. The engine was then reversed to pull it back, turning the furrow. A double system was used, the engine moving along the middle of the field with an anchor cart on either side.

The engine which Gooch designed was called *California*. A year or two later he built a second, *Australia*, which consisted of a typical locomotive boiler carried on four wheels. The cylinders were mounted on top and the ploughing drum underneath. A long connecting rod was used to couple the flywheel shaft to an underslung crankshaft which powered the winch drum through bevel gears and a dog clutch. Harold Bonnett in his *Saga of the Steam Plough* comments that Gooch's layout

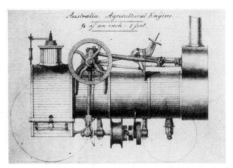

Australia, a ploughing engine built by Gooch for Lord Willoughby de Eresby. From Gooch's *Sketch Book*

anticipated future traction engine practice. It is interesting that he used small steerable wheels under the smokebox and large ones at the firebox end. Though *Australia* was not self propelled the large rear wheels suggest that he had the provision of a drive in mind, and by 1854 he had built a road locomotive for Lord Willoughby. It appears to have been quite speedy, as Gooch wrote that they 'had some good fun learning to stear it. I found it very difficult to keep her on the narrow roads . . . and often, if we went fast, made a dash onto the grass'.

The trials at Grimsthorpe showed that the ploughing system was more expensive than horses and Gooch saw little future for traction engines. Their developments came to a stop, Lord Willoughby generously giving his ideas away to anyone who wanted to make use of them.

Though this work provided Gooch with some amusement there can be no doubt that he and Willoughby had a serious commercial purpose in mind. The names which were chosen for the engines suggest that the opening up of the frontier lands was a part of their intentions. Their approach was not dissimilar to Fowler's, who, two years later, built his first steam plough and began the developments which made mechanised cultivation a commercial proposition. They had perhaps let a golden opportunity slip by, but by that time Gooch had little incentive to take new financial risks. Profits were pouring in from an enormously successful venture which had resulted from the aftermath of the atmospheric railway.

Gooch's opportunity arose because the

running costs of his engines were crippling the South Devon. The Great Western's rates were 1s. 4d. to 1s. 9d. a mile, which at first sight seem exorbitant, as the same engines cost only 9.8d. to 12.8d. per mile on their own line. The South Devon, however, was very hard on the stock, passenger locomotives costing 16.6d. per mile, so that the charges gave no more than a reasonable profit. The South Devon directors were therefore delighted when *Corsair* and *Brigand* came into service, as they proved as successful as Gooch had hoped. They were anxious to have more like them but were in no position to buy some themselves, as they had lost over £350,000 on the atmospheric venture. They approached the Great Western for help but money was scarce and the suggestion was turned down. Gooch then offered to find partners and raise the capital in return for a ten year contract to work the line. They accepted and instructed Brunel to negotiate an agreement with him.

Gooch took Edward Evans of the Haigh Foundry and Charles Geach, M.P., an ironmaster, as his partners. The Great Western's shareholders might well have expressed surprise at losing lucrative business to their locomotive superintendent, so he kept in the background, the contract being in his partners' names. His agreement with Geach and Evans was that he, as the instigator and manager of the venture, would receive two-fifths of whatever profits were left after 5% had been paid on the capital. On the assumption that he put up a third of the money this gave him over 60% of the profits, 40% for running the contract plus a third of the remainder, as well as his interest payments.

By May 1850 Brunel and Gooch had worked out a draft agreement. Locomotives similar to *Corsair* were to be used, charges being based on a complicated scale which started at 1s. 3d. per mile for a train of six carriages on the Plymouth to Newton line. The partners were to receive a minimum of £298 per week and at the termination of the contract the South Devon were to take over the stock and plant at cost less 2½% per annum.

It was 12 December before the agreement was signed. Gooch then issued orders

for ten locomotives, worth over twenty thousand pounds, to the Haigh Foundry and Longridges'. Edward Evans was annoyed that only five were to be built at Wigan but Gooch reminded him coldly that he had understood that no more could be managed in the time available.

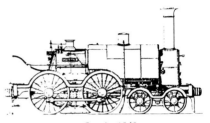

Corsair, 1849

The new engines were similar to *Corsair* and *Brigand*, though with larger grates, more tube area and coupled wheels 5ft. 9in. in diameter instead of 6ft. Gooch had no compunction about issuing Great Western drawings to the manufacturers. He mixed his normal duties and the South Devon work quite openly, both discussing the engines and ordering materials for Swindon in one letter.

Gooch was authorised to appoint a resident manager at a salary of up to £300 a year. On 12 December 1850 he wrote to William, his youngest brother, offering him the job. 'I will give you £200 per annum,' he said, 'and a percent of profits which should bring another £100 . . . I think it will do much better for you than anything you are likely to get in the North'. Gooch, it will be noted, was expecting the partners to share out at least £10,000 a year.

William Gooch, who was 25, had been a pupil at Swindon. He does not appear to have been in his brother's class, however, as during 1851 Gooch bore all the burden of launching the contract, writing letters finalising the design of the engines, urging their completion and ordering cranes, machine tools and coke ovens. In spite of his efforts by June it was clear that all the locomotives were going to be late. The Haigh Foundry, after grumbling at not being given more orders, had to subcontract two to Fairbairns'. Gooch told Longridge that he was reducing the price for his engines by £25 for each week's delay. He had to be hard as he was expecting the South Devon to impose heavy penalty charges on the partnership, though by October he had managed to negotiate an extension.

At last the locomotives began to arrive. By January 1852 six were in service and the seventh had left Wigan. William Gooch was in the saddle at Newton and the services were being taken over in stages. By the end of 1854 twelve engines were in use, three less than in Great Western days. The contract was run on a shoe string. Premiums were paid to the enginemen for coke saved and as a result goods trains were to be seen ascending the banks at less than 6 mph and running down the other side with steam off. The profits were enormous. In 1857, 202,605 train miles were completed in one six month period. The company paid an average of 1s. 6½d. per mile, so that the partners received about £15,600, whereas their running and repair costs were only £7,000. Gooch's share of the balance was presumably over £5,000 – £10,000 in a full year. In 1865, when they were working the Cornwall Railway as well, they shared over £36,000. Gooch was paid the vast sum of £21,713, a 63% return on his investment, which then stood at £34,550.

In spite of their robustness and power even Gooch's bogie-tanks suffered on the South Devon. At times William Gooch had to struggle just as hard as his brother had done in the early days of the Great Western. On 10 October 1854 only two engines were in good order. *Aurora* was stuck at Kingsbridge Road, *Comet* had a feed pump out of action, *Ostrich* had shed part of a tyre and four others were at Newton in various states of disrepair.

The *Corsairs* were the first large bogie engines to be built, so it is hardly surprising that Gooch had some difficulties with them. Ordinary engines did not have brakes, as they were fitted to the tenders instead. He naturally had to provide one on *Corsair*, but did not like the idea of brake blocks acting on the driving wheels, being afraid of uneven wear. Instead he used a sledge brake, with massive shoes which were forced down onto the rails. They proved so unsatisfactory that even *Brigand* was given normal brakes. He also tried india-rubber springs. Tom Tunstall, *Corsair's* first driver, complained that they gave a very rough ride.

One expert claimed that they suffered from a more fundamental problem. To accommodate the bogie the frames extended only under the rear half of the engine, the bogie pivot, front buffer beam and cylinders being bracketed to the boiler. As a result the driving forces were transmitted through the boiler plates and rivetted joints, causing fretting and leaks. He regarded this as a very defective arrangement. Nevertheless the twenty-seven bogie engines which were built averaged twenty-two years of gruelling service. *Comet* ran on the South Devon for nearly thirty-three years, not being withdrawn until 1884. There can have been little wrong with locomotives which gave such valiant service and made their designer rich.

CHAPTER

19

The year of 1851, Gooch wrote, 'was chiefly remarkable for the first of those exhibitions which have since become rather common . . . The Gt. Western Co. sent a locomotive, the *Lord of the Isles*, one of our large class of passenger engines, and I am safe in saying she was a beautiful job'.

At mid-century the Victorians looked back with awe and pride on the achievements of the previous fifty years. The *Illustrated London News* noted proudly that the large towns, grown out of all recognition, had become well lit and well paved. Those on rivers or near oceans enjoyed the advantages of steam vessels, and all had been brought closer together by railways and the electric telegraph. It was to celebrate such wonders that the Great Exhibition was organised. Under the enthusiastic leadership of the Prince Consort items ranging from works of art to huge machines were gathered together from all parts of the ever-growing world. Brunel was deeply involved and was no doubt anxious for the Great Western to put on a good show, so their principal contribution was one of the most striking of all the exhibits. As a result *Lord of the Isles* became a particular symbol of the broad gauge and gained a special place in the affection of the men of Swindon. In later years she appeared at Edinburgh and Chicago and, for her last showing, at Earls' Court in 1897. The editor of *The Engineer* recalled seeing her there. 'The drawings of these engines,' he wrote, 'give no insight into the character of the workmanship. To the modern eye this was quite rough. Smiths' work was left much as it came from the forge. That the chisel and the file had played their parts was

very evident. The dimensions of such parts as connecting rods seemed wholly inadequate. We had before us an object lesson in the difficulties the old time engineer had to overcome . . . Mr Gooch's audacity in building such locomotives with the inadequate machine tools and forging appliances of the day was only surpassed by Brunel in adopting the seven foot gauge.'

Many of the 5,416 parts of which *Lord of the Isles* was made began life in the foundry, where the biggest task was the cylinders, cast from toughened iron and made as hard as possible to resist the wear of the pistons. Most of the rest started amongst the dancing sparks and clanging hammers of the smithies. Gooch had a hundred and seventy six hearths, where the piston rods, levers, hand rails, steps and a multitude of smaller parts were forged. The bigger components, such as wheels, axles and connecting rods, were made using the steam hammers, which were served by the most skilled of the smiths and their sweating teams.

The task which caught the imagination of every visitor was the forging of the huge eight foot driving wheels. Each was made up of a hundred and one separate pieces of metal, hammer-welded into a structure whose integrity was vital to the safety of the passengers. A heavier, though less intricate, job was the forging of the crank axles. Quality was essential and all that Gooch had to pound shape and strength into them was a steam hammer with a one and a quarter ton head. The main shaft, which was about eight feet long, was made by 'faggotting', in which a bundle of rods was thumped into a solid bar under the hammer. Two heavy blocks of iron were then forged onto the shaft to provide the material from which the throws were machined.

The rough components passed on to fitting shops equipped with benches and rows of lathes and machine-tools. The crank axle went to the most imposing, a slotter which was the largest that Joseph Whitworth had ever made. This had a vertical ram which slid up and down, cutting bright slivers from the heaviest part of the forging to open out a square cavity as a first step in the formation of a crank throw.

The biggest lathe had two face plates and was capable of taking a crank axle complete with two driving wheels. This was first used to trim up the rims and bore out the bosses of the wheel forgings, an operation requiring great accuracy as eventually they were forced onto the shafts using a hydraulic press. The driving wheels were fitted with Gooch's patent steel tyres. The hoops were first heated, stretched to size on a mandrel and hardened by water quenching. They were then bored to size on the big lathe and shrunk onto the rims. To make doubly sure that they could not come off molten zinc was run into dovetail grooves.

The boring of the hard, inner surfaces of the cylinder castings was a slow, quiet operation. Gooch built a special machine for the purpose. This had a long boring-bar which passed through the cylinder and was rotated at a few revolutions a minute. The cutting tool, mounted on a lead-screw in the boring-bar, was moved lengthwise at two inches per hour by a difference gear.

Meticulous records kept by the clerks, or 'quill drivers', as Edward Snell called them, show that the boring of the cylinder cost 7s. 6d. and that a pair of cylinders, bolted to a steam chest and with the slide valves and covers fitted, cost £62 10s. 6d. Gooch's *Sketch Book* contains tables which give prices for every step in the manufacture of this and other assemblies, with percentages added for the overheads appropriate to each shop. His extraordinary attention to detail extended to keeping a check on the repair costs of every single carriage and wagon, the data being entered into piles of dusty ledgers. Hobsbawm, in his *Industry and*

Empire, remarks that in Victorian days 'rational cost-accounting or industrial management were rare, and those who recommended them . . . were regarded as unpractical eccentrics'. Gooch's stature as an industrialist is nowhere more apparent than in his accounting practices.

The noisiest part of his works was the boiler shop. The reverberating boom of the hammers could be heard throughout most of the factory and inside the building itself the noise was appalling. Great skill, however, was required of the boilermakers, fine craftsmen doomed to premature deafness. With little but hand methods available the construction of a boiler capable of withstanding a hundred and twenty pounds a square inch without leaking was a triumph. They began by rolling three large plates into curves, drilling holes around the edges and riveting them into a ring. Three such rings were then joined end to end to form the boiler shell and curved angle irons were riveted round the openings. The firebox and smokebox were attached to the angle irons and stays of copper or iron bolted through the whole length to stiffen the end-plates. The seams were caulked using blunt chisels and heavy hammers.

Each boiler contained many hundreds of rivets. The youngest lads in the shop heated them in the hearths, scrambling with one another for the best place in the fire. When a rivet was glowing brightly enough the lad took it in his tongs, ran to the boiler and pushed it through the next pair of holes. The 'holder-up', who was usually inside, pressed a large sledgehammer against the head and the riveter used a long-nosed hammer to clench it tight. The noise was terrific, especially for the holder-up, surrounded by the reverberating plates.

Another heavy operation was the expanding of the boiler tubes into the tube plates. Gooch used Alston's patent tubes, no mean feat of production engineering in themselves, being thicker-walled at the firebox end and tapering uniformly towards the smokebox. A mandrel was hammered into the tube ends to swell them into the holes and then a steel or cast iron ferrule was driven in to ensure a permanent seal.

The assembly of *Lord of the Isles* could not start until the frames were complete. Four

Swindon Works, 1851. From top and l. to r., steam hammer shop, boiler shop, expanding tyres to size on a mandrel, heating an eight foot wheel in a smith's hearth

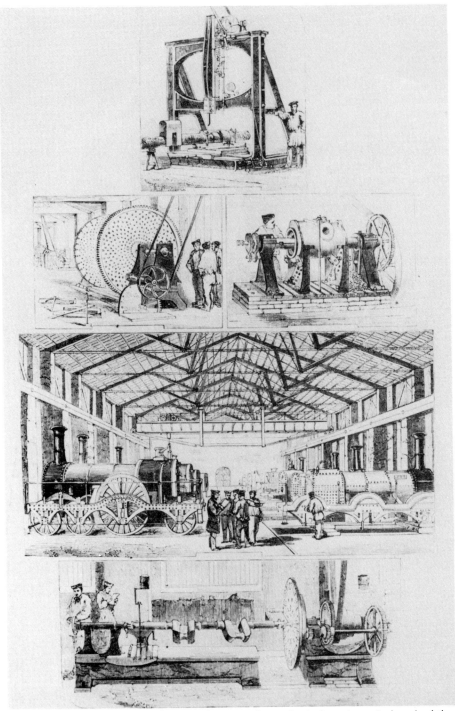

Swindon Works, 1851. From top and l. to r., slotter preparing crank axle throw, large wheel-turning lathe, boring machine for cylinders, erecting shop with hydraulic crane, turning crank axle journals

Lord of the Isles, completed at Swindon in March 1851

side plates, of the traditional curved and slotted form, were cut to shape and bolted in pairs on either side of 3-in. planks of oak to form the main longitudinal bearers. These were joined together by cross pieces of plate and angle iron and by massive timber buffer beams at the ends. The stout back-bone was carted to the erection shop and set up on sleepers, ready for the mounting of the cylinders and boiler. After these had been fitted the men were able to swarm about her to attach all the valves, levers, handrails, springs and so on. The boiler barrel was lagged by wrapping it in a layer of horse-hair felt, held in place by strips of well-dried pine.

The most dramatic operation was the lifting of the massive engine onto the wheels. Slings were attached to the frames and the hydraulic crane was used to raise her into the air. The four axles were pushed below the horn guides, the water was allowed to squirt out of the crane cylinder and *Lord of the Isles* descended slowly and majestically into place. The valve motion and connecting rods were then coupled up and she was ready for the painters and polishers. Her smokebox and chimney were finished in glistening black and her boiler in dark green, picked out with black bands edged with fine yellow lines. The venetian red frames were also lined in yellow around the sides, slots and curves. Bright red buffer beams and venetian red spokes completed the immaculate livery.

When she was perfect *Lord of the Isles* was despatched to Paddington. Then she was moved a mile or so to the shimmering Crystal Palace, drawn into the great glass hall and raised onto a plinth, where she dominated her rivals of the narrow gauge.

During the summer and early autumn the crowds poured into Hyde Park to see the wonders. Queen Victoria was probably the most frequent visitor, as she went almost every morning for the first three months. Excursions came from all over the land and Gooch took his place at the head of his men and marched them to the exhibition.

The Crystal Palace was only a mile and a half from Fulthorpe House. Gooch and his family must have driven past frequently, as during the year he bought his first carriage, a brougham. This perhaps marked a new status as on 1 January 1851 his salary had been increased to £1,500 a year, about as much as any employee could expect to earn. His health and the vigour of his professional life, however, contrasted sadly with his brother Tom's, who was again stricken by illness during the summer. He left with Ruthanna to winter at Lausanne, where he wrote his last business letters. At only forty-two he was forced to give up the work which he had enjoyed so much.

As the leaves began to turn interest in the Great Exhibition reached its height. On 7 October 109,915 people thronged the displays, which was a record, and on the eleventh the last of the six million visitors filed out. The railway companies were especially sorry to see it close, as their receipts had been up by a third. The final event was the presentation of over three thousand medals awarded for exhibits of special quality or merit. The Great Western received a bronze for *Lord of the Isles*, rather to Gooch's disgust. 'The highest class medal,' he wrote, 'was given to Crampton for an engine certainly the most faulty in construction exhibited. So much for the opinion of judges at such exhibitions.' The directors, with their customary courtesy, decided to present the medal to Gooch. In spite of his sour remarks he was proud enough to keep a copy of the board minute amongst his most treasured mementos.

Three weeks after the closure Gooch found himself on the witness stand at the case of John Gray versus the London and North Western Railway Company. As has already been mentioned, Gray was claiming that the Stephenson link motion infringed his patent of 1839. Gooch appeared as the principal witness for the defendants, standing up to Gray's counsel with great assurance. His evidence occasionally included characteristic exaggerations. He had known locomotives for twenty years, he said, 'in fact ever since I was born', and when questioned about the easy gradients on the Great Western he was stung to reply that 'we have got the worst in the world'. He was tart to the point of offensiveness when a clash came over his definition of the 'lead' of a slide valve.

'That is your lead?,' counsel asked him.

'It is everybody's lead,' he replied sharply.

'I was merely asking . . . whether you would not also apply the same term . . . to the opening . . . for the exit of the steam?,' counsel repeated mildly.

'Not if I wished to make myself intelligible I should not, because nobody would understand it so,' was his crushing retort.

Gooch's evidence demolished poor Gray's case. He was able to refer to valve gears which he had seen at Tredegar and Dundee and on *Lightning* at Hawks and Thompson's. The other witnesses supported and extended what he had said and the L&NWR won.

For some reason it was well into 1852 before *Lord of the Isles* went into service.

Soon afterwards Gooch came close to ending both her career and his own.

The Birmingham and Oxford Junction Railway, so hard fought for in 1848, was to open during the autumn. This was a most important occasion for the Great Western as the new line would link the main part of their system to their latest and most surprising venture — a narrow gauge system. In their battles with the L&NWR they had completed agreements with the Shrewsbury and Birmingham Railway and the Shrewsbury and Chester, two 4ft. 8½in. lines. The former ran through the Staffordshire iron-making district and the latter through the North Wales coalfield at Ruabon and Wrexham. They also had running powers to Birkenhead and Manchester, deep in enemy territory. The completion of the link was therefore to be celebrated with particular éclat.

The service from Fenny Compton to Birmingham, the final stretch of the new route, was to start on 1 October 1852. The ceremonies were to take place on the previous day. A special train, drawn by *Lord of the Isles* and driven by Gooch, was to leave Paddington at 9 a.m. to take a large party over the new line to Birmingham. After an appropriate welcome it would pick up more people and return to Leamington, where a banquet had been arranged.

When *Lord of the Isles* left the terminus the band of the Life Guards was on board as well as the distinguished passengers. Brunel was on the footplate with Gooch, showing considerable fortitude. The vibration on an *Iron Duke* could be terrific and a long journey was exhausting for those who were not used to it. The long curves on the main line were not too uncomfortable, as the centrifugal force held the wheel flanges firmly against the rails, but on the straights a bad rail-joint made them yaw viciously.

The special eventually left the Great Western for the Oxford and Rugby Railway. The inaugural trip marked its abrupt transition from a quiet branch line into a section of an important trunk route. Unfortunately Gooch was half an hour behind schedule when he reached it and could not afford to dally.

Somewhere ahead of him was the 9.27 a.m. stopping train to Banbury. This was a 'mixed', comprised of both carriages and goods wagons, and throughout the two years since the line had opened it had never been known to keep time. Today, as usual, it pottered along, doing a little shunting on the way. It reached Aynho, half way between Oxford and Banbury, 38 min. late. The guard began to unload cheeses from a van and the station staff set to work to uncouple a few wagons. The driver remained on the footplate, surveying the scene of mild activity.

In the meantime Gooch was making up time. At Heyford Crossing, 5 mls from Aynho, he was only 6 min. behind the mixed. There the Great Western signals had yet to be erected and so a policeman was on duty. He gave no warning wave, however, and the special raced on.

As Gooch neared Aynho he shut off steam in case he came to a signal. Then, on a long curve about a thousand yards from the station, he saw one set at clear and so opened the regulator again. Almost immediately he saw a second signal at the station standing at danger. He did everything that he could to pull up, but it was too late.

The driver of the mixed had heard the special approaching. As *Lord of the Isles* burst into sight, travelling at about 50 mph, he urged his engine into action so energetically that a coupling parted, leaving some wagons gently trundling in her wake. 'We soon went pretty smart into the wagons,' wrote Gooch, 'breaking some and sending some after the passenger train, which they struck . . . Our engine went jumping over the wagons and at last brought up in a ditch a little beyond the station . . . None of us sustained any injury, nor did anyone in our train feel any shock.'

According to the accident report only six passengers in the mixed complained of slight injury, but *The Illustrated London News* said that the crash was very great, many in the second class carriages being much cut and bruised. *Lord of the Isles* had a broken buffer beam after being derailed by an axle from one of the smashed wagons and demolishing the stonework of the platform before reaching the ditch.

Gooch found that the signal which had misled him was for a siding to a ballast pit and ought to have been removed. Once again the strength and stability of the broad gauge had been demonstrated, but it had been a narrow escape.

It was some time before the stranded passengers could be rescued. In the meantime the guests at Birmingham boarded another train for Leamington but this came off the rails as it left the station. It was four o'clock before all were assembled for the banquet, or nearly all, as Gooch had to stay to re-rail the engine.

The special left for home at about half past seven but did not arrive at Paddington until after one. 'Altogether it was a day of misfortunes,' Gooch wrote, 'and this was more annoying as we were particularly anxious to make a successful day, for our London and North Western friends were watching us.'

At the inquiry the Inspector of Railways severely criticised the unpunctuality of the mixed and the recklessness of the speed and timing of the special. 'There is no doubt the opening was pushed on too quickly,' Gooch admitted. 'We ought to have had another week.'

CHAPTER

20

During the rest of the fifties Gooch rose steadily from wealth to riches. On 28 December 1852 he became, as he put it, 'a landed proprietor', buying a 232 acre farm at Wanborough, near Swindon, for £13,000. This proved a good investment. He was already wealthy enough to retire as a country gentleman but that was never to be his style. Throughout his life he lived within the salary and fees which he earned. He enjoyed putting the balance of his huge income and the fortune which it generated to good use, but he never became dependant upon his capital or even the interest from it. His unspoken fear was that his schemes, like his father's, would wither, but with the secure foundation which he now had he was soon able to take bold risks.

The fifties brought profound changes to the Great Western. With the Gauge War behind them the board eased the timings of the West Country expresses. The new lines, mostly worked by Gooch's engines, were opened, and between 1852 and 1857 the mileage covered by his division increased by 60%, his responsibilities then extending as far as Milford Haven on the South Wales Railway. Many new locomotives were

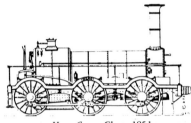

Hero, Caesar Class, 1851

needed, almost a third of all those that he designed being built in this period. Most were goods engines required for the freight traffic of the Midlands and Wales. No longer did each new class take him beyond the limits of his experience. His design work had become straightforward, even humdrum.

To meet the expansion the output at Swindon rose from nine engines in 1852 to seventeen in 1853. Over a hundred were required during the next four years, of which thirty-one had to be put out to tender as the works were so busy. The board voted £25,000 in 1853 for extensions to the shops. Space could no longer be spared for the Mechanics' Institution and accommod-

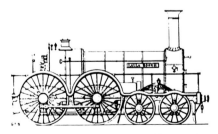
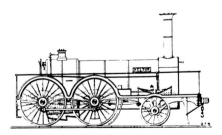

Lalla Rookh, Waverley Class, and *Fulton, Victoria* Class

114

Rob Roy, Waverley Class, after an accident at Bullo Pill in the sixties. Note the immaculately polished paintwork and brass splashers above her driving wheels. The stability of the broad gauge is well illustrated

ation had to be found elsewhere. This was done in style, the employees forming a company to build premises and a market-hall.

The first goods engines which were turned out were the *Caesar* class, eight 0-6-0's virtually identical with the earlier *Pyracmons*. Then came four tank engines, the *Banking* class, similar in layout but with larger boilers. These were the precursors of a long series of standard goods locomotives with even larger boilers, of which a hundred and two were constructed at Swindon between 1852 and 1863. They had no less than four times the tractive effort of the *Leos*.

No new passenger engines were required until late 1854 when the last seven *Iron Dukes* began to appear. Gooch's only novel broad gauge design during the fifties was the *Waverley* class, ten of which were built by Robert Stephenson and Company in

1855. These were 4-4-0 tender engines with inside frames and 17 × 24in. cylinders, needed for the heavier gradients in Wales and Gloucestershire. A list in Gooch's *Sketch Book* shows that, though they were very different in layout from their predecessors, many of their parts were from earlier locomotives. Their boilers had been designed for the *Standard Goods* class, their crankshafts, cylinders, guide bars and eccentrics for the *Caesars* and most of the other components for the *Iron Dukes* or bogie tanks. Gooch had carried his ideas on standardisation to such a pitch that only a bare minimum of expenditure on drawings, patterns and spares was required for the new engines to go into service.

The *Waverleys* each completed half a million miles during their twenty year lives. Gooch followed them with a scaled down version, the *Victoria* class, 2-4-0's with coupled wheels 6ft. 6in. in diameter.

The first was turned out at Swindon in August 1856. This was his penultimate broad gauge design and his last for six years

In 1854 Gooch had to turn his attention to narrow gauge engines. On 1 September the Shrewsbury and Birmingham and Shrewsbury and Chester Railways amalgamated with the Great Western. He took over the responsibility for their stock, concentrating repair work at Stafford Road, Wolverhampton. The manager there was Joseph Armstrong, who became an important figure in his life.

Armstrong was a month younger than Gooch. He had been born in Cumbria but brought up on Tyneside, where he was apprenticed to Robert Hawthorn. By 1836 he was working with Jim Hurst as an engineman on the Liverpool and Manchester Railway. After a spell as foreman under John Gray at Brighton he was appointed locomotive superintendent to the two Shrewsbury lines, becoming a Great Western employee when the amalgamation took place. His first job was to turn Stafford Road into a factory capable of producing all the Great Western's narrow gauge locomotives. Gooch was a good delegator and Armstrong grew to admire him greatly. 'A better business man he did not know', he was reported as saying. 'He did not believe there was such a man in any other railway company. He had sometimes labored hard to get up a report to submit to Mr Gooch, and occupied three or four pieces of foolscap with his statements. Mr Gooch would carefully read and consider it, endorse it "Yes – D.G.", and the thing was done.'

Gooch could not afford to wait for the extensions at Stafford Road to be finished and so set to work to design some narrow gauge engines himself. Between 1855 and 1857 thirty-six were produced, mainly 0-6-0's for goods service. Ten were ordered from Beyer Peacock's and the rest were built at Swindon, much to the disgust of his aristocrats there. All had inside cylinders and typical Gooch frames.

In 1854 Gooch persuaded the board to buy the Gyfeillon Colliery, near Pontypridd, as the Great Western had found themselves vulnerable to strikes and price rises. It became a part of his division, so that he had direct control over the quality

and stock levels of his coal supplies. During its first few years it saved the company £90,000. It also put money into the pockets of Gooch and a few of his friends.

During the year that the colliery was bought Gooch, acting as a private individual, placed an order with a shipbuilder at Chepstow for a 140 ton steam barge, the *Alma*, at a cost of £2,000. As soon as it was finished it was chartered to the Gyfeillon Colliery for the shipping of coal to the ports of the Bristol Channel. Both its ownership and the chartering were in the names of William B. Minet, one of his greatest friends, and William Castle Smith. Minet had been puzzled by a letter from Gooch. 'I certainly misunderstood . . . about the barges,' he said, 'but I shall be very glad to go into the business with you on the same footing in all respects as your arrangement with Geach and Evans with regard to the South Devon contract, which I believe is what you mean. Smith will find half the capital with me if you have no objection . . . I was glad to see that the result of the South Devon contract was so highly satisfactory as your letter stated.'

What Gooch had done was to charter his ship to himself, as the Great Western's officer in charge of the Gyfeillon. He was doing this covertly, as Minet's mystification indicates, and was using his friends as the front men. This was highly unethical, to say the least of it, and we may wonder why he went to such lengths for the sake of a mere barge. The answer, surely, is that he wanted some of the cheap Gyfeillon coal for the coke ovens of the South Devon contract. That is, he wished to sell some of the output of the pit which he controlled to Geach and Evans, his partners, another unethical situation.

The *Alma* plied her trade busily enough to need re-boilering in 1861. The coal was shipped in container boxes, a clear indication of what Gooch was up to, as that was how the materials were handled at his coke ovens.

His private work at this time involved him with the earliest inter-town railway in Australia. In May 1854 Stothert and Slaughter, the Bristol engineers, wrote to him to say that the Geelong and Melbourne Railway Company had given them an order for two locomotives and wished Gooch to act as their inspecting engineer.

The railway was to run for forty miles along Port Phillip Bay from Melbourne to the small port of Geelong. The first settlement in the region had only been established in 1834 but since then expansion had been at a phenomenal rate, especially after gold was discovered at Ballarat, 80 mls away. In 1852 no less than 94,000 people arrived and trekked to the diggings, most of them returning, depressed and hard-up, after only a short time. They poured into Melbourne at the rate of a thousand a week and conditions became chaotic. The government of the newly-formed colony of Victoria were struggling to create some semblance of order and amongst the various projects which were mooted were railways. The Geelong and Melbourne was the first to gain momentum, construction starting on 20 September 1853. In October 1854 the railway's London agents wrote to Gooch to ask his opinion of the drawings of two small express engines which they had received from Australia. Stothert and Slaughter, they said, had condemned them. Gooch thought the design so bad that a strong wind would stop them and was highly critical of their vertical boilers. He offered to produce drawings himself and was instructed to go ahead. By 27 November eight firms had sent him their prices for two neat tank engines, Stephensons' being the cheapest at £1,800 apiece. Slaughter's price was £1950 and Gooch told him that the wish had been expressed that he should have the order, provided they cost no more than from any other good firm. 'I have therefore written to him,' Gooch told the agents, 'to tell him you can get the engines at £1,750.' Gooch's attempt to undercut the lowest tenderer did not work, however, and the order was placed with Stephensons'.

Gooch ultimately bought all the materials and equipment for the line, including six more engines. Everything had been shipped by the end of 1855, so he requested payment of his fee. He had handled orders worth £63,512 4s. and asked 2½% of this, or £1587 16s. His bill was disputed, the most that the agents were prepared to offer being 1% . Gooch refused to accept this and nominated an arbitrator. Twelve hundred pounds was agreed as the inevitable compromise.

Disputes over fees were not uncommon but in this instance there was a fascinating sequel. On 22 November 1856 a letter was sent to him from Geelong.

Titania, one of the two small tank engines designed by Gooch for the Geelong and Melbourne Railway and built by Stephensons'.

Dear Sir,

I am very sorry to find that your claim on me for commission ended so unpleasantly, and I feel sure that if you had been aware that the money came out of my pocket you would not have charged quite so much . . . and as I can draw no more at the present I am in rather embarrassed circumstances.

I do not by any means think your charge high, provided it was paid by the company . . . Meanwhile I shall be glad if you would take this into consideration and refund . . . say £500 – **I do not think you would lose anything by it in the long run.**

We are railway mad out here . . . The Government are about making lines from Melbourne to . . . the Murray River . . . I have laid out a township . . . about nine miles from Geelong . . . called Swindon . . . Gooch Street runs from Maudsley Street to Archimedes Avenue'.

This letter, with its hints of future business, was signed by Edward Snell, Gooch's former chief draughtsman, who had become the engineer for the railway. As he himself received 5% of the cost of the materials ordered from Britain he had rather a cheek to complain.

During 1855 Gooch moved office. Brunel's splendid new terminus at Paddington was completed. The old station disappeared and the octagonal engine house with it. Larger shed accommodation was built further down the line at Westbourne Park. In the same year Charles Russell, who had been the chairman since 1839, retired, bringing an era to an end.

Russell had held a disparate board together skilfully and after his departure a gulf began to develop between the directors and chief officers. The new chairman, Spencer Walpole, M.P., had only agreed to serve for six months until the next Parliamentary session began. His first act was to set up a committee of directors to look into the company's prospects.

Whilst they were deliberating Gooch was working on a most important matter. Hardly any coal was carried for long distances by the Great Western, so he suggested to the board that they should buy some collieries and ship the output to London on their own account. They agreed and he recommended the Brandie Pits at Ruabon. Unfortunately a snag then developed. A judgement against the Eastern Counties established that railway companies were not empowered to engage in trade and so the scheme had to be dropped.

The Great Western were so anxious to have the traffic that Walpole asked Gooch if he would form a company himself to buy the pits and send a mutually agreed tonnage over the line at a preferential freight rate. He agreed and set up the Ruabon Coal Company, putting up £20,000, about half the capital, himself. Most of the remaining shares were bought by colleagues or friends and Gooch was made the chairman. The agreement was that they would despatch enough coal for distances of over 100 mls to be worth £40,000 per annum in freight charges. This represented nearly a tenth of the Great Western's goods traffic, so that Gooch was in the extraordinary position of being both a chief officer of the railway and one of its principal clients. Trouble was expected from powerful shareholders who were in the coal business, so Gooch wrote out his resignation and handed it to Walpole. Neither he nor the board thought it necessary to accept this but Gooch, in a most honourable gesture, left his letter in Walpole's hands ready for use at any time if the need arose.

The Great Western's shareholders were asked to ratify the agreement at their meeting in February 1856. It was a stormy session, as the lowest dividend since 1840 was announced and the report of the directors' committee was discussed. This expressed satisfaction with the way in which the company was being run but was pessimistic about the future profitability. The need for more business was obvious enough for the Ruabon Coal Company's preferential rates to be accepted by a large majority, but they were a sore point at company meetings for several years to come. 'I thus got a great deal of abuse by my trying to do good to the shareholders . . . and risking a good deal of money in doing so,' wrote Gooch. In 1858 one of the aggrieved coal owners put the question to the Court of Chancery. They decreed that the rates were perfectly legal, but Gooch had made some enemies.

Since his problems as a young man Gooch's health had given him no cause for concern. In April 1854, however, he had a sharp attack of an illness which kept him at home for three weeks. Then in September 1857 he had to have an operation. His disability must have been very uncomfortable or threatening, as no-one took the risks of surgery at that time without an extremely good reason. Pain whilst under the knife had been conquered a decade before by the discovery of anaesthetics but there were still the terrible dangers of sepsis. 'A man laid on an operating table in one of our hospitals,' the great Simpson said, 'is exposed to more chances of death than an English soldier at the battle of Waterloo.' For Gooch the risks were less. Hospitals, where dangerous concentrations of bacteria built up, were only for the poor. His surgeons operated on him in the relatively hygienic surroundings of his home. They arrived with their hands reasonably clean and perhaps with a clean apron and instruments, and so all went well.

Throughout the fifties profits continued to pour in from the South Devon contract. The only problems were over the hours which the footplatemen were being forced to work by the railway company. In 1855 William Gooch complained and Gooch sent a sharp letter to the South Devon's chairman. William warned him that he had annoyed their clients by what they regarded as interference in their business. This stung him into an even more forthright letter in which he said that he had to attend too many inquests not to feel strongly. 'My opinion of railway management,' he thundered, 'is that it is the duty of an officer to point out any source of danger in his department to those who have the power of correcting it. Who but one entirely reckless of his character and happiness would serve a company on other terms?' Thirteen hours a day was agreed as the absolute maximum, Gooch telling his brother that the men were then to go home whether the South Devon would pay or not.

William Gooch's time at Newton came to a sudden end in 1857. Minard Rea, the works manager at Swindon, had been ill with consumption for some time. He died on 18 June and Gooch asked his brother to take over. He was looking to his own succession, as he intended to retire from the company before too long himself. The directors gave an undertaking that William would become locomotive superintendent if and when Gooch left, and on that understanding he gave up his more lucrative post.

Royal journeys were still a frequent responsibility. Gooch looked after the King of Sardinia and Napoleon III and his Empress in 1855. Napoleon sent him a beautiful gold snuff-box as a memento. His most important occasion was the wedding journey of the Princess Royal and Prince Frederick William of Prussia on 25 January 1858. Within 2 min. of their arrival at Paddington after the ceremony the bridal party were whisked aboard the Royal carriages. 'Mr Gooch ascended the engine,' reported *The Illustrated London News*, 'the steam was shut off, and the train moved rapidly away amid prolonged cheers and hearty gratulations.' His reward was another snuff-box.

He also had weddings in his own family. On 19 October 1858 his younger daughter, Emily, married William Ponsford. She was just eighteen – 'much too young', Gooch wrote. Not to be outdone, Anna, the older girl, was married ten months later to Frederick Newton of Maida Hill. He was sorry to lose both his daughters so early: 'I had little opportunity of having them with me at home. I hope it is for the future happiness of both'.

A week after Emily's wedding Henry Tanner died peacefully at the age of seventy-four. Gooch attended the stately funeral at which Sunderland mourned his passing. He left £35,000, about £7,000 being put into trust for each of his daughters. Gooch, as one of the trustees, was no doubt given a good deal of work and Margaret had some hundreds a year to use as she pleased.

From the early fifties the Gooches spent their summers in lodgings at Windsor, leaving noisy London behind. It was easy to commute to Paddington, as the branch from Slough had opened in 1849. George III and his son had restored the castle to a lasting magnificence but the town huddled below was without decent public buildings or even drains and its back streets were worse than any industrial slum. Beyond the town, however, were the beauties of the willow-shaded river and the Berkshire beech woods. This was the Windsor which Gooch loved, and he had good friends living nearby. Capt. Bulkeley, one of the directors, had a house at Clewer, a mile to the west, and Edward Evans, who had retired from the Haigh Foundry, was living at Boveney Court, just over the river.

The tiny hamlet of Clewer stood beside the high-road to Maidenhead. A narrow lane flanked by a few cottages led to the Mill Stream, a backwater of the Thames. To the right was St. Andrew's Church, with its lych gate, spire and shady churchyard. Opposite were the gates of Clewer Park, a large house standing in nearly thirty acres of rich parkland. It was owned by a Dr Proctor and leased by the widow of one of the Ashley's, the Earl of Shaftesbury's family. In March 1859 it became vacant. Gooch, who had been looking for a house in the neighbourhood for some time, went to look it over, a large bed of violets took his fancy and he snapped it up. He leased it for a while before buying it. Clewer Park, which became his most treasured possession, stood until the 1950's and was then demolished to make way for a housing estate. All traces have gone except for the lodge gates beside the church. Amazingly, no photographs of it in its heyday have been found. Such evidence as exists suggests that it was a three storeyed Georgian house of simple symmetry and grace to which two wings of Victorian appearance were added prior to 1880, probably by Gooch, who wrote of making alterations. There were some fifty rooms and in the grounds were stables, hot houses and a private back-water and boathouses. The park, fringed by a belt of woodland, gave Gooch a walk of three-quarters of a mile around his domain. He spent a week there at Whitsun, if he was lucky, and from early July until late October or early November it was his residence. For the rest of the year it was swathed in dust sheets, home only to a housekeeper and laundrymaid.

Gooch took Clewer at a turning point in his life. Until then he had been known purely as a locomotive engineer and an employee of the Great Western. His fortune had grown to at least £100,000. All this had sprung from Brunel's initial confidence in him and from railways. His life was about to change, and this was because his old chief's was drawing to a close.

As Brunel's health failed two of his most splendid creations were nearing completion. One, the *Great Eastern* steamship, had brought him nothing but pain. The other, the Tamar Bridge, was faultless.

Brunel's last line was the Cornwall Railway, 53½ mls of broad gauge from Plymouth to Truro over tough country. His main problem was at the eastern end. On leaving Plymouth the line had to cross the River Tamar, 1,100ft. wide and 70ft. deep. The Admiralty required a clear headway of 100ft. His solution was the Royal Albert Bridge. It has two superbly proportioned tubular arch spans, the thrusts taken by suspension chains, a complex and elegant design which is his finest monument. On 2 May 1859 Prince Albert opened the bridge and on the fourth passenger traffic began. Gooch and his partners, Evans and Thomas Walker of Wednesbury – Geach had died in 1854 – were providing the locomotives, as on the South Devon. They bought nine more bogie-tanks for the purpose at £2,970 each, investing almost £30,000 altogether. Gooch prepared the specification for the locomotives very simply. He took the Great Western's printed specification for the similar engines which had been bought in 1854, crossed out their name and substituted 'Cornwall Railway'. After inking in a few alterations it was complete. The orders were placed with Stothert and Slaughter, to whom Gooch sent Great Western drawings, once again using his employers' property freely. The small amount of effort needed to launch the lucrative new business is plain.

Brunel could not attend the opening of the line. His health was so poor that he had wintered in Egypt. It was mid-May before he was brought to his magnificent bridge. A couch was placed on an open truck and he lay there whilst one of Gooch's engines drew him slowly beneath the soaring ironwork. But he was not finished yet and was summoning up his strength to complete his final project, the greatest ship in the world.

CHAPTER
21

The *Great Eastern* was to be twice the length of the *Persia*, the next largest merchant vessel, and three times the tonnage of the U.S. Navy's *Niagara*, the largest ship in the world. Her vast proportions had been chosen to enable her to carry enough coal for a round trip to Australia.

Her owners were the Eastern Steam Navigation Company. The hull had been built by John Scott Russell at his shipyard on the Isle of Dogs. Brunel's visionary genius and Russell's abilities as a naval architect had combined to create a vessel of great strength and beauty. Unfortunately

there had been a succession of financial crises. Brunel had estimated £1,000,000 as the cost of two ships but by February 1857, nearly three years after the keelplate had been laid, £450,000 had been spent on the first and she was still on dry land. Because of her length she was launched sideways, the most daunting operation which Brunel had ever undertaken. An accident brought the first attempt to a halt and then the inert mass had to be inched forcibly down the ways until at last she floated.

The launching had left the company £90,000 in debt and with another

The *Great Eastern* and the *Persia*, then the largest Cunarder

£120,000 to find before she could be completed, so the bare hull had been left, deserted and forlorn, at moorings close to the shipyard. The board were divided on whether to sell or re-finance her. Brunel sought the advice of his friend Thomas Brassey, who was able to marshall support for a proposal to form a new company to which the ship would be sold for a suitably low price and which would then complete her. A figure of £160,000 was settled upon and in November 1858 the Great Ship Company was formed with a capital of £330,000. The intention was to use' her on the North Atlantic run and a return of 15% was predicted. One of the shareholders was Daniel Gooch.

Brunel, though mortally ill with nephritis, managed to resume command of the project. The *Great Eastern* was unique in having both paddles and a screw and he was especially worried about the installation of the two immense engines. By the end of August 1859 she was nearly complete. Her six masts towered above the deck and the five tall funnels were in place. During the last hectic weeks Brunel dragged himself painfully about the ship or lay dictating memo after memo to his assistants. On 5 September, two days before she was due to sail, he had a stroke and was carried home.

On Wednesday 7 September 1859 the *Great Eastern* moved under her own power for the first time. On the Friday morning she left the Thames for the open sea. All went well until six in the evening, when she was off Hastings. Suddenly there was an explosion and an almighty roar of steam. The forward funnel toppled onto the deck. The grand saloon, fortunately completely deserted, was swept by scything fragments of glass. In the boiler room the blow-back flayed the stokers with steam, fatally scalding five. Miraculously no-one else was hurt. It was found that cocks which had been fitted temporarily to the water jackets around the funnels had been closed, making disaster inevitable.

Brunel was told the news and the blow was mortal. On 15 September he died. He was fifty-three. 'By his death,' wrote Gooch, 'the greatest of England's engineers was lost; the man of the greatest originality of thought and power of execution, bold in

his plans but right. The commercial world thought him extravagant, but altho' he was so, great things are not done by those who sit down and count the cost. He was a true and sincere friend, a man of the highest honour, and his loss was deeply deplored by all who had the pleasure to know him . . . I shall ever feel a deep sense of gratitude . . . for all his kindness and support from the day I first saw him in 1837.'

Only four weeks later nephritis also claimed Brunel's old friend and rival, Robert Stephenson. Sadly, Gooch wrote no panegyric for the man who gave him his first opportunities in locomotive engineering.

The *Great Eastern* was soon repaired and steamed to Holyhead on her trial trip. After weathering a severe storm she returned to Southampton. On 12 November Gooch went to see her, his first recorded visit to the ship. She had demonstrated that she could steam reliably lightly laden, but there were many alterations to be made before she could sail on her maiden voyage.

Gooch was doubtless at the Great Ship Company's annual meeting on 11 January 1860. Debts of over £40,000 had accumulated and more money was required before she could start to earn her keep. Critical motions were on the agenda and even the board's resignation did not mollify the shareholders, who eventually elected a committee to consider the position.

Whilst they were deliberating Gooch had other important matters on his mind. Money was continuing to pour in from the two railway contracts and he sought new avenues for investment. In January he, Charles Saunders and a few other close acquaintances bought a colliery at Hirwaun, west of Merthyr Tydfil. The Welsh steam-coal market was expanding rapidly, so they no doubt earned a good profit and provided more traffic for the Great Western. He also bought Bell Farm, close to Clewer, bringing his property to some four hundred acres. During 1859 and early 1860 he put at least £50,000 into various projects.

When the shareholders' committee of the Great Ship Company reported they recommended the formation of a new board. Gooch was amongst those who were elected. They raised £100,000 in debent-

The *Great Eastern's* paddle engines, built by Scott Russell. From a model in the Science Museum

The *Great Eastern's* screw engines, built by James Watt & Co., also from a model in the Science Museum

ures, of which he bought a large holding, and began preparing the *Great Eastern* for a voyage to New York. 'I went down to Southampton and took the direction of all the engineering departments of the ship,' he wrote, 'and we . . . worked hard to get her ready to sail in June.'

Brunel's mantle as engineer to the company had fallen upon R.P. Brereton, his former principal assistant, but the day-to-day responsibility lay with Alexander McLellan, the ship's chief engineer. Gooch's main task was to oversee his plans and expenditure on the board's behalf, but his words suggest that he become involved in the detailed engineering. He started a notebook in which he included watch-bills, tables of data and indicator cards, together with important technical information which had been prepared for the board. There is a copy of a well-known report on the state of the ship's structure and deck equipment, compiled by three eminent shipbuilders when she was at Holyhead. This listed numerous deficiencies, of which none was of great significance. He also copied down an abstract of a report on the engines written on 17 November 1859. This had been written at 28 Moorgate Street, in the City, but unfortunately the author's name is in Gooch's least decipherable handwriting. Amongst numerous 'matters of prudence' requiring attention were missing platforms, speaking tubes, tool racks and so on, the minor deficiencies to be expected on any new project. Attention was also drawn to more serious shortcomings. The boiler flues had been found to be too small, making the fires sluggish and leaving forty percent of the coal unburnt. There were doubts about the strengths of piston rods and cylinder covers. The stern gland bearing needed changing from wrought iron on white metal to a brass-encased shaft running in lignum vitae. The most important problems, however, concerned the ship's performance. On her trials she had reached 18 knots, but lightly laden. Calculations showed that she would only manage 11 knots at maximum draught, well below the design figure of 14 knots. Her fuel consumption was also too high. Steaming at 14.4 knots she had used 150 to 160 tons a day for the screw engines

and 100 to 120 for the paddles – 18,000 tons for a round trip to Melbourne, whereas her bunkers could only hold 12,000. The efficiency of her boilers and engines would have to be improved substantially if she was to meet her designer's intentions.

For the *Great Eastern* to reach her full speed her machinery needed major alterations. Scott Russell's paddle engines had only reached 2,991 hp for a few minutes under boiler conditions where over 4,000 would have been expected and Watts' screw engines had done little better, managing only 4,800 hp when the boiler pressure was enough for six thousand. This, the report concluded, was because the diameter of the paddle wheels and the pitch of the screw were too great. Modifying these to increase the power would, of course, also increase the fuel consumption.

Brunel, it is clear, had underestimated the *Great Eastern's* power requirements. 'Scaling up', especially to such an extent, is notoriously difficult and it is not surprising that, for all his care, his calculations had been optimistic. He had exposed his backers to great risks and the present owners had an expensive task on their hands if the ship was to do what he had originally intended. Preparing her for her maiden voyage across the Atlantic was, however, a straightforward matter.

McLellan and his men made good progress and soon tickets were being advertised at £25 for adults, £15 for servants and half price for children under twelve. Accommodation was prepared for three hundred but only thirty-eight passengers and eight guests made the voyage. They had a crew of four hundred and thirteen to look after them. The board was represented by three directors, of whom Gooch was one. His wife and Harry, their eighteen year old son, accompanied him.

They went aboard on Thursday 14 June, expecting to sail on the Saturday. Preparations continued until the last minute but when all the visitors had been sent ashore the Captain, John Vine Hall, said that he still could not leave as the crew were drunk. Gooch, in the first of a series of exasperations with Hall, was furious.

On the Sunday morning the *Great Eastern* at last sailed, 'with about twenty passengers, so that we had plenty of room', Gooch joked. For most of the crossing the weather was perfect and the ship was steady enough for skittles to be played every day. The passengers, the first to sail in a large luxury liner, could stroll for over a quarter of a mile around the main deck, its long sweep broken only by skylights and the captain's quarters. Below there were two tiers of magnificent saloons with cabins on either side. The best of the first class were reached by little bridges with elegant wrought iron balustrades which led to heavily curtained doorways. Behind each was a family suite for as many as eight. 'The snug berths . . . the noble deck-parade, the cosy smoking room – everything in short reminds one of a West-End club or a huge hotel rather than a ship,' wrote one reporter. 'Add to this the almost certain absence of all pitching . . . the ice and the French cook, and what more could the most fastidious Sybarite require?'

The *Great Eastern* ran the 3,188 mls to Sandy Hook in 10 days 19 hrs, averaging 12.3 knots and arriving on 28 June. Her daily runs ranged from 254 to 333 nautical miles – 10.6 to 13.9 knots. Gooch, however, was annoyed with Vine Hall, who, he commented sarcastically, 'thinking we would like to see the flying fish and other curiosities found in the Gulf Stream, took us a good way south out of our course, and altho' we all enjoyed the voyage very much . . . the credit of the ship needed that we ought to have made the run in nine days, which she would have done if the right course had been steered'. He was hardly fair, as the captain's experience was in the East India trade and he had never made an Atlantic crossing before. The great circle course had many navigational hazards, so he had taken the more southerly of the two steamer routes.

The engines gave little trouble during their first long run but the coal consumption remained high. The daily average was 264 tons for 295 mls, at which rate the bunker capacity would be used just to reach Melbourne.

New York gave the *Great Eastern* a tumultuous reception. A vast fleet of yachts, ferry boats and coastal steamers sailed out to meet her. The shore was lined by thousands of people and as she came through the Narrows the saluting guns thundered. It was late afternoon before she reached her wharf. The welcome then continued on board, Gooch being glad when at last he could slip away to his berth. 'I did not go ashore', he wrote. 'It had been a really hard day's work. I will, however, never forget the beauty of the scene'.

For the next ten days he became a showman, as the company hoped to earn a great deal of money by exhibiting the ship. He found the experience distasteful. A charge of $1 had been advised, but this was too much, as the newspapers pointed out caustically. Droves of people came to stare and to enjoy the funfair which appeared on the dockside, but few boarded. When the price was dropped to 50¢, however, as many as eighteen thousand a day went over her. There were also publicity stunts, set up by the company's American agents, which Gooch detested. 'Photographers wanted our photographs (in which I did not indulge them)', he wrote, 'and the first night we went to the theatre, we, as modest people, went into the body of the house, but had not long taken our seats when a person came to invite us to go into a private box. This we did, and were greeted with God Save the Queen'. The ship's officers enjoyed the fuss, which annoyed Gooch as he felt that they cared more about showing off in their uniforms than they did about their duties. Vine Hall, he punned, 'certainly was a mighty **vain** man'. 'All this sort of humbug lasted a very short time', he wrote thankfully. 'We soon began to get out of favour . . . and before we left New York for good it was our first amusement every morning to read the abusive articles in the newspapers'.

Gooch escaped from the ship after about ten days, leaving for Washington to meet Colonel Mann, an old friend, who was involved in trade from the Southern States. He arranged for Gooch to be received by President Buchanan, who told him that if Lincoln won the forthcoming presidential election the South would secede. He then returned to New York and went by boat and overnight train to Niagara, being impressed by the American 'bed carriages', as he called them. Each of the berths was wide enough for two and he managed to get a pair, one for Harry and the other for Margaret and himself. They enjoyed the Falls greatly, finding that the grandeur grew on them day by day. Blondin performed on the tight-rope over the river whilst they were there – 'I cannot say the sensation was a pleasant one', wrote Gooch. They finished their three-week trip by travelling to Toronto and the St. Lawrence, returning to New York via Lakes Champlain and St. George on the steamers.

The *Great Eastern's* next fund raising exploit was a two-day cruise to Cape May at the mouth of the Delaware. Many of the fifteen hundred passengers were far from pleased, as the catering and sleeping arrangements were hopelessly inadequate. The directors kept well clear of disgruntled passengers and indignant pressmen. According to Gooch, however, most people enjoyed their sail greatly and passed resolutions praising both the ship and Brunel.

A week's excursion to Annapolis Roads, on the Chesapeake, followed. Only about a hundred boarded but at Old Point Comfort, where she arrived on the morning of 2 August, thousands were waiting to see over her. Many were slaves brought by their masters in what one suspects to have been a public relations stunt – Gooch wrote that 'the kindest and most friendly feeling seemed to exist among them and I have never seen more happiness expressed in the face and manner of the working classes than appeared in these slaves'.

On 9 August President Buchanan and some of the members of his administration visited the ship. Gooch was able to speak to him about trade with America. He was hoping that the *Great Eastern* would be used to transport cotton to Britain and the President, he said, thought well of the scheme. Then, with important business behind him, Gooch was able to travel to New York to make preparations for the return voyage.

The *Great Eastern* left on 16 August. 'I think I never was so entirely glad of anything,' Gooch said, 'as I was when I felt, on that day, that our ship's head was turned towards England and I was quit of America. Of all the experiences I ever had in my life of dishonesty in business matters, none ever equalled the ordinary practices I met with . . . in the dealings of the Yankees . . . The jealousy between North and South made it a matter of offence to them that we took the ship to the South. I left . . . with a feeling of rejoicing I never before experienced.' Pleasure at her departure was mutual, as the Great Ship had outstayed her welcome.

The *Great Eastern* was first steamed hard for Halifax. She arrived in forty-six hours, beating the previous record by 5½ hr. and covering 58 sea miles between two lighthouses in 3 hr. 5 min. – 18.8 knots, a tremendous speed. They reached Milford Haven on Sunday 26 August 1860 after a 14 knot crossing. A dozen ships of the Channel Fleet were at anchor and their crews manned the yards, giving the huge ship a truly British welcome which warmed the hearts of all on board.

A special train was waiting to return them to London but it remained empty. 'It is not often passengers wish to sleep another night on board after a voyage,' Gooch wrote, 'but such is the comfort of the *Great Eastern* that all felt regret that it was time to leave her.'

CHAPTER

22

During the winter the *Great Eastern* lay beached on a gridiron at Milford Haven. Her poor performance had been put down to fouling of her hull, but as she towered above the mud it was plain that she had not suffered from her three years in salt water. In May 1861 she sailed to New York on her second voyage. Only about a hundred boarded, but her reputation was spreading. On the return trip to Liverpool she carried 212 and three thousand tons of cargo, averaging 14.8 knots over one 24 hr. period. As she steamed into the Mersey enormous crowds gave her yet another rousing welcome.

Five weeks later she sailed for North America on a dramatic mission. The American Civil War had broken out and there were rumours that Lincoln was about to declare war on Britain and France in an attempt to draw the divided states into a common cause. To counter the threat to Canada the Government decided to send troops to Quebec. This was a chance for the *Great Eastern* to demonstrate her vaunted abilities as a troopship. She sailed for the St. Lawrence with 3,400 people and two hundred horses on board. She was steamed at speed regardless of risks, narrowly missing the Cunarder *Arabia* off Newfoundland. For the next month she lay at Quebec, being visited by enormous numbers of people. No less than five hundred booked for the return trip to Liverpool. By the end of August she was again on show, nearly thirty thousand looking around her in a week.

On 10 September she began her fourth west-bound voyage. A new captain was in command. 'We were in capital spirits about her,' wrote Gooch, 'and I arranged after she sailed to go to Mr Baker's house, near Worcester, who was at that time chairman of the Ship Co., to talk over her future, believing a bright one was in store for us.'

After dinner they were settling before a comfortable fire when a telegram arrived with the astonishing news that the *Great Eastern* had been sighted off the Irish coast, far from where she should have been. This spoiled their evening and they went off to bed despondently. Twice that night Baker came dashing into Gooch's bedroom with more messages. 'I will never forget the appearance of the old gentleman,' he wrote. 'He stood at the foot of my bed . . . wrapped up in a white flannel dressing gown and one of those old-fashioned night caps on his head.' It was, however, the next day before they heard what had gone wrong.

Two days after leaving Liverpool the *Great Eastern* had run into heavy weather. A boat was torn from the davits and the screw was run astern with helm on to avoid the wreckage. The numerous helmsmen had the wheels – there were several – torn from their grasp. The rudder-head, to which the steering-chains were attached, fractured. All means of steering were lost and the ship swung into the trough of the waves, rolling alarmingly. Her paddles were smashed to pieces. All efforts to regain control were fruitless until a passenger, an American engineer called Hamilton Towle, persuaded the captain to let him build a jury rig to work the rudder. The *Great Eastern* was then able to limp into Queenstown and the news was telegraphed to London. Towle was awarded about £3,000 as salvage money, a heavy sum on top of the repair costs. Once again the company's finances were sorely stretched. 'We, however, set about the work,' said Gooch, 'and during the winter got her all ready again for sea.'

In the meantime Gooch had an important project under way on the Great Western. In January 1860 he had persuaded the directors to agree to the construction of mills at Swindon for rolling all the company's rails and plates. They were to have a capacity of 12,000 tons a year and cost over £18,000. He expected to save a pound a ton. To build and run the plant he took on Thomas Ellis, a grandson of his old foreman, who brought all his workmen from Wales. The 'Welsh Mills' became a great success but proved a bone of contention with the ironmasters, who lost a valuable market. As a result Gooch made new enemies and others emerged as a result of a further major change in the Great Western. He found the situation growingly distasteful.

The unpleasantness started with the Oxford, Worcester and Wolverhampton Railway. This, it will be recalled, had been fought for in the greatest battle of the Gauge War. Parliament had decided that it should be a broad gauge line but, to the fury of the Great Western, its board, under the leadership of a man called Parson, built it to the narrow gauge. Then, on 1 July 1860, they joined with two other narrow guage lines, the Worcester and Hereford and the Newport and Abergavenny, to form a new company, the West Midland Railway. This gave a route from South Wales to Oxford and over Great Western mixed gauge track, laid as a result of the 1846 Acts, to Reading. Narrow gauge trains could then travel from South Wales to within 36 mls of Paddington. As a break of gauge so close to the terminus was absurd the Great Western agreed to convert the Reading to Paddington line to mixed gauge. On 14 August 1861, less than two years after Brunel's death, the first narrow gauge train steamed into the terminus.

The West Midland and Great Western then had so much in common and competed so directly with the South Wales Railway that all three decided to unite. On 1 January 1862 a Joint Committee was formed which ran them virtually as one pending the preparation of an Amalgamation Bill. Once this had been passed a single board would run a vast new Great Western Railway with 1,106 mls of line, 546½ mls of the broad gauge and 559½ mls of the narrow. With such a fine balance the demise of the 7ft. gauge would be certain.

The ringleaders of the old Oxford, Worcester and Wolverhampton board were appointed to the Joint Committee. Gooch grew to detest them, and the feeling was mutual. He dreaded the amalgamation. 'I would have new men to work with,' he wrote, 'strangers to me, and those likely to come from the West Midland not standing very high in character. I therefore quite resolved to leave them.' He proposed to resign in 1862, after twenty-five years service, but as the time approached Saunders and his colleagues persuaded him to change his mind.

The new arrangements brought further freight traffic so Gooch had to build more goods engines. Between 1860 and 1864 twenty-four broad and thirty-two narrow gauge 0-6-0's were turned out at Swindon. The works were once again unable to meet all the requirements and another thirty-two were sub-contracted. The only broad gauge passenger engines which were built were ten 2-4-0's of the old *Victoria* class, which were made at Swindon.

Gooch produced his last locomotive design at the end of 1861. The Metropolitan Railway Company were building the first underground line from Paddington Station to Farringdon Street. The Great Western took a large stake in the venture. It was a most difficult undertaking, as John Fowler, the engineer, had to work his way amongst a tangle of water mains, gas pipes and sewers. Some form of locomotion was needed which would not fill the tunnels with smoke and steam. Fowler proposed the use of 'smokeless steam locomotives', in which white hot firebricks would be put into the boilers instead of coke. A prototype was built but proved, said Gooch, 'quite useless'.

Gooch carried out tests to see how far an engine could travel with the blast off, coasting along on the steam stored in the

A Conversatzione of the G.W.R. Literary Society at which some of Gooch's collection of paintings were on display

boiler. The results were encouraging, so on 1 November 1861 the Great Western accepted a contract to work the railway. Gooch then built the world's first condensing locomotives, the *Metropolitan Tanks*. They differed from ordinary engines in having two large water tanks under their boilers. In the open they were worked normally, but as they entered the tunnels a change-over valve was operated. This diverted the exhaust steam into the tanks, where it condensed. At the same time dampers were closed below the grate. The engine could then work for a while without choking the passengers – or so it was hoped.

The *Metropolitan Tanks* were ungainly and clumsy but completely functional. They were the only broad gauge locomotives to have outside cylinders, as Gooch had to make room for the condenser tanks. The first were needed in a hurry, six being ordered from the Vulcan Foundry and six from Kitson's at Leeds. Five arrived at the end of July 1862, an excellent achievement by all concerned. There were delays in the completion of the line, however.

During the summer Gooch enjoyed the second Great Exhibition, which was held at Kensington. 'The picture gallery was very good and four of my pictures were selected to go there,' he wrote. His standing and pride as a connoisseur are evident. His collection eventually reached nearly eighty, including a Constable. Almost all were by contemporary artists, most of whom are highly regarded today.

The *Great Eastern* made three voyages to New York during 1862. There were only 138 passengers on the first outward trip but for the return there were nearly four hundred and as much cargo as she could carry. Her eastward crossing broke the record by 12 hrs. Her second trip was also a great success, but on her third, whilst slowing down off Montauk Point to pick up the pilot, she scraped over a reef. She was able to continue unaided into New York, listing a little, where the divers found that a gash 80ft. long and 4ft. wide had been torn along her hull. Any other ship would have gone to the bottom but only the outer skin of Brunel's unique double-walled hull had been ruptured. 'This was a most unfortunate accident for us,' Gooch wrote, 'and I fear to some extent a careless one . . . The excuse made was that these rocks were not shown on the chart.'

The ship was perfectly fit to be sailed to Britain for a full examination but her captain decided to have the repairs done at New York. An ingenious technique was used in which a long caisson was fitted around the gash and sealed to the hull. This served as a kind of diving bell from which patches were riveted into place. The work cost £70,000. It was January 1863 before the *Great Eastern* was ready to sail for Liverpool. When she was put onto her gridiron it was found that the repairs were not watertight and that there were nine more holes. The captain's decision had pretty well ruined the company, Gooch said.

Shortly before the *Great Eastern* returned Gooch was busy with the opening of the Metropolitan Railway. He spent the first day in the tunnels, checking on his engines. Next day he felt the effects, falling at Fulthorpe House and lying unconscious for several minutes. He was too ill to return to work for some weeks. This grim time brought the news of the *Great Eastern's* latest troubles and of the death of his sister Anna, who had been suffering from cancer for some time. She was the first of John and Anna Gooch's children to pass away.

In March Joseph Whitworth turned his Manchester business into a limited company. Gooch became one of the seven shareholder directors, as he wanted to be sure of a good position for his son Harry. He was also interested in a gun barrel which Whitworth had invented, feeling that it would be an interest for him when he came to retire from the Great Western. He was still far from well and his doctors advised him to take a long holiday. On 17 March he began a leisurely tour of the continent which lasted for eleven idyllic weeks. He set off with Margaret and Harry for Paris and then went on to Marseilles and Nice. There they took a carriage and four and, with Sardelli, their courier, to look after them, drove along the Riviera through Genoa and La Spezia to Pisa. Gooch felt his health improving day by day.

After Florence and a short stay in Rome they moved on to Naples, 'a charmingly situated town but rather given to bad smells . . . It drove me away before I had intended'. He was well enough to climb Vesuvius, though he found it hard going and was glad to rest at the top and eat eggs roasted in the ashes. A longer visit to Rome followed before they sailed to Leghorn and went through the mountains by carriage to Zurich. There he found a letter from Charles Saunders which asked him to hurry back. On 1 June he was again at home, fit for any fray.

Saunders' troubles were with the Metropolitan Railway. There had been a row because they wanted to increase the underground services but the Great Western felt that this would not be profitable to them. To bring their smaller neighbour to heel they threatened to withdraw from the contract. Their bluff was called and from 11 August the Metropolitan ran the trains themselves. They used narrow gauge stock hired from the Great Northern, whose locomotive superintendent, none other than Archibald Sturrock, added condensing pipework to some of his engines at lightning speed. The dispute soon blew over and the Great Western's massive locomotives again began to rumble through the tunnels, but handling through-traffic to the city, rather than the underground trains.

The rivalry did not ruffle the warm friendship between Gooch and Sturrock. The Metropolitan grumbled that the Great Western's locomotives were filling the tunnels with sulphurous fumes, whereas Gooch's colleagues were sure that Sturrock's were to blame. To stop the wrangling Gooch arranged for his engines to use the same coke as Sturrock's. 'So long as I work the Metropolitan,' Sturrock told him, 'I can supply your engines with coke . . and shall do so with pleasure . . . You shall be charged the same price as the Metropolitan.' There were also complaints that his locomotives were leaking water onto the line, adding to maintenance costs. They were his least successful design. The exhaust pipes leaked both air and water. There were also risks of drawing water back into the cylinders, as the non-return valves did not work satisfactorily. Worst of all, the tanks were not big enough, so that they soon overheated. They remained in service for only eight years, far less than any of his other locomotives, but this is hardly surprising, as they were highly novel.

During the summer Gooch's long service as locomotive superintendent began to draw to a close. On 1 August 1863 the Act which united the Great Western with the South Wales and West Midland Railways became law. The new directors were elected, amongst whom were Potter, Parson, Watkin and Brown, 'men who were little guided by the principles that govern gentlemen of honour', Gooch said. Potter was a former Great Western director who had complained of Charles Saunders' power in 1856. The rest had been members of the renegade board of the Oxford, Worcester and Wolverhampton. Potter was voted in as chairman and only a month later Saunders, who was sixty-six and in poor health, retired. His duties were then divided between his nephew, F.G. Saunders, as Secretary, and James Grierson, the young Chief Goods Manager at Paddington, who became General Manager, a new post.

To tighten their grip on the running of the company the directors formed several committees. Parson, Watkin and Brown were appointed to one which was to oversee the affairs of the locomotive division. Its chairman was C.R.M. Talbot, who had

doubts about Gooch. He had been chairman of the South Wales Railway, which was worked by the Great Western under contract. At their shareholders' meeting in 1861 he blamed him for a heavy loss, claiming that he had not been treating them fairly. The rates were most profitable to the Great Western if light trains were used and Talbot said that Gooch had instructed his men to take only half the load which their engines could manage.

With so much mistrust around the table it is hardly surprising that the committee's first meeting ended with Gooch walking out. It was, he said, 'well calculated to carry out what, there is no doubt, was their object, viz. to disgust me with the concern in order that they might put in their own men'. He was begged to attend their second session, agreeing only when he was promised that a different course of conduct would be followed.

All went well, but at the third he had a row with Parson, a rogue who before long was flung off the board. He again walked out, this time never to return.

The eruptions were caused by two reports. The first declared that the West Midland's locomotive repair costs were much less than the Great Western's – 7.39d. per train mile against 8.80d. The writer stated that 'the only reasons I can give . . .

Ethon, the last of Gooch's many *Standard Goods* Class to be built

are . . . undivided management . . . fort-
nightly examination of expenses . . . less
expensive system of carrying out the work'.
Gooch prepared a scathing rebuttal. It was
obvious, he said, that larger engines
drawing heavier trains would cost more per
mile, and what was the comparative state of
the stock? He thundered his astonishment
'that an individual claiming to be a Practical Railway Officer should attempt to
make such a report without previously
communicating his intention to me or even
making the slightest inquiry into the facts
concerned with the department'.

The other document attacked two of the
Great Western's most profitable assets. The
first, the Gyfeillon Colliery, conflicted with
Potter and Brown's mining interests and it
was recommended that it should be sold.
The second, the rail mill at Swindon, was
claimed to be losing £14,000 to £17,000 a
year. Gooch sprang to their defence,
writing to Potter in strong terms. He
pointed out that the pit, besides giving
security of supplies, was producing coal of
excellent quality at less than the Cardiff
price. The Welsh Mills, he said, had
produced iron at £6 17s. 3d. a ton during
1863 against £7 10s. at Newport.

Potter, to Gooch's annoyance, did not
submit his note to the board, so he sent a
copy to all the old Great Western directors,
hoping that they would pull together. As a
result the rail mills survived. They
remained in operation until 1964,
completing a hundred and three years of
service. He was, however, unable to
prevent the sale of the Gyfeillon.

Whilst the disputes were raging Gooch
suffered another sad blow. On 24 November
1863 Anna Gooch died at the age of eighty.
'What a good mother she has been to me, to
us all,' he wrote, 'an example of all that
makes human nature true and noble.'

Gooch was too powerful and respected
for his enemies to be able to get rid of him
easily and so, in spite of his rows with most
of the board, he avoided dismissal. He was,
however, determined to leave. In March
1864 he asked Potter what he would do
about the board's promise to make William
Gooch locomotive superintendent if he
resigned. Potter assured him that he would
do his best to honour the arrangement.

Accordingly, on 4 April 1864, Gooch
wrote to him.

My Dear Sir,
  I have today written to Mr Saunders
asking him to inform the Board of my
intention to retire . . . I can with much
satisfaction look back on the twenty-seven
years I have been on the line. They have passed
over without one expression of dissatisfaction
by the Board . . . or one angry word or
feeling with a Brother Officer or disagreement
with our men. And allow me to thank you for
the kindness I received from you during the
many years when you were on the Old Board,
and for the kind expressions of confidence you
expressed in me on a recent occasion. I will ever
take a deep interest in all that concerns the
welfare of the Great Western, not only as
holding a large stake in it, but from my long
and happy association with so many of its
Directors and Officials.
  I trust you will excuse my referring to the
claim I believe my Brother has, and Mr
Armstrong also. I also mentioned that I felt
better men cannot be obtained, and trust that
you will think it only **just** to them and to the
Service that those who have **well** and
faithfully served the Co. should not be set
aside without **proved** incapacity . . .
  Reports have come to me circulated without
my knowledge that the locomotive department
of this line has been conducted very expensively. Such a result cannot be shown by
figures or documents. On the contrary I say,
and the Public Accounts will prove it, the line
has been worked at a much less charge upon
the traffic than any other of the principal
railways. It has been also stated that the
engines built at Swindon are built at an
extravagant cost. The enclosed statement will
show you the fallacy of this assertion as well
as the former . . . What . . . are the Great
Western Shareholders to gain by a change in
the direction? You will I trust forgive my
urging this matter so strongly to your consideration but I feel it is a duty I have both to
Armstrong and my Brother and also the
company.
  If the line is placed under new management
I am sure either Armstrong or my brother will
work cheerfully with or under the other, and

in either case the company will be well and faithfully served, and with the practical knowledge I have of such matters I trust I am not presumptuous in expressing this opinion strongly.

I am,
My Dear Sir,
Yours ob^{ly},
Danl. Gooch.

It is sad that Gooch had to conclude his years of service by defending himself against the attacks of lesser men in the interests of his brother and Joseph Armstrong. His words, however, were of no avail and he was soon to find that Potter had not the slightest intention of keeping his promise.

CHAPTER

23

On 5 April 1864, the day after Gooch had written his letter of resignation, it was announced that the *Great Eastern* had been chartered to contractors who were preparing to lay a telegraph cable across the Atlantic. It was he who had negotiated the agreement, and it was hardly a coincidence that he gave up his post at precisely the same time.

The world's first successful submarine telegraph cable had been laid from Dover to Cap Gris Nez by Gooch's former chief draughtsman, Tom Crampton. It consisted of a copper core insulated with gutta percha and protected by an outer armouring of iron wire. Since then a number of similar, but far longer, lines had been laid. As yet, however, there was no link between Europe and America.

The shortest crossing was between Newfoundland and Ireland. Surveys had shown the sea-bottom there to be a smooth plateau, ideal except that it was well over two miles deep. An American, Cyrus Field, launched the project by raising capital in Britain in 1856. He gathered a brilliant group of engineers and scientists around him, including Professor William Thomson, the future Lord Kelvin. No single ship was capable of carrying the immense cable and so two were used, the Royal Navy's screw frigate, *Agamemnon*, and the United States Navy's *Niagara*, the largest ship in the world. They set out from Valencia, in Southern Ireland, in 1857 and 1858. The first attempt failed because the brake of the cable-laying machine was applied too fiercely and the cable snapped in mid-ocean. In the second Trinity Bay in Newfoundland was reached but there was a fault

and after only a brief period the signals became unintelligible.

The 1858 expedition was a glorious failure. Many lessons had been learned. Gutta percha had been shown to be a highly suitable insulator for the great depths, but a thicker and more buoyant cable was required. Improved manufacturing and stowing procedures were essential. The next attempt, it was clear, would have to be better equipped and organised. An enormous amount of money would have to be put at risk.

Over the next few years the idea languished but the American Civil War made the need for swift communications between the two continents even more apparent. Field and Curtis Lampson persuaded the British and United States governments to offer financial guarantees if success was achieved. Some capital was raised and a Consulting Scientific Committee, consisting of five F.R.S's, was formed. Both Thomson and Joseph Whitworth were members. Towards the end of 1863 they received tenders for the making and laying of the cable. The committee unanimously recommended that from Glass, Elliot, of Greenwich.

The new cable was to weigh almost twice as much as its predecessor. During the voyage it was to be kept in huge tanks filled with water, so that a check could be kept on the insulation. Altogether three times the tonnage of the 1858 expedition would have to be transported. The *Great Eastern* was the only ship in the world which could carry such a load. If she was not available Glass, Elliot would have to charter at least three large vessels and face the risks of splicing cables together in the deepest parts of the Atlantic.

During 1863, whilst the project was gaining momentum, the *Great Eastern* made three trips to New York, carrying many passengers. When leaving Liverpool for the second voyage she was so heavily laden that some of the cargo had to be put on board after she had crossed the bar. Gooch was there to see the operation, sailing in her as far as Queenstown. In spite of the record amount of business the season was very unprofitable. The Cunard and Inman lines were engaged in a price war and the *Great Eastern's* owners had to follow suit. Expensive repairs were necessary after the ship again broached-to, part of one of the paddle wheels being damaged. Losses amounted to £20,000, which added to the debts left after the Montauk Point incident, so that Gooch and his fellow directors had a grim report to present to the annual general meeting on 2 October. 'The position . . . is most critical,' they said, 'and immediate steps must be taken either to raise additional capital or to dissolve the company.'

The shareholders appointed a committee to consider the situation. Its chairman, William Hawes, had connections with the Brunel family. His view was that the ship should be used on voyages to the Far East or Australia, as her designer had intended, rather than uneconomic trips to America. He carried his colleagues with him and a row was certain at the re-convened meeting on 4 November. The chairman, William Barber, had sold his shares because of the lack of confidence in the board and so Gooch, as one of the two surviving directors, had the uncomfortable task of chairing the meeting.

Hawes' committee had established that £60,000 were needed to repair the ship and fit her out for another voyage. They recommended that she should sail to Australia. Their report was adopted and the directors were empowered to raise the cash.

The company's liabilities were then £543,350, of which £105,350 were 'bonds' – mortgages and debentures. More than half were held by Gooch, Thomas Brassey and William Barber, who now began a brilliant coup. Brassey was immensely rich,

Barber had shown a lack of spine by resigning from the chair and so it would seem probable that the ringleader was Gooch.

The bondholders came to the conclusion that they were unlikely to get their money back unless they took action. Having first call on the assets they decided to force the company into liquidation by seizing the ship and putting her up for auction. What part Gooch and his two friends played in this decision is not known, but it must have been a major one, as they held the bulk of the votes. To try to forestall them the despairing shareholders began to organise a gigantic raffle, with the *Great Eastern* as the prize. A Herr Fabricius of Frankfurt, where lotteries were legalised, issued a prospectus on their behalf, but it came to nothing.

The auction took place in the Cotton Room of the Liverpool Exchange on 14 January 1864. A large crowd assembled. By a bitter irony the man on the rostrum was Joseph Cunard, the principal partner in the firm of Cunard and Wilson, who was a brother of the late shipping magnate.

When Cunard called for bids there was a long pause. At last an offer of £50,000 was made, but the bidder's name was not announced. This attempt to flush out interested parties had no effect, so after another long wait the audience was advised that a nod or a wink would be worth a thousand pounds, 'and very cheap at the price'. As this, too, brought no response Cunard declared a reserve of £130,000 and moved on to better business. 'It is said that the *Great Eastern* will again be offered for auction in a short time', the newspapers noted.

It no doubt surprised Gooch and his colleagues that no-one had come forward to buy the ship on behalf of the Atlantic Telegraph expedition. Seeing their opportunity they decided to buy her themselves provided she did not cost more than £80,000. They first formed a new company, The Great Eastern Steamship Co. Ltd., with a capital of £150,000, and exchanged their bonds in the Great Ship Company for shares in the business. The other bondholders were then told that they were prepared to pay cash for up to £80,000-worth of shares to provide the capital to buy the ship. The bondholders were invited to join in by trading their bonds for shares.

Most took the plunge and were then readily persuaded to agree to the ship being put under the hammer again, but with an important difference – there would be no reserve price.

The trio steamrollered the decision through with great speed, as it was on 25 January, only eleven days after the auction, that Cunard, Wilson announced that the *Great Eastern* would be offered for sale again in three weeks time, 'peremptorily and without reserve'. The shareholders and creditors must have been outraged, as their last hope of getting any money back had now gone.

On 17 February Joseph Cunard again took his place before an excited crowd. In the front row were Barber and John Yates, the secretary of the new company.

'To the greatest mercantile community in the world,' Cunard began, 'we offer the greatest ship that ever was, and probably that ever will be.'

When the laughter had subsided he stood awaiting their response.

'Twenty thousand!', called Yates. Cunard was horrified.

'The spare gear is worth more than that,' he shouted. 'Twenty thousand for a ship that cost nine hundred thousand! Are you really in earnest?'

'Twenty-five thousand!'

This was from John Rae, a Liverpool shipowner, who had only come as an onlooker but now saw his chance. Cunard's assistant scurried over to ask if he had the necessary 10% deposit with him. To Yates's relief he had not and so Cunard returned to the first offer.

'If I don't get a higher bid I must knock her down at this. Once, twice, third and last time at twenty thousand?,' he asked.

'Guineas!,' cried a Mr McGhee, to another shout of laughter.

'Twenty-two thousand!,' said Yates.

'Now shall I say guineas?,' called Cunard.

'You said you would take a nod or a wink?,' asked McGhee.

'Yes.'

'I'm winking!'

Yates knew that he was only being teased

and so he brought the joking to an end.

'Twenty-five thousand!'.

All were silent until, to a few cries of 'Shame!', Cunard's hammer fell. 'Strange to state,' wrote Gooch, 'a ship that had cost a million of money and was worth £100,000 for the materials in her, was sold to us for £25,000.'

Their brutal stroke had given the three accomplices at least a two-thirds share in a re-capitalised venture unencumbered by mortgages or creditors. Gooch, in typical style, remained in the background until the sale was complete. He then became chairman, no doubt an indication that he had masterminded the coup, and set to work to charter the *Great Eastern* to Glass, Elliot. Within seven weeks terms had been agreed. It was announced that the *Great Eastern* would be handed over to the cable contractors on 1 May, the arrangement being that they were to meet all the expenses of modifying her and fitting her out for the expedition. In return her owners were to receive £50,000 of fully paid-up shares in the Atlantic Telegraph Company. These would be a splendid asset if the voyage was a success, but worthless otherwise.

At that moment all work on the project was at a standstill for lack of funds. In March John Pender, one of Gooch's fellow shareholders in Whitworth's business, had been elected to the board of the Atlantic Telegraph Company. He immediately proposed a way of raising the outstanding capital. The Gutta Percha Company, who were to make the copper core and insulation of the cable, and Glass Elliot, who were to add the armouring and lay it, were merged. The new concern, the Telegraph Construction and Maintenance Company – 'Telcon', for short – formed a sound basis on which the money was raised with little difficulty. On 7 April, only two days after the chartering of the ship had been announced and three after Gooch had written his resignation, Telcon was registered. John Pender became the chairman and Richard Glass the managing director. Gooch bought £20,000-worth of shares and was invited onto the board. These events, we may be sure, were far from coincidental.

On 5 May Telcon formally took over the contract to lay the cable for the Atlantic

Telegraph Company. Their price was £300,000 in cash and £237,140 of shares. They immediately ratified the arrangements for the chartering of the *Great Eastern* and the project began to surge ahead. The expedition was to sail in the summer of 1865, leaving barely a year to equip the ship and make over 2,000 mls of cable. Gooch's stake in Atlantic Telegraphy was then enormous. Besides his investment in Telcon his shares and bonds in the Great Ship Company had cost perhaps £20,000 and he had put about £8,000 into purchasing the ship, a total of £48,000. To recover what he had lost and earn a return on the rest he was dependant upon the laying of the frail cable.

The first step was for the ship to be sailed round from Liverpool to Sheerness, on the Medway, where the tanks and machinery were to be installed and the cable stowed. Gooch and his friend Dr Pavy were on board and enjoyed the short voyage. Telcon's engineers were there as well to discuss how she might be modified. During the rest of the year he was often at the cable manufacturers' or on the ship. Within Telcon he had no executive function – the responsibility of implementing the board's policies lay with the company's staff. As a director and greatly respected engineer, however, he no doubt kept an eye on how funds were being spent and offered advice when he saw the need. His role as chairman of the ship's owners was more positive. He and George Beckwith,[*] her new chief engineer, had to approve the modifications made to the *Great Eastern*. The work was extensive, the fourth funnel and second class saloon being ripped out to accommodate the three huge cable tanks, 50ft. across and 20ft. deep. Workshops, forges and a mass of machinery were also installed on the main deck. Gooch drafted out a watch-bill for the engine room staff – 12 engineers, 1 blacksmith, 2 boilermakers, 132 trimmers. He was especially concerned that the ship would be stable with the enormous weight stowed just under her main deck. A naval architect prepared a comforting report for him. He calculated her period of rolling as about eight seconds, considerably greater than the longest time between successive waves in the North Atlantic, so that she would be safe.

When the *Great Eastern* arrived at Sheerness she was not looking her best. Weeds and slime were to be seen below her waterline. The seams in her deck planking were in need of caulking, the mirrors and gilding had disappeared from the Grand Saloon and the handsome gold and white panelling had been replaced by imitation graining which had toned to a dirty brown. Telcon's men immediately began to smarten her up. Soon, thanks to Gooch's shrewdness, Brunel's superb ship would come into her own.

---

[*] Beckwith was presumably a relative of Henry Tanner's partner in his coal-fitting business.

CHAPTER
24

As soon as Gooch had handed in his resignation, Potter began to make arrangements to replace him with a man of his own choice, ignoring the promise which he had made. Gooch soon heard that Charles Reboul Sacré had been asked to attend the next board meeting to be given the post. This was more than he could stand.

Sacré had been one of Sturrock's pupils at Swindon. For the last six years he had been both chief civil and chief mechanical engineer to the Manchester, Sheffield and Lincolnshire Railway. He was a fine locomotive designer, but suitability was not the issue. Gooch immediately took up the attack, sending letters to all the directors with whom he felt he had influence, telling them that either his brother or Armstrong should be appointed. For once they stood together and Potter was outvoted. By 28 April 1864 the skirmish was over, but it was Armstrong who was given the post.

Even by mentioning Armstrong's name Gooch had weakened William's case. He remained half-hearted about him, saying afterwards that it was for the best that the offer went to Armstrong. 'Had my brother been appointed he would not have been comfortable with . . . such . . . men always pulling against him', he wrote.

Armstrong began to take over in June 1864. Gooch worked in double harness with him until 7 September. He then concluded his twenty-seven years service, bitterly regretting having remained for the last two. John Gibson, the Carriage and Wagon Superintendent, also resigned during 1864. William Gooch was not even given his job as a sop, Armstrong being asked to take over the dual function, and so he too decided to leave. 'To assist him', as he put it, Gooch formed a company to buy the Vulcan Foundry. William became the managing director.

Purchasing the factory where he had once been a boy and a pupil gave Gooch great pleasure: 'I have since often thought of my mother's words when I went from home in Jany 1834, when she told me not to be content until I was manager'. There was more than sentiment in the investment, however. When Charles Tayleur died in 1854 Edward Tayleur became the sole owner. By the early sixties he was in difficulties, the output dropping from thirty-two engines in 1862 to seven in 1864. The order book was still healthy, as in the new company's first year twenty-eight were turned out. Tayleur had evidently run out of working capital and Gooch was able to drive a hard bargain. He wrote to his brothers and friends asking them to come in with him and the firm, the Vulcan Foundry Company Ltd., became something of a family affair. The share capital was £46,500, of which Edward Tayleur was allotted £20,000 as the price of the business.

William, John and Daniel Gooch each bought £5,000-worth, the remaining £11,500 going to William Castle Smith, Gooch's partner in the *Alma* barge, and three others. They took over the responsibility for the old firm from the previous January, the retrospective date confirming that Tayleur had been in trouble.

The Vulcan Foundry soon turned the corner. By 1867 it was valued at £124,055, nearly three times the original share capital. By 1882 the turnover had risen from less than £30,000 to £106,000 and it was worth £174,000. The books were usually just about balanced, the business being developed as a capital asset rather than a source of income. It made William Gooch wealthy enough to leave over £74,000 when he died.

As soon as he left the Great Western Gooch took charge of Whitworth's London office. 'It was an amusement to me', he said, 'giving me an object in life, without which I could not get on with any happiness'. He had an uphill struggle on his hands. Whitworth was trying to persuade the government to adopt his guns but had succeeded in upsetting all the people who might have been of use to him. After careful experimentation he had developed

Whitworth gun barrel.

an improved form of rifle barrel of hexagonal bore. His novel approach, which gave greatly improved range and accuracy, could equally well be applied to heavy artillery and by 1864 he had produced muzzle loading armaments ranging up to a seventy-pounder gun. By 1864 he had rifles in service in good numbers and his heavier weapons were vying with Armstrong's in the 'Battle of the Guns'.

Gooch visited the arsenals and dockyards where Whitworth's field pieces were under test and was highly critical of what he saw. He felt that they were badly run because their managers had not, as he said, 'worked their way from the vice upwards . . . They were civilians who have not had any practical experience, or . . . military men — Capt. Smith or Capt. someone else'. He made these comments in the course of his first political speech. He had been asked to stand as a Conservative candidate for

Cricklade, the constituency of which Swindon formed a part. There were two seats, as was usual for the boroughs. At the 1859 general election A.L. Goddard, of the town's ruling family, had taken one for the Tories and the other had gone to a Liberal. The Conservatives were determined to win both at the election due in 1865. Shortly after he resigned Gooch was approached: 'Mr Merryweather, Sir John Wild and other landowners were anxious to get in a second Conservative, and I have no doubt thought my influence with the Swindon men would secure my election'. After some hesitation he accepted.

His first speech was made at the Mechanics' Institution on 22 March 1865. A large audience gave him an enthusiastic reception. 'I appear before you tonight in a somewhat new character, and I must crave your indulgence for my shortcomings,' he began. 'I have not had time to acquire any large extent of knowledge on those questions which, from a political candidate, you might expect to hear discussed.' In the brief but vague speech which followed he showed that this was not mock-modesty, as he aired only four points and outlined no policies. His most positive statement came in a reference to his life of contact with men like themselves: 'I know your feelings, your wants and your many virtues; and I also know how far you may be trusted, and I feel you may be trusted very far indeed'.

He was referring to the question of greatest interest to the men. Few of them had a vote. Cricklade, which covered 248 sq. mls, had an electorate of only 1,746. There were growing pressures for change and even Gooch would not be able to keep the Liberal out unless he was sympathetic. When question-time came he was asked if he was in favour of the vote being given to householders who paid £6 or more a year in rent, a rule which would have included most of the railwaymen. 'This country is a progressive country', he replied. 'The Conservative body advocates an extension of the franchise, but not to the extent that all would like to see . . . I do not think it would be well to give one section of the community an over-riding control. If such were the case the Government would become worse than autocratic.'

Soon the meeting turned to the formal business of supporting his candidature. He was left in no doubt about the feelings of his former workmen. 'On the charge of changing our colours,' said one, 'we have known Mr Gooch for twenty years. He possesses a thorough knowledge of the commercial and engineering worlds. Whatever the world might call his opinions, we know that in practice he is liberal and a friend to religious liberty.' But there were at least a few present who were not so pleased, especially the Rev. Mr Pillgrem. 'Having listened to Mr Gooch's address,' he complained, 'I find that it is not to the electorate at large, but simply to those in the employ of the railway . . . We have not heard an expression of political opinion. It was all milk and water.' His words were drowned in a storm of interruptions and a Mr Simpson sprang to his feet. He was not there to support Mr Gooch because he was a Whig or a Tory, he bellowed, 'but because he is a fair, honest and just man – one with a headpiece that may be worth fifty heads of young lords', a reference to the Liberal candidate, Lord Eliot.

Polling was likely to take place after Gooch had sailed in the *Great Eastern* so he had to begin canvassing immediately. He was expected to seek out every one of the electorate in person and set off accompanied by two of his election committee, George Dick and George Adams. Adams was his chairman, an extraordinary testimony to his regard for his old chief, as he was an ardent Liberal and had been an active Chartist in his time. They travelled Wiltshire daily for several weeks, Gooch enjoying himself apart from the actual buttonholing of electors. 'The asking of votes is a detestable office,' he wrote, 'and more particularly from small shopkeepers, a shoemaker most of all.' These strange words and a statement in his memoirs that the election cost him £2,600 suggest that he had to offer bribes.

At that time there was no limit to what a candidate could spend on his election, but he had to declare the total to Parliament. Gooch confessed to £1,978 8s. 9d. – over £600 less than the figure in his memoirs. Even this was more than twice as much as Goddard declared, and the average for the boroughs was only £1,000.

A batch of Vulcan Foundry locomotives being unloaded at Sydney in the eighties

Election expenses varied widely between candidates. Besides meeting the costs of the poll and paying their agents and canvassers they had to provide carriages to take their supporters to the booths, an unusually large expense at Cricklade because of its size. They were also expected to make handsome donations to local good causes, but in a third to a half of the boroughs even this was not enough and votes had to be bought. In the worst cases even the magistrates were involved, but in the less corrupt it was usually the small shopkeepers and their like who succumbed, so the meaning of Gooch's comment is clear.

The high spot of the campaign was not, on the face of it, a political occasion. By a most convenient coincidence the whole population of Swindon turned out to honour Gooch only a month before polling day. This came about because nearly a thousand of his friends and workmen had raised a subscription when he left the Great Western. Their intention was to present him with a portrait of his wife. The great John Millais was given the commission, but time passed without the sittings starting. As the election drew closer the subscription committee decided to change tack and to give Gooch an illuminated address and Margaret some handsome jewellery instead.

The presentation took place on Saturday 3 June. 'The candidature of the hon. gentleman for the representation of Swindon . . . added to the interest, although the proceedings were not intended as a political display', said the local paper, but as both George Dick and Foote, Gooch's election agent, were heavily involved we may have our doubts.

The sun was blazing down as the long procession wound through the flag-bedecked streets to collect the guest of honour at the station. A huge crowd then gathered in front of the Mechanics' Institution, clustering around *Lord of the Isles*, which stood on a special siding close to the platform. The presentation was made by James Grierson, who listed Gooch's many good works at Swindon – the Mechanics' Institution, the schools, in which he had taken an active interest, the Engineman's and Fireman's Mutual Assurance Society and the annual excursion trips, which the

directors had granted at his request. He closed, to the accompaniment of loud cheers, by saying that 'if there be one reason more than another which calls forth our respect . . . it is that during all the time he had charge of the locomotive department . . . while heartburnings and strikes might be heard of in other parts of the country, Swindon and the Great Western knew of no such things'. He then read out the address and Gooch replied, saying that he took pleasure that three of his sons, who had been brought up amongst them, were present.

After the speeches Gooch was handed the illuminated address, enclosed in a purple velvet case ornamented with gold. He also accepted a diamond bracelet, a pearl pendant and a pair of diamond earrings on behalf of his wife, for Margaret Gooch did not attend to receive these generous gifts in person. In offering thanks on her behalf Gooch said that she was sorry not to be there, but he made no excuse for her, not even a white lie. At the celebration dinner he again apologised for her absence, but gave no reason. We may be sure that she was hurt that, in the interest of politics, the Millais was not to be. She had diamonds in plenty but amongst their paintings there was none of her. Within three years her husband was to regret this as sadly as she did on the day which he called 'the highest . . . in my life'.

Whilst Gooch was canvassing the preparations for the cable expedition neared completion. The *Great Eastern's* engines were overhauled. Her strength was tested by putting 1,400 tons of water into her stern compartments and 1,100 into her bows. At the Gutta Percha Company's works the insulating compound was extruded around seven twisted strands of copper to form the core of the cable, upon which Glass, Elliot's wound ten steel wires, wrapped with hemp, as armouring. Eighty miles of cable were produced each week and put aboard two frigate hulks for transportation to the ship.

On Wednesday 24 May the Prince of Wales visited the *Great Eastern* and was shown round by John Pender and his senior colleagues. A few days later the directors went to see the making of the final piece of cable. 'No sooner had the signal been given that the last inch had really and positively passed through the machines than a simultaneous cheer and waving of hats announced the completion,' *The Illustrated London News* reported. A month later the *Great Eastern* left for the deeper waters of the Nore with 7,000 tons of cable, 2,000 tons of tanks and 7,000 tons of coal on board. Her new master, Captain James Anderson, one of Cunards' most experienced seamen and a man very much after Gooch's heart, was in command.

By Monday 10 July Gooch had cleared up all his business affairs and could embark on the *Great Eastern*. In his cabin he started his shipboard log. 'Success will open a useful future for our ship,' he wrote, ' . . . and satisfy me that I have done wisely in never losing confidence in her; and the world may still feel thankful to my old friend Brunel.' The expedition was expected to sail on the Wednesday, which was nomination day at Cricklade. He was only too glad to have an excuse for keeping out of the way and William Gooch stood in for him. 'They had a very rough time of it,' he wrote, 'for as usual there was a great row and I was glad to be saved the annoyance and excitement of it'. On the day itself he wondered if his absence was making any difference, 'yet if I knew it would have I am certain I would have been here all the same. There is no comparison between the importance of the two tasks. My getting into Parliament or not will make no earthly difference to anybody, and to myself, the not doing so will add much to my comfort and, probably, health. Yet, having made the attempt, I will be disappointed if I fail.'

At Cricklade the Town Hall windows were used for the nomination ceremony. A crowd of about two thousand gathered, their behaviour, according to the press, being hardly orderly. After the Acting Returning Officer had opened the proceedings Goddard's proposer, Hussey Freke, appeared and the fun began. 'Mr Goddard lives amongst us,' he bellowed, 'and his political principles are well known to us, for he is a tried man.' 'Interruption', noted the North Wilts Herald, and we can imagine the wit crying, 'He **ought** to be tried'. Freke was then heard reasonably quietly

until he was unwise enough to say that 'Englishmen would rue the day if ever the Government passed into the hands of the party whose only cry was change'.

Goddard's seconder was given an easy time but when Major Calley emerged to propose Gooch there was an uproar. 'Some persons in the crowd held up printed bills, the nature of which we were unable to perceive,' the Tory press stated diplomatically. 'We are familiar with the candidate's principles,' Calley declared when at last a lull came, 'and they are principles which are acceptable to the country at large.' This remark led to a storm of interruptions, in the midst of which one man, puzzled about Gooch's allegiances, asked, 'What are you?'.

George Adams, Gooch's seconder, was given a fair hearing by an audience mainly composed of his workmates but Hitchcock, Lord Eliot's champion, was met by a howl of disapproval. He was heard to say that Goddard belonged to the stand-still-and-do-nothing party. 'We next have Mr Gooch,' he continued. 'We must regret his absence. That circumstance alone prevents me from saying one word that would be personally offensive to him or disagreeable to his supporters.' This remark provoked the crowd to fury and, later in his speech, when he turned to Parliamentary reform, a fight broke out and they began to sing, 'Slap! Bang! Here we are again!'.

Lord Eliot's seconder, Major Prowse, quietened the mob by telling them that they would miss a treat if they did not hear him. 'The Conservatives like Reform as a Jew likes pork,' he roared – a dig at Disraeli. 'I have known Major Calley since he was a boy, and he was always a consistent Tory. Mr Adams I have found a very straightforward, very consistent but very advanced Radical. Now unless one of these gentlemen has ratted – and God forbid that I should impute such a thing to either – their position today is very peculiar and it is really a question of a toss of a coin as to what colour Mr Gooch's supporters belong.'

Next came the show of hands, declared as in Gooch and Lord Eliot's favour. After Hussey Freke had demanded a poll Goddard, Lord Eliot and William Gooch spoke briefly. The Liberals then set off around the town behind the Purton Band and Gooch's supporters paraded after the New Swindon musicians. 'There were sundry fights and much excitement,' it was reported, 'but no serious casualties occurred.'

Polling took place the next day. A voter in a two seat constituency had two options. He could either 'plump', giving a vote to only one candidate, or 'split', giving a vote to each of two, but could not give two votes to one man. This made campaigning tactics complicated. Gooch said that he had asked his supporters to give their second vote to Goddard but had received little help in return, presumably because Goddard was afraid of being pushed into third place by him.

During the morning there was trouble at Cricklade. A large crowd of youths wearing Liberal colours arrived carrying bludgeons and stones and began to annoy the Conservative voters. Soon a gang of New Swindon men turned up to protect them. A battle royal developed, which the police did their best to break up, though they were heavily outnumbered. The superintendent was struck on the head and a magistrate was hit on the leg by a large stone. Eventually the fighting died down and the New Swindon men left the town. There were lesser skirmishes throughout the afternoon, but little came of them.

The result was declared from the windows of Cricklade Town Hall at six o'clock. The show of hands had been no indication of the voters' feelings, as Goddard was first with 978 votes, Gooch was runner-up with 878 and Lord Eliot was last, 106 further behind.

The figures for the individual polling stations showed that Gooch's influence at New Swindon had indeed gained the Tories their second seat, but he was disappointed that Goddard's tactics had cost him the lead and swore vengeance.

After the Town Clerk had finished the candidates were given the opportunity to address the crowd. Goddard, who knew what to expect, did not arrive from Swindon in time. Lord Eliot, whose supporters were present in great strength, was rapturously received when he appeared at the window wearing a yellow rosette. There were cries of 'Gooch's bribery!', which were even reported in the true-blue North Wilts Herald.

After Eliot had shouted that he was not discouraged William Gooch took his place but the crowd would not hear him. As he and the rest of his brother's supporters tried to leave for their headquarters at the White Hart Hotel they were attacked and had to run for it. Foote, Gooch's agent, was hit on the back and a large stone smashed in his hat, though fortunately did not injure him. After they reached shelter the hotel was put under siege. All the windows were shattered and stones were hurled over the roof into the yard. The police enforced enough order for them to leave the town but the crowd rampaged again.

A telegram which was sent to Gooch went astray and it was late on the Friday, when someone arrived with *The Times*, before he heard that he had been elected. 'Well I sleep tonight as an M.P.,' he wrote. 'Do I feel any happier? No! Has it in any way satisfied an ambition? I say no, for I do not feel I ever had any particular ambition for the honour. I value it chiefly for the warm-hearted feeling it has called forth in those associated with me for a long, long time. Having, however, taken the office, I pray God it may enable me to do some good for my fellow creatures, and I will endeavour to do my duty.'

CHAPTER

25

When the news of the election arrived the *Great Eastern* was almost ready to sail. Then the stays failed in one of the screw boilers. The fires had to be drawn for new ones to be fitted, so it was 12.15 p.m. on Saturday 15 July before she began to move slowly towards the sea.

Gooch's worries began the next morning. As she steamed through the Channel the *Great Eastern* came up with her smallest consort, the *Caroline*, which had the heavily armoured shore-end cable on board. This had to be laid from the telegraph station at Foilhummerum Bay, Valencia, into the deeper waters of the Atlantic, where the *Great Eastern's* cable would be joined on. The little steamer was in difficulties, rolling and pitching frighteningly in conditions which the world's largest and most heavily laden ship was shouldering serenely aside. Eventually she was taken in tow but the hawser frayed through and she had to struggle on unaided. By Tuesday Gooch was wondering if she would last out the night, afraid for both the fifteen people on board and the shore-end. 'It was a great act of folly to have put it into such a vessel,' he wrote.

The *Caroline* survived and by Sunday 23 July the shore-end had been laid. The *Great Eastern's* cable was spliced on and, to rousing cheers, she steamed away. Her two escorts, the warships *Terrible* and *Sphinx*, kept station ahead and on either side to intercept any merchantman which threatened to cross her bows.

The cable was running out over the stern pulley at about 4 knots. As the first control over the speed it ran over six grooved pulleys fitted with jockey wheels and brakes. Next it took four turns around the drum of the paying-out machine, which had a powerful brake, arranged so that a constant tension was maintained. Finally it passed through a dynamometer, where the tension was measured, and hissed over the stern pulley into the sea.

As confidence grew Anderson increased the ship's speed to 6½ knots and everyone settled to their duties. Gooch's task, as the chairman of the ship's owners and a director of Telcon, was to represent both boards. He was the most senior person present, though Samuel Canning, Telcon's chief engineer, and Captain Anderson were in charge of day-to-day matters. Major issues would have to be discussed with him, and it was his job to deal with any contractual disputes which had to be settled on the spot. His opposite number for the Atlantic Telegraph Company was Cyrus Field, who had Professor Thomson and Cromwell F. Varley to advise him.

Telcon's team was a strong one. Anderson was assisted by Staff Commander Henry Moriarty, R.N., a navigator of great ability. His first mate was Robert Halpin, an ex-blockade runner of Civil War days. Canning's staff included his chief electrician, de Sauty, whose tests on the cable were coordinated with similar activities on shore, where Richard Glass was in charge. Under them was the large and enthusiastic crew. Amongst George Beckwith's assistants in the engine-room was Alfred Gooch. He was nineteen, and one of several young men who went along for the excitement and experience. Many journalists had been anxious to go but room was only found for Dr William Russell of *The Times*, famous for

The paying-out machine at the stern of the *Great Eastern*, 1865 expedition

his despatches from the Crimea of a decade before. His two young sons were with him. Two artists, Robert Dudley and Henry O'Neil, were also included, and there were two stowaways – a black cat and a jackdaw which perched on the dynamometer for hours on end.

O'Neil savoured every moment of the trip. He enjoyed the village atmosphere of the deck, with its blacksmiths' forges, carpenters' shop and pens for the animals – oxen, a cow, sheep, Hampshire pigs and innumerable poultry.

De Sauty's 'electricians', as the electrical engineers were called, kept a continuous watch on the cable from the testing room, a darkened cabin into which wires were led from the tanks. Their most sensitive instrument was a galvanometer, invented by Thomson for the 1858 expedition. It had a tiny mirror, suspended from the finest of threads, which reflected the light of an oil lamp onto a long scale. Minute changes in the electric currents flowing through the cable were translated into movements of the light-spot. As long as it remained on scale all was well, but if it slid out of sight the gutta percha was faulty.

Their monotonous vigil continued until Monday 24 July, when 84 mls had been laid. Then, at 3.15 a.m., they saw the spot glide rapidly across the galvanometer scale and vanish. The insulation had developed a serious fault.

Gooch was awakened by one of the ship's signal guns, fired to warn the escorts. He dressed hurriedly and went on deck, where he found that the paddles had been stopped. Canning had high hopes of recovering the fault, as they were still in shallow water, and his men were already preparing the gear. To avoid having to manoeuvre the ship whilst she was going astern the cable had to be drawn back on board over the bows. The difficult task of transferring it from one end of the ship to the other was completed and the picking-up machine, a winch mounted on the foredeck, was started. Almost immediately its boiler failed. A steam supply was hastily piped from the engine room and soon the cable was being coiled back into the tank. Unfortunately the picking-up machine was not up to its job and half a knot was all that could be managed.

In the meantime the electrical tests

continued, but the results were puzzling, even suggesting that the trouble was as far away as the shore-end splice. The fault did not prevent messages from being sent to Valencia and by 10 p.m. arrangements had been made for another steamer to join them and for the *Caroline* to go out to the splice. Gooch then went off to his cabin. 'I can do no good on deck and the night has come on wet with a small rain,' he wrote in his log. 'I shall now see if I can get a few hours' sleep.'

By breakfast time 10 mls had been wound in but the electricians were still not certain where the fault lay. Gooch discussed the situation with Anderson and Canning. They decided to waste no more time, but to return to the splice and start afresh. Canning, however, had been connecting up another boiler and wished to try it out, so he continued hauling in whilst the others went to the dining saloon. This was fortunate, as just as they were finishing breakfast the fault came on board.

On examining the cable it was found that a piece of the steel armouring had been forced into the insulation, piercing it through to the copper. There was concern as to whether there had been sabotage, but Gooch felt sure that the sharp sliver could not have been pushed in by hand, and it showed no marks of having been driven in using a tool. He came to the conclusion that a scrap of armouring had stuck to the cable and been squeezed in as it passed through the drums.

The damage was soon repaired and the *Great Eastern* again began to gather way. Suddenly Canning came rushing out of the test room. 'Stop the ship!,' he shouted.

'My heart seemed to sink within me,' wrote Gooch. 'He told us all signals through the cable had stopped. I felt as though I could have jumped into the sea. Oh, what a cast-down it was . . . I felt so wretched that I went to my cabin to lie down, for my head ached . . . Sleep I found impossible. I tried to read. This was little better, but in about twenty minutes O'Neil came into my cabin . . . The electricians had got some signal through the cable.'

Their colleagues at Valencia had made a mistake, it seemed, but all was now well. 'What a miserable two hours they have given us,' Gooch wrote as the *Great Eastern* continued on her way. With sighs of relief all settled to their routines once again. Anderson continued his contest with Moriarty as to which was the more accurate navigator. Russell's youngsters amused themselves by making a pet of one of the sheep. Thomson and Varley pored over abstruse calculations whilst others worked at journals or sketches. There was a terrific noise from below, as the lower saloon had been turned into a carpenters' shop where half a dozen men were hammering away, damaging the gilding and tearing the wallpaper in the process, to the evident horror of Gooch. Others of the saloon party amused themselves by playing quoits or shuffle-board on deck. The evenings were enlivened by whist, chess or other games. Sometimes there was music, as O'Neil, Jules Despecher, a Frenchman on board as an observer, and Dr Ward, the ship's surgeon, were excellent performers. Everyone developed an enormous appetite. The day started with two or three mutton chops and a plate of ham and eggs. Luncheon was even more substantial. At five o'clock sherry and bitters preceded dinner, a sumptuous meal accompanied by the finest of wines. Tea, toast and marmalade followed later and biscuits and cheese were available at ten. 'As regards Construction I know nothing', said one of the voyagers, 'but I can safely assert it is a most excellent Maintenance Company'.

By Saturday 29 July over a third of the cable had been laid. Then, at 1.20 p.m., all communications with the shore were lost. The *Great Eastern* was in two thousand fathoms of water, so that there were doubts whether the fault could be recovered. Fortunately the sea was glassy smooth and once again the picking-up machine began to turn.

'Our good captain is most anxious and attentive,' Gooch wrote later. 'He has never left the bridge since this trouble began, and will, I have no doubt, remain there until all is again at work. These are indeed very anxious hours.' All went perfectly, however, and the fault came on board at 9.30 p.m. By 3 a.m. the repair was finished but as the *Great Eastern* gathered way the splice caught in the machinery and had to be re-made. It was eight o'clock on Sunday morning before she finally steamed away. Immediately afterwards a fresh breeze sprang up. 'Had we had this . . . during the night,' Gooch said, 'there is no doubt we would have lost our cable.'

Victorian attitudes to the Sabbath allowed them to repair the fault on the Sunday but they had to wait until Monday to find out what had gone wrong. Once again a sliver of wire had cut through the gutta percha, and this time there were strong feelings that there had been sabotage. It was decided that eight of the saloon party would take turns as sentries to prevent further mischief. 'I have to go on watch tonight in that wretched tank at twelve o'clock,' Gooch wrote. 'It is anything but an agreeable task to stand for two hours in a tank of cable covered in tar, and like a girl with a skipping rope, jump over the cable as it runs out . . . or else sit on the edge of an iron bar with your legs upraised.'

By 5.30 a.m. on Wednesday 2 August the *Great Eastern* was 1063 nautical miles from Ireland. Suddenly one of the men heard a click, as if a projecting wire had struck on something. 'Broken wire!,' he called to the watchman on deck, but no warning was passed to the brakesmen. Immediately the electricians detected another serious fault.

Two miles of cable were recovered without difficulty but then the boiler of the picking-up machine ran out of steam. Whilst they were waiting the wind changed. The *Great Eastern* swung round until she drove over the cable, jamming it on one of the projecting hawse-holes and forcing it across her stem. 'To relieve this,' wrote Gooch, 'a man was sent down to make a chain fast to the cable below it. This was done and the cable freed.' The picking-up engine was then re-started, but when only three or four yards had been drawn in the cable snapped and vanished into the Atlantic. 'All is over, I fear, for this year,' Gooch wrote sadly, 'and all our labour is lost.'

The loss, said O'Neil, changed all their natures. 'Our very occupations seemed hateful; the piano was shut, Anderson lost his ever-hopeful smile, and Messrs. Can-

ning and Clifford forgot their usual courtesy. Mr Gooch went below, vainly attempting, through sleep, to obtain oblivion . . .

Moreover, a certain demoralization took place. Hitherto I had never seen anyone light a pipe or cigar in the saloons, and now smoking was prevalent . . . This dreadful breach of discipline was regarded with utter indifference by Captain Anderson and Mr Gooch, the latter himself being one of the chief culprits.'

Not surprisingly the *Great Eastern* had no special equipment to search for a lost cable in such deep water. There were, however, 5,000 fathoms of stout buoy rope on board in hundred fathom lengths. Canning decided to shackle these together and try fishing with a grapnel. The ship was sailed back along her course for 14 mls and before the day was out they made their first cast. 'Of this I have no hope, nor have I heart to wish,' wrote Gooch.

The *Great Eastern* was allowed to drift with nearly 3 mls of the line trailing behind. At first light the picking-up machine was started. Almost immediately one of the gear wheels broke and the steam capstan had to be used instead. As the rope crept over the bow pulley the dynamometer reading rose steadily. Soon they were certain that they had hold of the cable, but when 700 fathoms had been hauled in a shackle broke and their quarry plunged back to the sea bed.

To give a lighter lift for their second attempt the ship was steamed to within about seven miles of the broken end, but then she had to wait for a suitable wind. 'Every one . . . has been very low in spirits,' wrote Gooch, 'none more so than O'Neil. I have not heard a note of music from him . . . nor do any of them seem inclined for a rubber at whist, but they sit talking over our troubles. If we had each lost a dear friend we could not be a more melancholy party.'

Four days passed before the skies cleared and a favourable breeze blew. The rope was lowered and from mid-day until seven o'clock the *Great Eastern* drifted southwards. She then swung head to wind, the dynamometer reading rose to three and a half tons and there was no doubt that she

The ending of the last attempt to recover the lost cable, 1865 expedition. Gooch is the figure in the cap at the extreme right

had hooked. Steadily, but very slowly, the rope was drawn in. Another gear-wheel failed in the picking-up machine, so once again the capstan was coupled on. Then, after over 12 hr. of laborious work, another shackle broke.

For the third try only 2 mls of buoy rope were left and nine hundred fathoms of weaker manilla had to be added to the line. Their chances of success were slim, so Gooch, Canning and Anderson decided to get rid of the shackles which had cost them dearly and to take every step which they could think of to reduce the risks. As the men set to work the weather worsened. Whilst the gale blew the smiths forged new tackle, the carpenters built up the capstan drums and the riggers checked over the rest of the gear.

At 7 a.m. on 10 August the third attempt began but was unsuccessful as the chain at the lower end became entangled in the prongs of the grapnel. The next day another cast was made. By four in the afternoon the strain on the dynamometer showed that they had again hooked. The screw engines were used to hold the ship stationary against the wind and the capstan began to haul.

As the slender manilla rope came in over the bow pulley the dynamometer reading slowly climbed to three tons. With a jerk it shot up 600lb then moved steadily to 4 tons. Seven hundred fathoms were drawn in, leaving only two hundred to go before reaching the strong buoy rope. Then there was another sudden strain. The line broke close to a shackle and plummetted into the black depths, taking their hopes with it. 'No sooner had it broken,' wrote Gooch, 'than the wind began to blow hard from the south with a heavy rain . . . and a state of weather existed that would have rendered our hauling-in the cable quite impossible.' 'I fear the season will be too late for us to be ready to pick up and complete the present cable this year,' he continued, already in no doubt that the task could be carried out. 'It will have to be postponed until the spring. I wonder whether I will come or not? My present feeling is not to do, yet I have a strong longing to witness the completion of the work I have begun. Well, we will see.'

The *Great Eastern* was soon heading eastwards with all canvas set and every ounce of steam raised. They had a fine passage, steaming into Crookhaven harbour, close to Valencia, at 7 a.m. on 17 August. Nothing had been heard of her for a fortnight, so she was hailed with a delighted cry by the press agent, who shouted that many thought they had gone down.

Gooch had cabled to say that he would be home on Sunday 20 August but on the Saturday morning the *Great Eastern* put into Brighton. She was not expected and crept towards the town in a thick mist. Then, at eight o'clock, when the haze lifted, she was revealed, lying majestically about a mile off the pier. 'The landing was an amazing scene,' Gooch wrote. 'Thousands . . . crowded the shore, and if we had been people coming down from the moon we could not have excited greater curiosity.' He took the train homeward and arrived at Clewer at two o'clock.

So ended five anxious weeks. 'How time softens all disappointments,' he wrote. 'I begin to look back upon our broken cable as a matter to be regretted, but not one to discourage me in the ultimate success of our work . . . It is, I believe, true we can come out with proper tackle and pick up the end, and go on to lay the next with certainty . . . It is therefore no failure, but a postponement of our final triumph; we are not beaten, but checked.'

CHAPTER
26

In the autumn of 1865 the directors of the Great Western were due to appoint their chairman. Potter tried to use the occasion to strengthen his hold on the company. 'A couple of days before the election,' Gooch said, 'he went to . . . several of the most influential directors, stating that he was willing to retain the chair on certain conditions, the nature of such conditions being that he should have more power – in fact almost unlimited power . . . This, much to his disappointment, was rejected.' At the end of September he offered his resignation and, to his surprise, it was accepted.

None of the board members felt equal to succeeding him so they decided to approach a shareholder who knew the company inside out and was a highly successful businessman – Daniel Gooch. At first he declined, as there were too many directors with whom he had no wish to work. Spencer Walpole pressed him to accept, offering him £5,000 a year if it was a question of salary. Gooch, however, did not want a full time position, saying that 'if I take it I would only do so on the same terms as former chairmen had held the office. I will not, by receiving larger pay, become the servant of the company'. His former colleagues, who were dispirited by the frequent changes introduced by Potter, also begged him to take over and eventually he agreed. The directors then had to find him a seat on the board. This was not easy, as the Great Western's Act did not permit casual vacancies to be filled until the Annual Meeting. Sir Watkin Williams Wynn, who was a director as an outcome of the amalgamation with the Shrewsbury lines, solved the problem by standing down and nominating him

in his place. So on 2 November 1865, at £2,000 a year, Gooch became head of the company which he had served for so much of his life. 'I could not help feeling some gratification at the position I had taken, after the treatment I had received . . . only a year before,' he wrote. 'It was certainly a victory over the West Midland lot.'

He was now in charge of one of the largest organisations in the world. The turnover during his first twelve months totalled almost £4,000,000. Nineteen million passengers and 8,000,000 tons of goods were handled, about a thirteenth of Britain's railway business. There were 1,200 mls of line, over eight hundred locomotives and more than seventeen thousand carriages and wagons. He had no intention of being a mere figurehead, but when he began to look into the company's finances he was horrified at what he had taken on. Huge liabilities had been incurred with no consideration of where the funds were to come from. Expensive obligations had been entered into with neighbouring lines. Half a million pounds-worth of rolling stock had just been ordered and new stations were being built at Reading and Slough without firm estimates of their cost. To keep the business afloat temporary loans had been raised amounting to £1,400,000, but how these were to be repaid was not clear. 'I now regretted the step I had taken,' he wrote, 'feeling a very difficult and anxious path lay before me, but having put my hand to the plough I had no alternative but to go on and do my best.'

Gooch regarded his predecessor as responsible for the appalling mess, a clear indication of the power of the chairman. He was convinced that Potter would have taken the Great Western into bankruptcy if he had not resigned: 'He was reckless in expenditure and a vain, soft-headed fool, blown about by any wind.' Potter advised him to spend £3,000,000 extending the company, but Gooch felt that, even if they could have raised the money, this would have been 'a wicked folly'. He was disgusted that he had pledged support for a proposal to build a railway from Lydney, on the South Wales line, to Wootton Bassett. This would have taken £80,000 a year from the Great Western's traffic, but it suited him because of the benefits to his coal company. Gooch also would have stood to gain from a shorter route to the South-East, but he put his duty to the shareholders first and squashed the scheme.

Potter had also been behind a proposal for a new carriage and wagon works. This was needed because the old shops at Paddington had become inadequate and the West Midland's had burned down the previous year. Several large towns were keen to provide a site and had begun to vie with one another. People at Swindon were especially interested and on 7 July, less than a week before polling day at Cricklade, a letter had appeared in *The Standard* from Foote, Gooch's election agent. He claimed that statements that Warwick or Reading had been chosen were premature, as the directors had not yet made up their minds. His view was that Swindon would be selected. Potter, however, ruled out the town, as there was no access for narrow gauge stock. On 11 July it was announced that the factory was to be built at Oxford. The dons were aghast but the board were undeterred. This was another project which Gooch brought to a halt. No more was heard of it for two and a half years, when £26,000 was voted for a more modest establishment at Swindon. His constituents were no doubt well satisfied with the decision, which was taken in an election year.

His first board meeting took place on 16 November 1865. All the directors, including those who had done everything in their power to get rid of him two years before, gave him their full support. He needed a united board and worked hard to create one. Their first task was to find capital to finish the essential projects and to pay off the short-term loans, so they decided to put through a Bill for a preference share issue.

The Annual Meeting took place on 2 March 1866. Gooch was given a most kind reception by the shareholders. He was not willing to continue as chairman unless he was elected as a director in the customary way, so one of the board agreed not to seek re-election and he was appointed in his stead.

Gooch had 'a quiet, somewhat phlegmatic style of getting through the heavy business devolving upon him', it was said. He was no doubt at his grimmest at this first meeting, as the dividend was only two percent and he had to make it plain that a difficult period lay ahead. His policies, he said, would be to avoid further obligations for new lines and extensions, and to make friendly arrangements with neighbouring companies. He promised that he would keep capital expenditure to a minimum, but nevertheless money would have to be found to get rid of the broad gauge, as he was under strong pressure from South Wales. It would be an expensive business, he warned them, but the directors would have to raise the funds somehow. Within a year a start was made.

At this time Gooch had to sort out his eldest son's career. Harry Gooch, who was twenty-four, was increasingly unhappy at the way Joseph Whitworth was treating him, so his father bought him an interest in some slate quarries at Bettws-y-Coed. A limited company was formed, of which he became the managing director. This was perhaps a wedding present, as only a few weeks afterwards he married the girl next door – Mary Croskey, of Tunstall House.

Much of the enthusiasm for recovering the Atlantic Telegraph cable had evaporated. 'Shooting season came on,' Gooch grumbled, 'and everyone seemed to think shooting down poor birds vastly more important than making efforts to raise more cash.' He urged that they should first attempt to lay a brand new cable and then try to complete the old one. This bold course, giving a double chance of success, was eventually agreed upon. The Atlantic Telegraph Company were threatening to sue Telcon and John Pender was able to appease them by offering to do as Gooch suggested for £500,000. They proposed to raise the money by an issue of 12% preference shares. Unfortunately, as they already had a preference holding, this was illegal and the year closed without there being any firm plan for an expedition in 1866. Cyrus Field came over to try to raise the capital but had little luck. In desperation he called at Fulthorpe House. Gooch suggested that they form a new company to fund the project, whose shareholders would receive 25% interest if it was a success. The remainder of the profits would go to the present shareholders. This seemed the only course, so the new concern, the Anglo-American Telegraph Company, was set up immediately. Gooch became a director and pressed his colleagues on the Telcon board to invest £10,000 each, to give the public confidence. This led to long faces, but he put his name at the head of the list and they all followed suit. The rest of the capital then materialised, Telcon again taking some of their contract price in shares. Gooch added another £10,000, bringing his total stake to about £70,000.

Telcon's performance over the next few months was astonishing. By the end of June 1,600 mls of cable had been made and loaded into the *Great Eastern*. The ship and all her gear were put into even better order than in the previous year and the cable machinery was improved in the light of their experience. Gooch had little involvement with the work, as he was preoccupied with the affairs of the Great Western and his obligations as an M.P.

The Conservatives had been disappointed with the election results. Only a handful of seats were gained, leaving them in a minority of seventy. Another somnolent Parliament was anticipated under Palmerston, whose benign rule was acceptable to both parties, but he died. Earl Russell took over as Prime Minister with Gladstone as his Chancellor and leader of the Liberals in the Commons. Their opponents were headed by Lord Derby and Benjamin Disraeli.

The new Parliament met for the first time on 1 February 1866. On 13 February Gooch was elected to the Carlton Club. During March he dined with Disraeli, finding him a more genial fellow than he looked when the House was sitting.

At that time only a few of the Divisions of either House were recorded in full in Hansard and it was 17 February before Gooch was listed in one of these. Only in this way, or on the rare occasions when he was made a member of a Select Committee, did his name appear in the proceedings of Parliament, as he never made a speech or asked a question. 'I have taken no part in any of the debates,' he wrote many years later, 'and have been a silent member. It would be a great advantage to business if there were a greater number who followed my example.'

The most controversial issue to come before the House for some years was the long-awaited Parliamentary Reform Bill, introduced by Gladstone on 12 March. He and Russell were committed to increasing the electorate but their party was deeply divided over the issue. Disraeli saw a chance to overthrow the Government and suddenly the session came to life.

To try to hold his party together Gladstone put forward a middle-of-the-road measure, with a limited extension of the right to vote. The important question of a re-distribution of seats was left to a later Bill. He went too far for the fifty Whigs who formed one wing of the Liberals and not nearly far enough for the ninety Radicals on the other. There were also forty dissidents who were against any reform at all. Disraeli was determined to keep the different factions at loggerheads whilst preserving unity amongst his own forces.

The first attack came from Gladstone's own side. At the Second Reading two Whigs proposed an amendment requiring the Government to prepare a Bill immediately which dealt with both the franchise and re-distribution issues. On 12 April a heated debate began and there were eight nights of speeches before the division bells rang. The atmosphere was electric as the result was announced. Gladstone had scraped home by 318 to 313, a humiliating win. 'On this view I voted against the Government,'

Gooch said. 'Gladstone lost his temper and bullied his party, and did his cause and himself much harm.'

The Government's first defeat came on 28 May. A relatively unimportant Conservative amendment was put forward requiring the Bill to be extended to include means to reduce bribery and corruption. Gladstone opposed it, as he felt that the measure was complicated enough already. Gooch evidently agreed with him, as he took a staunchly independent stand, voting with the Government in their defeat by 248 to 238. After a further battle the Committee stage was reached and on 7 June Gladstone was shaken when a Conservative motion was defeated by a mere twenty-seven votes. Gooch stood firmly with his party on that occasion.

It was clear that a concerted heave would overturn Russell's administration. Disraeli and Colonel Taylor, his Chief Whip, pulled the Liberal rebels together. They decided that Lord Dunkellin would move an amendment restricting the increase in the electorate in the boroughs. This was an issue of confidence and if it was carried the Government would have no choice but to resign. Taylor sent out the ultimate in whips, Gooch keeping his as a souvenir. He also sent him a personal letter asking him to be present, presumably because it was feared that he might backslide again. On 18 June, however, Gooch did his duty, being amongst the Ayes in one of the most important and exciting divisions of the century. When Dunkellin appeared to read out the results there was such a storm of cheering that it was several minutes before he could make the announcement that the amendment had been carried by 315 to 304. A week of chaos followed, as the Queen was reluctant to let Russell go. Once the inevitability was brought home to her she invited Lord Derby to form a Government. Disraeli, whose brilliant tactics had swept the Conservatives to power, became Chancellor and leader in the Commons.

On 16 July, when Disraeli took his place on the Government front bench for the first time, Gooch was not there to cheer him. There had been so much jealousy between Canning and Anderson that he decided to go with the cable expedition to keep the peace. He joined the ship at Sheerness on Friday 29 June. 'Yes, I am again seated in

The *Cable-istic Extravaganza*. The mermaids are swinging on the cable. 'Field' is speaking to 'Gooch', whose bow ties appear to have been regarded as characteristic.

this familiar cabin,' he wrote in his log. 'What is my present hope? Is it the same as last year? Do I feel the same confidence? No. The hope is as strong, but not the confidence; the experience last year showed me on what a slender thread our success hung, how little might destroy our hopes.'

Mid-day on Saturday was the time fixed for them to sail. Punctually to the minute the *Great Eastern* moved away. She was even more heavily laden than in the previous year, as she had the remainder of the 1865 cable on board as well as the whole of the new. Her hull had been cleared of weed and barnacles. Beckwith had strengthened her boilers and all the flues had been cleaned. As a result she was soon doing 7 knots at a lower boiler pressure and engine speed than had given 5 knots the previous year. Gooch was disappointed, as he had expected at least another knot or two, but was pleased to find that she burned only 183 tons of coal in steaming through the Channel, 78 tons less than in the previous year.

A good many guests were on board for the trip to Ireland. They worked hard to give the expedition a cheerful send-off, even putting on a *Cable-istic Extravaganza*, in which the principal voyagers were portrayed. Gooch, played by George Elliot, appeared in the finale with a bevy of mermaids swinging on the telegraph cable:

Neptune   Come out of that! Is that how you disable,
Our new Manilla-twist galvanic cable?
You're sitting on the messages! Get up!

Gooch   My dears, beware of sitting on,
Or tampering with the cable.

Field   But give the messages a shove,
And help them, if you're able.

At Bear Haven more coal was loaded into the bunkers and work on the cable-laying machinery was finished whilst the shore-end was being laid. The *Great Eastern's* guests waved her farewell as she sailed to make the splice. Then, at 3 p.m. on Friday 13 July, Anderson set her on her course and once again cable was splashing into her wake. HMS *Terrible* was on guard ahead. Two chartered steamers, the *Medway* and the *Albany*, lay astern, one on each quarter. Both were equipped with grappling ropes and hauling-in machinery to assist in recovery work. Anderson increased speed to 5 knots as his crew settled to their vigils. There were 501 on board – sailing dept. 164, engines 175, stewards 50, electricians 19, cable 88, plus 5 others. The small saloon party was much quieter than the previous year's, with no music or cards to enliven the evenings.

The paying-out machine was the one used in 1865 but with the addition of a powerful steam engine and clutches, so that a damaged cable could be recovered quickly over the stern. The electricians had devised a method of testing the insulation continuously, enabling a fault to be spotted at the instant that it occurred. A powerful new hauling-in machine had been installed in the bows, capable of up to 1½ knots. Between them the three ships were carrying 20 mls of wire rope of ample strength for grappling. Gooch was well pleased with all the careful preparations: 'I cannot see why we should fail. I have tried often to find out a weak point, but in vain,'

A length of the new cable was laid first. It only differed from the 1865 version in that the final wrapping of hemp over the armouring had not been tarred, so that there was nothing for sharp pieces of wire to stick to. They then laid some of the old cable, whilst they were still in shallow water. Gooch thought this a false economy, and though the speed was reduced and an especially careful watch was kept he was worried. All went well, however, apart from a fright when one of the electricians accidentally leaned on the alarm switch.

On 17 July, as he lay reading in his berth, Gooch thought he heard a change in the noise of the ship. Dressing hurriedly he went on deck, where he found a tangled mass of cable lying between the tanks and the paying-out machine. Some of the coils of un-tarred cable had sprung upwards, because of their lack of stickiness. They had then become entangled with the cable passing out of the tank, to be deposited in a writhing heap on the deck.

The cable at the stern pulley was secured

with a stopper and Canning, Halpin and a group of men set to work to tug the knots free. Anderson kept watch at the taffrail, using the paddles and screw to ease the strain. For the next 3 hrs he kept the *Great Eastern's* stern at one spot, a magnificent feat of seamanship. The ship was then able to resume her steady course, the electricians' tests showing that the gutta percha was still faultless. On a few further occasions the cable started to snag but the squads were watchful and were able to free the coils in time. Gooch, however, could no longer sleep soundly.

By 25 July shallower water had been reached and he knew that success was certain: 'What a relief this is to us all. It has been a hard fortnight . . . a long time to feel that from one minute to another you might be involved in misfortune.'

At four o'clock on the morning of Friday 27 July he was awakened by gunfire. The ship was moving slowly through a thick mist, with land just visible to port. Already they were in Trinity Bay and as the fog lifted the scrub-covered hills of Newfoundland were revealed.

Soon after nine the *Great Eastern* reached the spot where the shore-end was to be spliced on. The cable was cut and carried to the *Medway*, which had the heavier cable on board. Then, to the astonishment of all who saw her, Brunel's ship turned slowly about her axis, her screw going ahead and her paddles astern, before steaming to her anchorage in Heart's Content Bay. Her first task had been accomplished.

A little after mid-day the cable was within a hundred yards of the water's edge. Gooch and Canning landed to decide where to bring the end ashore and when the last few yards had been laid there was wild excitement, the seamen and cable hands jumping into the water, shouting and cheering. The *Great Eastern* and her consorts immediately fired a salute, smoke hiding the ships as round after round crashed out.

At four o'clock the cable reached the wooden building which was to serve as the telegraph office and there was more jubilation. One of the cable hands even put the end into his mouth whilst the rest danced round him, cheering at the tops of their

Unravelling the tangled cable, 17 July 1866

voices. 'It was a strange sight – nay, a sight that filled our eyes with tears,' wrote Gooch. 'I am glad two of my boys were present to enjoy and glory in their part of so noble a work.'

Before the first messages were sent everyone who could be spared filed into the tiny church at Heart's Content to offer thanks for their success. Gooch, as the expedition's leader, then despatched two telegrams, one to Richard Glass, in which he expressed his deep sense of the untiring zeal with which all had performed their duties, and the other to Lord Stanley, the Foreign Secretary. 'God grant it may be a lasting source of benefit to our country,' he concluded. A night of wild jollification then followed.

The Foreign Secretary's reply had arrived by breakfast time. He asked for a message from the Queen to be forwarded immediately to the President of the United States, expressing her hope that the cable would serve as an additional bond of union between their two countries.

Gooch was eager for the *Great Eastern* to set off for 'the fishing grounds', as he called them, but first she had to be coaled. In the meantime the celebrations continued. Dozens of people arrived to make a free hotel of the ship. One of them, a Dr McKee, gave Anderson a pure-black New-foundland dog, nine months old, called Norval, which he in turn presented to Gooch. The two became inseparable. Mr Ridley, at Harbour Grace, arranged a grand ball, sending his carriage to bring as many as could squeeze into it. Gooch endured the 16 mls of appalling roads and enjoyed the dancing immensely. After five weeks of the *Great Eastern's* all-male society he fancied that he had never seen so many good-looking women in one room before.

The Atlantic Cable was already a commercial success. On 3 August fifty messages were exchanged, worth about £1,200 – £24 a telegram. Within a few weeks, when the line south from New-foundland had been completed, traffic was at the rate of £900,000 per annum. High dividends were certain for those who had risked their capital so boldly.

On 1 August the *Albany* and the *Terrible* left to start grappling for the 1865 cable whilst the *Great Eastern* finished bunkering. It was 9 August before she and the *Medway* were ready to follow. They sailed for the rendezvous through the heaviest seas which Gooch had ever experienced. He was com-fortable enough, but life was hard on the *Medway*. 'Charlie is on board her', he wrote, 'and I fancy is wishing himself back in the *Great Eastern* tonight'.

On 12 August they reached the other ships. Already the *Albany* had managed to attach a buoy to the cable. The next after-noon the *Great Eastern* began to lower her grapnel, but soon the breeze died and the line was drawn in again. 'Canning lost many valuable hours in thinking instead of acting, as was too often the case with him,' complained Gooch.

The following day was too rough for grappling, so that it was noon on 15 August before the next cast was made. By eight in the evening they had hooked. The new hauling-in machine was started but after 350 fathoms had been recovered Can-ning decided to buoy the line and wait for daylight, which Gooch thought a bad mis-take. Whilst they were attaching the buoy an eye broke. Two miles of wire rope went to the bottom.

The next attempt was more successful and on 17 August the grapnel emerged with the long-lost cable hooked onto two of its prongs. The fleet resounded with cheers, but it was far too taut, snapping as they were preparing to secure it.

Because it had been under such a strain they decided to try lifting at two places some miles apart but neither ship hooked on. At a further attempt the *Great Eastern* had more luck. The cable was raised 1,200 fathoms and buoyed. The *Albany* did the same, but then the weather broke.

The frustrating work continued. By 22 August even Gooch had lost patience. 'At dinner today we were anything but jolly,' he said. 'A sense of failure seemed to hang upon everyone's mind, although no one will admit any doubt of success. I hear remarks, "Oh, we must stay here till Christmas rather than fail", but this is simple non-sense. If we cannot do it now, no length of time will enable us to do so. We are nearly the end of August, and bad weather will be the ruling feature . . . I am quite willing to hope and try a few days more; but then it will be time to go home.'

Friday 24 August was Gooch's fiftieth birthday. It was too stormy for grappling, but flags crackled at the *Medway's* yard-arm and Charles Gooch's congratulations were brought to him. Perhaps there was a celebration, as their first ox was killed that day.

Time after time the cable was hooked and lost. On 27 August the *Albany* brought a loose end to the surface. 'It may well be we have only some of the cable broken off by the hauls we have had,' Gooch wrote, and so it proved, as when Moriarty was able to take a good sight he found that they were 12 mls from their proper course.

After one more day Gooch used his authority. 'I began to despair of getting the cable by the plan we were trying,' he wrote. 'It had been so often hooked by the various ships, and probably broken and pulled out of place, that we might never get it. I therefore proposed that we should at once go along the cable about ninety miles, where we had an excellent observation when it was laid . . . and also only in 1650 fathoms, a great advantage over 2000 . . . Many objections were urged by Canning and Anderson to this shift of ground. Anderson said it was admitting defeat. Canning soon yielded the point, and I was glad to see the ship's head turned east.'

It was Friday 31 August before the weather was good enough for the first cast on the new ground. The *Great Eastern* hooked straight away and began to haul. When the cable had been raised eight hundred fathoms the line was buoyed. She steamed 2 mls to the west, hooked on without difficulty and again lifted and buoyed. The *Medway* did the same another 2 mls further on, so that the cable was supported at three points. The smaller ship was then ordered to haul in hard, to break it and make a free end. This too was done successfully.

All was now ready for the *Great Eastern* to try to bring their quarry to the surface. The hauling-in machine began to turn. Fathom by fathom the wire rope came over the bows and was coiled into the forward hold until, at a quarter to one on the morning of 2 September, the cable emerged from the Atlantic.

Stoppers were then attached, the western end of the bight was cut through with a saw and, in perfect silence, the signal was given to start winding. The cable rose, passed over the bow-pulley, through the hauling-in machine and onto the foredeck. Still there was complete quiet, though some crossed the platform to touch it, as if to make sure it was real. The end was carried into the testing room. The leaders of the expedition crowded in and stood back as the checks began. Willoughby Smith, the chief electrician, began signalling to Foilhummerum. For ten long minutes nothing happened. Then, wrote Gooch jubilantly, 'the little magic light flashed upon the scale, and one wild burst of pent-up feelings was given by ringing cheers, which were taken up by those outside, and oh, what a load was lifted from my heart . . . This had been a night of intense anxiety. I felt it was our last hope . . . I feel now very glad I persevered in carrying my point of changing our ground'.

By breakfast time the splice had been made, telegrams of congratulation had been exchanged with Valencia and the *Great Eastern* was on her way to Newfoundland. Gooch was more anxious than ever, as it would have been hard indeed if they had failed to complete the cable after such a struggle. But all went smoothly and on 8 September the *Great Eastern* was riding at her anchor in Heart's Content Bay with a second perfect cable to her credit.

On the night of their return there was a celebration attended by a large party from St. John's. A pressing invitation to a return banquet was declined as the ship was too expensive to be kept waiting. The visitors were turned out and they sailed for home the next morning.

On Tuesday 18 September the *Great Eastern* steamed past the lights of Anglesey, heading for the Mersey Bar. The next day Gooch, with Norval at his side, arrived at Clewer. He had been away for almost eleven weeks. There, awaiting him, was his fiftieth birthday present from his wife, a silver hot-water jug. With it was a slip of paper, shyly inscribed, 'D. Gooch Esqr, with his wife's dearest love, Aug. 24th 1866'. This was one of the last occasions on which he was so addressed, as the honours were about to be bestowed upon the key figures of the expedition.

Gooch's pleasure during the last weeks at sea had been disturbed by the jealousy between some of the staff as to which of them ought to have the most credit for their success: 'When we returned the year before no one was anxious to struggle for the credit of the failure, but now there was nothing but bad feeling and I had constantly to interfere to keep things all right'. He was able to play a part in ensuring fairness, however, as a fortnight after his return the Home Secretary, Spencer Walpole, told him that the Prime Minister was going to offer him a baronetcy, and wished to know about the contributions made by other members of the expedition.

The announcements were made at a banquet at Liverpool at the end of September, which Gooch did not attend. Sir Stafford Northcote read out a letter from Lord Derby which said that the Queen had been pleased to direct that 'a knighthood should be conferred upon Captain Anderson, the able and zealous commander of the *Great Eastern*; Professor Thomson, whose distinguished science has been brought to bear with eminent success upon the improvement of the submarine telegraphy; and on Messrs. Glass and Canning . . . whose skill and experience have mainly contributed to the admirable construction and successful laying of the cable. Her Majesty is further pleased to mark her approval of the public spirit and energy of the two companies who have had successively the conduct of the undertaking, by offering the dignity of a baronetcy of the United Kingdom to Mr Lampson . . . to whose resolute support of the project in spite of all discouragements it was in a great measure owing that it was not at one time abandoned in despair; and to Mr Gooch, M.P., the chairman of the company which has finally completed the design'. Cyrus Field, as a citizen of the United States, could not be given a title but the Prime Minister acknowledged his unique contribution in the most handsome terms.

The scene in the testing room whilst Willoughby Smith attempts to contact Ireland. Gooch is second from the left, with finger extended.

On 13 November 1866 *The London Gazette* formally announced that Gooch had been created a baronet. 'Any acknowledgement of my services by the Government had certainly never formed a part of my hopes,' he wrote. 'I had gone into this matter . . . from a desire to assist in completing so great a work, and would have been quite content with the feeling I had had success . . . I earnestly pray that the dignity thus conferred upon me . . . will never be disgraced by myself or those who, in the course of nature, will succeed me.' He had achieved a rare distinction. During the whole of the century less than four hundred baronetcies were awarded, mostly to men of high birth. Gooch was the first engineer to be granted the title, and one of the handful who rose from a workman's wage to such an honour.

CHAPTER

27

Soon after Gooch returned the Great Western's financial position became extremely serious. In May 1866 the important banking house of Overend, Gurney failed. During the autumn there were disclosures of malpractice in the London, Chatham and Dover Railway Company. Confidence was lost and investment in railways was hit hard. This could not have come at a worse time for the Great Western, who were in desperate need of cash. Some of the £1,400,000 of debentures fell due for repayment every month and the £1,300,000 of temporary loans had to be cleared.

At the shareholders' meeting in October it was decided that an issue of £2,600,000 of 6% preference shares should be made. The market was so bad, however, that less than a tenth were taken up. By the end of the year liabilities could not be met and Grierson, the general manager, expected a receiver to be appointed at any minute. 'We could not get money in any way,' Gooch wrote. 'I deeply regretted ever having involved myself in so difficult a concern.'

On Friday 8 March 1867 the Annual Meeting was adjourned for three weeks whilst he tried to borrow £1,000,000 from the Government. The very next day he and two of his fellow directors went to see Disraeli. They asked for a five year loan, offering £2,300,000 of unsold preference shares as security. Gooch argued that support to the company would do a great deal to restore trust nationally, but they were turned down.

Having failed with both the public and the state, Gooch had to find some other solution. He called the main shareholders together and suggested that the dividend be paid with 6% preference shares rather than cash. They agreed, supporting a motion to that effect at the re-convened meeting. This released enough revenue to clear some of the debts, more being obtained by drastic economies. Maintenance was pared to the bone and services were cut. Thanks to Gooch's determination the crisis was passed, though bankruptcy stared them in the face for some months. His skilful rescue operation was seen as one of his finest achievements.

Gooch felt that the fragmented board was at the root of many of the problems. He advised a reduction in numbers from twenty-five to sixteen. When the necessary private bill had been passed Potter, Fenton and Brown were amongst those to go. 'They had acted badly towards me,' he said, 'and I now saw all those who, in 1864, did their best to get rid of me by arrogance, now themselves out of the board.' The stronger and more congenial directorate had no hesitation in re-electing him. He abolished the hated departmental committees, the board and a finance committee directing the company's affairs. On 26 July 1867 he proposed terms of reference for all the chief officers, clarifying their responsibilities and powers of discretion, setting up an organisation which survived in its essentials throughout his long tenure of the chair.

In the aftermath of the cable expedition distinctions showered upon him. On 8 December *The Illustrated London News* printed an article on *The New Baronets and Knights of the Atlantic Cable* in which he was the first to be praised. 'He is, wherever practical experience and unflagging energy

Engineering's portrait of Gooch, 1868

are required, a most valuable labourer,' the writer said. The Duke of Sutherland presided at a dinner held in his honour. He was made a Deputy Lieutenant of Berkshire, one of some forty-five of the county's most notable or aristocratic men. Later in the year he became a Justice of the Peace, serving on the Windsor Bench, and in the following February *Engineering* published a sternly dignified portrait of him which must surely have given him pleasure.

At that time the *Great Eastern* was being prepared for her next voyage. She had been chartered to a French company, as there was to be an International Exhibition in Paris that summer. The intention was to bring visitors from the United States in droves. A vast amount of work was done on her, well over a thousand workmen swarming over her at Liverpool. Accommodation was prepared for over three thousand, the charterers paying for most of the outfitting and for new screw engine boilers. Her most serious deficiency, the feeble steering gear, was put right. Brunel had called for a steam-powered rudder in his specification

but in the event only manual steering was provided. For the 1867 voyage a powerful steering engine specially invented by J. McFarlane Gray was installed. This embodied the first true servo-system.

On 25 March all was ready. 'We start in the morning,' wrote Anderson, 'the grandest ocean passenger ship the world ever saw. Whether this will prove her mission or not I cannot conjecture. The outlay – £120,000 – is enormous and I am sorry for . . . all concerned.' Over a thousand made the outward passage, but only 191 booked for the return. The charterers made a disastrous loss and had to cancel the rest of the trips, leaving the owners heavily out of pocket. 'We made rather a bad bargain,' Gooch said. 'The French Company saddled us with all the wages of the crew, and large expenses which we never contemplated having to meet . . . We lost £25,000 – £30,000'.

Gooch's second session as an M.P. started quietly. He did not take part in a division until it had been under way for six weeks. Over the next few days he voted on several minor issues, including one in which he favoured the limitation of flogging in the Army to fifty lashes. The important business of the year then began – Disraeli's Reform Bill.

Since the defeat of Russell's Government the country had seethed for reform. Lord Derby and Disraeli, however, only proposed to put some bland Resolutions before the House. Their caution was understandable, bearing in mind their minority, but the public, the bulk of the Conservatives and, indeed, the Queen herself wanted the matter settled. Disraeli sacrificed his support from the influential right wing of his party and announced a bold measure – 'a franchise on a very extended scale', Gooch said, 'a leap in the dark, as it was called. I supported this, feeling that any intermediate solution would only be a temporary one, that it was better to get down to this at once than to have continued agitation on the subject'. Radical though Disraeli's ideas were the backbenchers on both sides made the Bill even more extreme as it passed through the House. Rebels amongst the Conservatives occasionally voted against the Government. On 7 May Ayrton, the Radical member for

Tower Hamlets, proposed that borough ratepayers should qualify after being residents for one year rather than two. Gooch was amongst the 278 who rallied behind him and defeated the Government by eighty-one.

The Act which finally emerged gave virtually all householders and many lodgers in the boroughs a vote. Nearly nine hundred thousand were added to the electorate, almost doubling it. The most disgruntled communities, the large industrial towns, were given thirty-eight additional seats by depriving the smaller boroughs of their second member. Cricklade was not amongst those affected, but Gooch would have a different situation to face at the next election, as a great many of the Swindon workmen would then go to the polls for the first time.

Though the session had been historic Gooch found his duties as an M.P. irksome. 'The late hours do not suit me and it is a great tie upon my time', he wrote. 'What with Parliament and the railway I see no chance of even a few weeks rest and I often ask myself why, at my time of life, I should not have some leisure to travel abroad and feel now and then I can call a day my own.' For a man with so many other responsibilities he was a conscientious M.P. During the 1867 session he took part in forty of the 164 divisions. On the average one in three voted, but this included the hard core of inveterate debaters, so he was certainly in the top half as an attender. He had a good excuse for not being in the chamber, however, as Spencer Walpole had appointed him to an important and hard-working Royal Commission on the Trade Unions.

During the last few years there had been concern at shootings, explosions and even a murder at Sheffield, all the work of union members in attempts to intimidate others to obey rules or join their ranks. Because of a wall of silence the police had not managed to bring any of the culprits to book. The culminating incident took place on 15 October 1866. Agents of the Saw-Grinders' Union exploded a can of gunpowder at the house of a lapsed member. There was a great outcry, both the Master Cutlers and the Government offering rewards for information leading to arrests. Responsible unionists were alarmed by the reaction. They were also concerned at the outcome of an apparently trivial court case. The Boilermakers' Society had sued a branch secretary to recover £24. Courts up to the Lord Chief Justice's ruled that they could not try the action, as the union, being 'in restraint of trade', had no right to the protection of the law. Not since the repeal of the Combination Acts in the twenties had the unions been regarded as criminal conspiracies, but this judgement implied that they were only partially legalised. The union leaders saw this as dangerous to their standing and pressed for Parliament to regularise their position.

As a result of the pressures a Royal Commission was appointed in February 1867. The chairman was Sir William Erle, a jurist who was very much against the unions. The employers were represented by Gooch and William Mathews, 'businessmen of great energy and keen opponents of the tradesmen', as one of the Commissioners described them. As it was unthinkable for working men to represent themselves Frederic Harrison, a brilliant barrister, was appointed on their behalf. He was supported by Tom Hughes, the author of *Tom Brown's Schooldays*, who was the unions' principal spokesman in the House. The other seven members were selected by Walpole as an uncommitted middle ground.

The Commissioners were empowered to send examiners into districts which they thought warranted investigation. The Sheffield events were already being probed, the three investigators being successful where others had failed, as they could grant amnesties to people who were incriminated by their own evidence. Due warning was given that the full weight of the law would fall on anyone later convicted of a crime to which he had not confessed, so sinister figures fell over themselves to tell their stories. The ringleader was a Thomas Broadhead. He had hired one man to blow up another for £5, and had arranged for legs to be broken and for a horse to be hamstrung. Canisters of gunpowder had been dropped down chimneys on his behalf and funds embezzled to pay the bills. It became clear, as the unionists had expected, that the outrages were the work of a tiny minority. A similar investigation into Manchester building workers yielded the same conclusions.

In the meantime the Commission concentrated on their more general study. In all they held forty-seven public hearings, publishing the evidence verbatim in ten reports which appeared at intervals during the next three Parliamentary sessions. Amongst those questioned were leading trade unionists, representatives of employers' associations, working men who were opposed to unionism and experts on the benevolent society activities of the unions. Their statements made it clear that the unions were respectable bodies which posed no threat to law and order. The effects they might have on businesses and the economy were, however, more controversial, so behind the scenes discussions were often heated. Erle, the chairman, could not control his temper and was quite incompetent, according to Harrison. The meetings were dominated by Lord Elcho, with support from his brother-in-law, the Earl of Lichfield. John Roebuck, the M.P. for Sheffield, a Radical who had become a bitter opponent of the unions, played a major part but was tart, angry and negative. Tom Hughes, like Gooch, was too busy to give the Commission his wholehearted attention, but proved a loyal comrade to Harrison. Gooch and Mathews were kept well supplied with facts and figures by their side, but the unionists, Harrison thought, were even better served.

Gooch's experience of organised working men went back to his time at Tredegar. There had been union members at Swindon since the earliest days. A branch with over a hundred members was amongst the founders of the Amalgamated Society of Engineers in 1851. Only a small proportion of those eligible to join did so, however. His railwaymen were not unionised at all, and it is clear that he knew how to control his men without their feeling the need to band together. Their trust in him was made evident in 1862 when Cobbett introduced a Bill to limit the hours of enginemen. 'A Great Western Engine Driver' wrote to *The Times* to complain that he and his colleagues had been classed with those who had petitioned Parliament, but they had authorised no one to use their names: 'As long as our respected and esteemed chief superintendent, Mr Gooch, is at our head, we want no other protection than his, for we all know that we can get no protection so just and generous as we receive at his hands.' As a successful paternalist Gooch was an ideal advocate for the employers. They believed that what was good for their business was also good for their employees, that there was a way to riches open to any capable workman who cared to work hard, and that the general level of wages must be kept down for a company, and indeed the nation, to survive. Trade unions did not fit into their scheme of things. Gooch particularly disliked the unions' attempts to limit the output of the best men. He asked a shipbuilder whether he thought they tried to hold the most intelligent workmen back to the level of the rest.

'That is the . . . picture,' he answered.

'Taking the interests of the working classes . . . do you think that it is desirable that they should be reduced to a level of dead mediocrity without the power of rising beyond that?' Gooch asked.

'I believe that the working man himself is really the worst sufferer of all.'

The unions, however, were far from happy about their members being pitted against one another, preferring a society in which there would be a fair wage for all, rather than fortunes for a few.

'Employers have generally sprung from us,' said one of their leaders, in what seems to have been a direct dig at Gooch. 'They have gone up at such a rapid rate that in twenty-four or five years they actually do not know you when they meet you, though you may be as intelligent as Lord John Russell. They are always talking about losing so much, and yet they thrive on their losses. And if the employers would be content with less margin of profit . . . you may depend on it that they could afford to give better wages.'

'Is it not one of the advantages of this country as contrasted with foreign nations that the highest positions in society are open to everyone who has merit?,' Gooch countered, no doubt thinking of his baronetcy.

'I daresay it is,' came the reply. 'I would rather be an Englishman than a Frenchman. I am somewhat like the man who said: England! – with all thy faults, I love thee still.'

It was contract piecework which enabled the best of the men to rise. The Amalgamated Society of Engineers opposed the system, as most of the workmen had no say in the prices and no share in the profits.

'But the fact is,' Gooch said to their general secretary, 'that those men who take contracts are the most intelligent class of workmen, and are more qualified to judge-..than the men who work with them.'

'It does not always follow . . . From my experience it is generally the most pliable one that gets the job.'
Gooch pounced on a unionist who said that 'a man should not be free to over-exert himself'.

'I presume that skill means something more than better execution of work,' he said. 'It means more rapid execution of work . . . I want to see whether the skilled man may not be able to . . . work with . . . less exertion to himself, so that he may be able to do a greater amount.'

He was also irritated by attempts to interfere with the use of lads as cheap labour.

'Would your union consent to . . . apprentices doing the work that men do?,' one of the Commissioners asked.

'Yes, they do it now in particular districts.'

'In the higher skilled work?'

'No. The employers do not find that to their advantage.'

'But supposing they did?'

'We would endeavour to prevent it.'

This was too much for Gooch, who angrily took over.

'What chances have English houses to compete . . . if the manufacturer has no power in deciding the mode of carrying on his business? . . . If he found he could dispense with nine-tenths of the mechanics and employ boys at a lower rate, why should he not be free to do that, on his own premises and using his own capital?'

'You are perfectly at liberty to employ as many boys as you like', came the defiant reply, 'but we object to the system and will not work with you.'

Some of the exchanges make it clear that paternalism was doomed.

'But the interest of the employer and the employed is to work together, is it not?,' Gooch asked one of the greatest of trade unionists.

'There I differ,' he replied. 'Every day of the week I hear that interests are identical . . . It is their interest to get the labour done at as low a rate as they possibly can, and it is ours to get as high a rate of wages as possible, and you can never reconcile these two things.'

Gooch's own interests were continuing to prosper. During 1867 he had enough capital to spare to lend the South Devon Railway £25,000 for a year at 6%. The security was £35,000 of their 5% preference shares, and one wonders whether the struggling company managed to redeem them. A slowly developing venture, the sinking of the Hafod Colliery at Ruabon, came to fruition. Gooch's company had begun the two shafts in 1863, coal production starting in August 1867.

It is extraordinary that during such a busy year Gooch also managed to write his memoirs. Pride in his baronetcy caused him to undertake the task. 'I feel it may not be uninteresting to those who succeed me . . . and my other children, to know something of him upon whom the title was first conferred,' he said. 'I must first express my gratitude to God for the many and great blessings which He has bestowed upon me. I feel and acknowledge all is due to His goodness, that many who have run the race of life with me, while falling greatly short in the result, have equally merited advancement.' He worked swiftly, beginning in the October and finishing by Christmas. In the succeeding years he wrote an intermittent journal, keeping with his manuscripts newspaper cuttings, souvenirs and some of the exquisite arrangements of pressed flowers and ferns which he made.

Gooch made few references to his wife in his memoirs. His remarks on their engagement – of being anxious and unhappy at his position, of feeling that he had been too hasty – were so frank that it is clear that he knew that she would never see them. Perhaps he already sensed that she had only a short while to live.

What was perhaps the zenith of her life occurred on 25 June 1867 – the Queen's Ball at Buckingham Palace. 'My wife persuaded me to attend,' Gooch wrote. 'It was a gay affair but not one I should care about often attending. I was glad to see it over.' They were amongst seventeen hundred who filed into the palace between gleaming ranks of Coldstream Guardsmen. Beyond the great doorway Yeomen of the Guard marked the way to the glittering ballroom. The Queen herself did not make an appearance but at ten-fifteen Prince and Princess Louis of Hesse, the Prince of Wales and other members of the Royal family entered and the orchestra began to play.

Early in 1868 Lady Gooch began to suffer from a disease of the liver and kidneys. 'Altho' for some months she has been complaining of not feeling well, yet I anticipated no danger,' Gooch wrote in the May. 'The week before last she went out for a drive every day until Friday. On Saturday she was downstairs all the afternoon. On Sunday she got up and sat for a few hours in my dressing room, where I joined her about one o'clock . . . As she felt fatigued I advised her to go to bed.'

An obstruction of the bowel had developed. The efforts of the eminent surgeons who attended her were unavailing. After a few days of intense agony she grew too weak to feel the pain and her family were sent for. Her sister Jane and all her children except Frank, who was in the Army in India, were with her until the end. Harry and his wife were the last to arrive, reaching Fulthorpe House on the Thursday evening: 'Poor soul, when I told her they had come she wanted to get up and see if their room was comfortable'.

When he reached his mother Harry was sobbing. Gooch was close to her with her hand in his. She thought the sobs came from him and said, 'Oh, Dan love, don't'. A letter which she had been expecting for a fortnight arrived from Frank. Gooch never forgot her thankful expression when he told her that it had come, but she was too exhausted to have it read to her and drifted away into a sleep from which she never wakened. At half past six on the morning of Friday 22 May 1868 her life came to its end.

She was buried in the shade of an old tree in the churchyard at Clewer. 'There must have been some presentiment in my mind of this blow that has come to me,' Gooch wrote, 'for it is only a few months since I asked . . . if I could have reserved a piece of ground . . . where I fancied I should like to make my last resting place.'

He was accompanied to the graveside by Tom, John and William Gooch – George Henry did not attend. A large number of the residents of Windsor and Clewer were present. 'Her amiable disposition and many acts of kindness had caused her memory to be revered,' *The Illustrated London News* said in a brief obituary.

Her passing left Gooch deeply stricken. 'Oh God, how hard is this blow,' he wrote in his journal, 'the loss of one who has been my constant and loving companion for more than thirty years, one so pure, so unselfish . . . How much I owe to her for what has been good of my life; how much I regret any pain I have given her . . . My greatest treasure on earth is taken from me. My fireside will be for ever lonely. Oh God, give me strength to bear the burden.'

CHAPTER

28

Full of loneliness and despair Gooch began to pick up the threads of a life which now seemed pointless. At Clewer the sun blazed down throughout a long and glorious summer but he was overcome by the knowledge that he would not share the beauty and peace with his wife again. His Paddington home was even more depressing. The two houses were being turned into one and the workmen had left a sad mess. He could take little interest in the alterations, feeling no more than an agent for his successors.

In his grief there was much remorse. 'How good and loving she was to me,' he wrote, 'How much more has her care been for me than I felt it at the time. How much I under-rated the blessing God had given me in her. Oh my beloved Peggy, how earnestly I would try and make up to you for any sorrow I may have caused you in the past if it were possible you could again come to me.'

To ease his loss he turned to work. He had been at the Trade Union Commission only three days before his bereavement. On 23 June, just a month later, he resumed attendance. In March he had been appointed to the Select Committee on Admiralty Monies and Accounts. Until Margaret died he had only been to four of the twenty meetings, but he was at six of the ten between 18 June and 14 July. The archaic accounting practices at the Royal Dockyards brought a return of his testy incisiveness.

The half-yearly meeting of the Great Western went well, as he was able to tell the shareholders that future dividends would be paid in cash. Then, with his responsibilities eased, he decided to go to Ireland for a holiday. His daughter Anna kept him company. They spent three weeks travelling the beautiful but troubled land. Their only disaster was at Athlone, where the hotel was wretched, with dirty beds and a nauseating smell of burnt fat in Gooch's room. For the most part they had good weather and he enjoyed the sightseeing and scenery as much as could be expected.

Whilst he was in Ireland he took every opportunity to study the political situation. During the year widespread disaffection had erupted into a series of Fenian outrages. Both sides of the Commons were anxious to introduce measures to bring about a lasting peace. Disraeli thought the unfair system of land tenure the problem, but another important grievance was the status of the Irish Church, the minority Anglican faith. As the legally established church it was supported by the state, though only an eighth of the population were members. Gladstone thought it should be disestablished immediately. On 1 May he had introduced a Resolution on the matter. The Government had been beaten by sixty-five votes, bringing Disraeli's insecure reign to an end.

The new Parliamentary registers were not to be ready until November. Neither Disraeli nor Gladstone wished to go to the country until they were complete, so there was an uneasy truce whilst all began their campaigns. Gooch, though by no means keen to seek re-election, was preparing himself. At the hotel in Killarney he argued politics in the smoking room and discussed the religious problems with a young lady who sat by him at dinner. He was especially interested in the views of the farmers. Their main wish was for lower rents, he found, but he thought their crofts so small that even if they were made a gift of them they would not be able to earn a decent living.

Gooch returned home by way of Harry's at Bettws-y-Coed. 'I have not been here before but in company with my dear wife,' he wrote sadly. 'We have spent some happy days here, and what is the future for me? . . . I was never fitted for a solitary life. I need the home happiness of a wife.'

At Cricklade both parties were in disarray. It was thought that Gooch was not going to stand again, so a Walters F. Pratt offered himself as the second Conservative. At first it seemed unlikely that the Liberals would put up a candidate but with so many artisan voters they stood a good chance. George Glyn, Gladstone's Chief Whip, obtained £1,500 from Lord Yarborough to start a contest. George Howell, the secretary of the Reform League, came down to marshall support. 'I have been to Swindon,' he told Glyn, 'and intend setting things all right with the railwaymen there.' As a result Gooch heard on 4 October that the Hon. F. Cadogan had come forward as the Liberal candidate. Three days later, though still uncertain whether to stand, he held a meeting at the Mechanics' Institution, where he was well received. The next day Pratt withdrew and Gooch's election address, written as long ago as 18 August, appeared in the press. 'I have no inclination to go on with the contest,' he confided to his journal. 'I have not perfect faith in the Conservative Party as a whole. I have no intentions to be used to secure Goddard's election.'

It was plain to Foote, Gooch's agent, that Cadogan was going to head the poll. When he heard that there was a likelihood of a second Liberal he was afraid that neither Conservative would be elected. He advised Gooch that either he or Goddard should drop out. 'I don't think men of either party would like to see you out. Mr Goddard should therefore give way . . . **otherwise both seats will assuredly be lost.**'

Goddard, whose family had represented the borough since 1807, would not stand down. Foote, however, had doubts whether another Liberal would appear, feeling that they were rattling sabres before offering

terms, and so it proved. Knowing that they were unlikely to keep Gooch out they put it to Foote that if they were helped against Goddard they would not field a second man. 'If I gave support to the Liberal side,' Gooch wrote, 'or, rather, took no steps to get the Swindon men to vote for Goddard, they would vote for me largely, and so leave Goddard in the cold.' In the circumstances this was all that he could do. Goddard later complained of support being withheld where, 'from solemn assurances', he had believed it would be given. Gooch must have taken quiet satisfaction that he had paid Goddard back for his 1865 tactics.

On 25 October Gooch wrote to Disraeli to warn him that he could expect to lose one of the Cricklade seats. 'Personally I have no wish to be in Parliament,' he said. 'My work as Chairman of this Company is as much as I ought to have on my hands but I feel the Railway Company should have as one of the Members for Cricklade one who will give his attention to their interests.'

Whilst the manoeuvring was going on Gooch began his campaign. At his New Swindon meeting he was received with acclaim. 'I am not a talking member', he confessed. 'I have, however, been connected with many important matters . . . and if you do not read my speeches in the daily papers, you must not think it is because I am idle.' He reminded his audience that he had supported the Reform Bill and he declared his belief that the problem in Ireland was not the Irish Church question, 'but the present system adopted by the landlords . . . The grievance is owing to the absenteeism on the part of those who are drawing their thousands a year from land they never see'. In a later speech at Wootton Bassett he took a more bigotted view: 'We all know what the Jesuits did in former times and what seeds of discord they sowed even into our families, and, therefore, I pray God their power may never return to them'.

There were further ungentlemanly tactics. A letter to the press referred to Cadogan's connection with 'the Veillard contract and the Commissioners of the International Exhibition of 1862'. How, the writer asked, was the refreshment contractor induced to pay Cadogan, the

The 1868 election cartoon

secretary of the Commissioners, so large a sum as £2,400? Less libellously, Gooch's side produced a cartoon showing the three runners in 'the Cricklade Races'. 'The Countryman (Dark Blue)', a be-smocked Goddard on a donkey, lies second to 'The Baronet (Light Blue)', a dapper Gooch perched on top of *Lord of the Isles*. 'The Cad (Yellow)' is third on a pig, gesticulating crossly as Gooch's fireman (Foote?) rains coal on him. 'The Baronet . . . is a wiry and tough animal, with a clever head well set on his shoulders, and an eye that sees through everything', said the race card. 'The Cad is a dark, wicked Country animal with plenty of spite . . . The tip – lay all your money on The Baronet'.

The dissolution of Parliament took place on 11 November. At the last minute Gooch was offered a safe seat at Gloucester but declined, as he felt comfortable enough at Cricklade.

Tuesday 17 November was nomination day. 'What a farce that ceremony is,' Gooch complained. 'It is perfectly useless for any effect it has upon the result . . . We had to speak to an excited and not very quiet rabble in the street . . . I made a very short speech and was listened to pretty fairly by the mob . . . All passed off very peaceably.'

There were no reports of disturbances on polling day. In his speech at New Swindon Gooch had said that he was appealing to them 'not as the chairman . . . Every man in the service of this company . . . is at liberty to use his vote as he thinks proper'. Nevertheless *The Swindon Advertiser*, which

took the Liberals' part, reported that 'Gooch's people were most thorough'. Earlier there had been complaints of intimidation and of 'the screws' being put on the Great Western workmen. During polling a row of managers and foremen stood behind the poll-clerks. Towards the close Armstrong positioned himself where his men had to pass between him and his senior staff. The pressure was no doubt to ensure that at least one vote was cast for Gooch.

As anticipated 'The Cad' romped home with 2,644 votes. 'The Baronet' followed with 2,452, Goddard being a poor third with only 2,009. Gooch polled far less than he had been promised 'Where the falling-off took place I have not yet heard', he commented grimly. The Cricklade pattern was repeated nationally, Gladstone's majority rising to a hundred and ten.

Gooch found the first Christmas after his bereavement hard to bear. Jane Tweedy, widowed since 1859, spent the holiday with him at Fulthorpe House and was a great comfort. He had a further blow in February, however, as his eldest sister, Barbara, died. She was sixty-one. 'She has never been strong; her end was peace,' he wrote.

His main distraction was the Royal Commission, whose work had reached a climax. 'Neither thither, nor any other whither have I been, save for a gasp of fresh air on a Sunday,' wrote Frederic Harrison. 'No! I have not been in Fairyland, but in Blue-Book-land, a very different and ogre-like country. I have been harried out of existence by our Commission. We have had constant, daily fights, and I have had to write volumes of notes and memoranda and letters.'

The Commissioners were working on their eleventh report, their conclusions and suggestions for legislation. A draft prepared for the chairman was so oppressive that Harrison and Hughes fought it tooth and nail. Their determination led to clause after clause being thrown out. The final document went before Parliament in mid-March. 'I wish it had been a stronger one against the unions,' wrote Gooch. 'I fear it will not do much good in its present form.' He was right, as the proposals were too hard for the unionists to bear.

The Commissioners were so divided that there was both a Minority Report, to which Harrison, Hughes and Lord Lichfield put their names, and a Majority Report, which the others signed. Gooch and his colleagues stated that the objectives of the unions were to increase wages and reduce hours, rather than to act as benevolent societies, and that their main weapon was the organisation of strikes. They believed that unionism had fostered a spirit of antagonism, though they had been unable to identify any adverse effects on the nation's business. They were satisfied that the unions' rules put them beyond the protection of the law as it stood. They wished to correct this, but at a price. They also wished to protect the right to form a union, though only if membership was voluntary. Picketting, they felt, ought to be carefully controlled, but they regarded the law as already adequate to prevent the worst abuses.

Their proposals were that unions should be registered, as the friendly societies were, and that the full protection of the law should then be granted to them. Registration, however, should only be permitted if the rules conformed to certain requirements. Restrictions on the use of apprentices or of labour saving machinery would be a disqualification, as would regulations against piecework, favouring closed shops or permitting financial support to strikes by other unions.

The minority group regarded the surrender of cherished principles as an unfair price for the unionists to pay in return for so little. Their proposals were that the right to form unions and their protection by the law should be granted without onerous conditions being imposed. No Bill was introduced until 1872, but the measure then put through by the Liberals was based closely on their more generous ideas.

The attempt by Gooch and his colleagues to control the unions' aspirations now seems naive. They had, however, foreseen lines of battle which are still drawn. The bargain which they offered was the only one open to them, and no doubt they saw the Minority Report as an abject capitulation. Though there was no immediate outcome from it their work was fundamental. Gooch had taken part, albeit as a reactionary, in a historic study.

At home he was still pitifully lonely. 'What am I to do? My dear sister Jane Tweedy has been a great comfort to me . . . If she could remain permanently with me it would be a great blessing, but that is not possible.' His thoughts, now more of the future, led to a prophetic dream. In February he went to bed feeling weary of life and prayed to the spirit of his wife for comfort: 'I could not have been long asleep when, if it was a dream or a reality I know not, but she stood so plainly at my side, looking Oh how sad. Yet she mentioned to me the name of a lady who is almost a stranger to me, one who I have certainly not met more than half a dozen times but who I have often heard my dear wife speak of in kind terms, and one who stood very high in her good opinion. In such a matter she was generally right'. He often though of his dream as the year progressed.

Gooch had succeeded John Pender as the chairman of Telcon. During 1869 he became heavily involved with arrangements for the making and laying of the French Atlantic cable. The Societé du Cable Transatlantique Français had raised the money for a telegraph from Brest to North America. The *Great Eastern* was to be used to lay the main cable to St. Pierre, a small French possession off the coast of Newfoundland. He was delighted that this gave the ship another job to do, as she had been idle for too long, and he was to sail with the expedition.

They were to leave on Saturday 19 June

1869 from Portland. The whole Great Western board came to see him off, giving a dinner in his honour at Weymouth the previous Tuesday. 'Nothing could be more gratifying than the kindness and warmth of the expressions used towards me in the speeches,' he wrote. 'Mr Talbot kindly stated that altho' he had been opposed to my election as chairman, yet he was now very pleased to have been overruled.'

Next day Gooch boarded the *Great Eastern*, settling down in his old cabin with Norval as his companion. Sir James Anderson was again with the expedition, but this time as a director of the French company. Halpin, his former first mate, was in command. It proved a difficult voyage, in spite of all their experience.

The splice was completed in Brest Roads on the Sunday evening, Gooch having to be firm with Canning, who was anxious to wait for the next morning. Their first three days at sea passed uneventfully, but then the electricians detected a fault. Paying-out stopped almost immediately yet a mile and a quarter of cable had to be recovered before the failure came back on board. A small puncture was found in the gutta percha. There was no obvious cause, which was most worrying.

The next night an even more disturbing problem developed. Willoughby Smith, Telcon's chief electrician, reported that there was a small fault in the cable, but he could not say where. At two in the morning Gooch called a meeting with Anderson and his engineers, to discuss what should be done.

Gooch had three options. They could carry on, accepting the tiny fault, which could cost Telcon as much as £100,000. Alternatively they could start recovery, in the hope that the damage was not too far away. Finally, they could sail for shallower water, splice on afresh and re-lay. He asked Anderson and his party for their views, hoping to be able to do what they thought best for their interests. To his disgust they offered no opinion. He made up his mind that he would not give them the opportunity of influencing him if there were any more difficult decisions to be taken. Characteristically, he decided to press on.

The *Great Eastern* continued on her way but only a few hours afterwards a further fault developed, this time a serious one. The damaged region was recovered quickly and again a neat puncture was found. 'It is very trying, and enough to turn ones hair grey,' Gooch complained. The small fault continued to be a worry. Next day it vanished, only to re-appear some time later. 'How difficult it is to get a line 2,600 miles long without so much as the prick of a pin in it, and to get this safely stretched across the ocean,' he wrote.

Two days later there was a third major fault. It was blowing a gale but recovery had to begin. When the strain on the dynamometer reached 5 tons the cable parted, Fortunately they were using a new technique, bringing it in over the stern and carrying it through the paying-out machine to the picking-up winch in the bows. The break occurred between the two machines, so that the cable did not vanish into the sea. 'It is most likely to go there, and we have a better chance of securing it . . . I am therefore of opinion that this is the best arrangement,' Gooch said.

There were no more problems and a week later they were in shoal water. Halpin gave them champagne, but what pleased Gooch most was that the insulation resistance of the supposedly faulty cable was higher than that of the previous two. On 14 July he was able to send Napoleon III a telegram. He thankfully handed the cable over to Anderson, leaving any question of a fault to be settled between the two boards. 'The work and anxiety of this expedition,' he wrote, 'has been much more severe than the former ones . . . We have also had most unpractical and unreasonable people to deal with.'

A few weeks later Gooch was at Brighton. 'Strange enough,' he said, 'I met a lady walking on the promenade who has often been in my mind of late. I do not think I would have known her had she not been with her mother, whose face I seemed to recollect. I stopped, or I am not sure whether they did not stop and speak to me first. Why did my heart beat so? It brought back suddenly a dream of long ago. Is it God's will that I am again to have a happy home and be cared for by a loving wife? A vain hope, for my nature is not likely to gain the love of a woman much younger than myself and I feel sure my heart will never care for one who does not really love me or who, like my beloved Peggy, would devote her whole soul to me . . . But why do I write thus on an incident so likely to happen? They were staying in Brighton, and I being there for a day, what so likely that I should chance to meet them; but why should I so often have this girl in my thoughts? Oh Peggy, has God indeed permitted you to lead me to a happiness in the future? It is in God's hands; may he guide me for good.'

Though Gooch's journal does not give us the name of the lady we may be quite sure that she was Emily Burder, the youngest daughter of the late John Burder, solicitor. Her home was at Paddington, and less than a quarter of a mile from her distinguished acquaintance's office.

Emily was just twenty-eight, twenty-five years younger than Gooch. She had been born at Crown Lane, Norwood, but since her father's death had lived at No. 60 Queen's Gardens, one of Paddington's tall terraces. Her mother had been left well provided for, her household requiring the services of a footman, a cook, a housemaid and a kitchenmaid.

Emily had perhaps caught Margaret Gooch's eye as a suitable match for one of her boys. By 1869, however, she must have seemed destined for spinsterhood. Whether Gooch engineered the meeting and wrote the account of his dream to convince her that she was Margaret's choice, or whether the romantic story was true, is up to the reader to decide. Gooch was far too wise, and probably far too shy, to call on the Burders. He was one of the most eligible widowers in Britain, and an apparently chance encounter was a good way of sensing Emily's reaction to him. However it began the relationship which developed between the mature young woman and the rather austere middle-aged baronet was not one of arid social convenience. They grew to care deeply for one another, his strength match-ing her delicate health, the age difference closed by her pride in his achievements and willingness to join in every aspect of his life.

As the year drew to a close Gooch's family was much in his mind. Charles Gooch left to work for the New Russia Company in their mines and ironworks. Harry's son, potentially the third baronet, was christened at Clewer. Frank Gooch was gazetted as a Captain in the Fourth Hussars at Meerut. His promotion, as was customary, was purchased. Christmas Day was more cheerful than the previous one. Besides Alfred Gooch and Jane Tweedy he had Harry and his two married daughters and their families with him. Anna and Emily each had six children, making, with Harry's two, fourteen grandchildren: 'What a patriarch I felt . . . One dear face was missing.' His thoughts were now positive, his grief eased: 'Soon will this year be of the past. What will another year bring? Who can tell? . . . Sufficient for the day is the knowledge thereof.'

We can infer that it was on 4 May 1870 that Gooch proposed to Emily Burder, for in the years which lay before them she invariably gave him the most beautiful of greetings cards on that date. Their marriage took place on 17 September 1870 at Christ Church, Lancaster Gate. Their honeymoon began at the Regent's Hotel, Leamington. Where they spent the next few weeks is not known, but by Sunday 23 October they were at Newcastle.

'We had a carriage this morning,' he wrote, 'and started at 8.30 for Bedlington to spend the day with my old playfellow, George Marshall . . . How familiar the road seemed to me . . . I found my friend very well, and a hearty welcome. We went to church . . . and afterwards walked down the village and half way to the iron works . . . I was very glad to pay another visit to the scenes of my boyhood.' Emily must have been enthralled to hear his stories of an upbringing so different from her own.

CHAPTER

29

After his honeymoon Gooch's life reverted to its old pattern of a happy, well run home, his work and the House of Commons. Emily, or 'Bay', as he called her, cared well for him. His leanness filled out, his weight increasing by a stone and a half to almost twelve stones. 'I have gained a good deal,' he joked. 'My wife says it is because I married her.' Fulthorpe House became an establishment of some grandeur, with seven indoor servants. Sir Daniel and Lady Gooch, however, spent a considerable part of each year out of London, leaving smoky Paddington behind in search of the quiet and country air which they loved. At Easter they usually went to a seaside or spa town. Then came their long spell at Clewer, broken by a holiday of five or six weeks in the early autumn. They preferred Britain, sometimes staying briefly with family or friends, but mostly taking rooms in a homely hotel.

The first important family event after their marriage was the wedding of Frank Gooch to Teresa, another of the Croskey girls, on 30 March 1871. Emily joined fully in the numerous engagements which were the lot of the chairman of the Great Western. Each year she took her place beside him on the platform at the Mechanics' Institution, where he introduced one of their distinguished friends to present the prizes. They were frequently invited to grand state occasions – Foreign Office receptions, the Prince of Wales's levées, the Queen's Ball, and so on. Gooch often officiated at royal journeys, though no longer from the footplate. In 1874 Czar Alexander II, the Prince and Princess of Wales and sundry other royals were taken

from Windsor to Paddington by a special train in which Gooch, Grierson and other officials travelled. He and Lady Gooch were at the State Concert in the Albert Hall a few days later, when Mr Arthur Sullivan was the conductor. As prominent residents of Windsor they were on visiting terms with Princess Christian of Schleswig Holstein, Queen Victoria's fifth child, and her husband, who lived at Cumberland Lodge. 'These parties are very pleasant,' Gooch said airily. 'I sat next the Princess and she was very chatty and kind.'

By this time he had achieved considerable fame and was regarded as a shining example of self-help. During the seventies *Touchstone*, in an article illustrated by a portrait, said that there were few men in the United Kingdom to whom the world was more deeply indebted. 'To his energy and ability, to his sturdy courage, and to his great fertility of mind, we owe it that the Old and New Worlds are on speaking terms with one another . . . What he has done will doubtless serve as an incentive to others.' His name was so well known that Matthew Arnold felt no need to explain who he was when he wrote of 'that beautiful sentence Sir Daniel Gooch quoted to the Swindon workmen . . ., Mrs Gooch's golden rule . . . the sentence . . . repeated to him every morning when he was only a boy going to work:- "Ever remember, my dear Dan, that you should look forward to being some day manager of that concern!" This fruitful maxim is perfectly fitted to shine forth in the heart of the Hyde Park rough also'.

His achievements as chairman of the Great Western were also widely known. His friend Sir Theodore Martin was a Parliamentary solicitor as well as a distinguished literary figure. This had given him frequent opportunities to see the calm and wise way in which he implemented his policies. Gooch, he said, had that modest estimate of himself which was generally the concomitant of real power. 'Of speech he was chary', he continued, 'and his general demeanour was marked by that reserve of manner which is often mistaken for coldness. He was a man such as Wordsworth spoke of in the lines -

*You must love him ere to you
He will seem worthy of your love.'*

Gooch said that his duties as chairman were onerous, because he did not accept the post with the intention of being 'more of an ornament than a reality'. His policies of rigid economies worked. Dividends rose steadily, 2⅝% in 1869 being followed by 3⅜, 4¹³⁄₁₆, 6 and then 6¼%. During the hard years from 1866 to 1870 annual receipts increased by nearly 10% and the number of passengers by well over a fifth. Over the next five years receipts grew by a further third and passengers by another 60%. The complicated financial structure of the company was unravelled. The numerous amalgamations had brought together a total of forty different share issues, each with different claims on the Great Western's profits. A Bill was put through to consolidate these into a mere three. New business was sought by starting packet-boat services to the Channel Isles, France and Ireland. The market price of the ordinary shares, which had dropped to 38½ in 1867, climbed to a comfortable 130 in six years. Gooch presumably made a good deal of money out of his success.

At the half yearly meeting in March 1871 he declared the highest dividend since 1853. He also announced that they were going to issue a million of 5% preferred stock and that the gauge from Swindon to Gloucester and beyond the Severn was to be narrowed. Barely a year later the last 7ft. gauge train ran in South Wales. He announced an even higher dividend in 1872. The shareholders were in no doubt as to where the credit for the restoration of the company's fortunes lay, passing a resolution awarding him a testimonial of 5,000 guineas.

New Swindon gained the first benefit from the generous gift. The Medical Society converted a small building and two cottages into an accident hospital with two surgeons and two qualified assistants. It was financed by a trust fund of £2,000, half from the Medical Society and half from Gooch's money. He spent much of the remainder on a service of plate. When the formal presentation was made at a private ceremony at Fulthorpe House, Lady Gooch was not forgotten, being given some exquisite diamond and pearl jewellery.

As a gesture of his appreciation of the testimonial he asked the directors if they would like a portrait of him for the boardroom. Louis Desanges, a fashionable painter, carried out the commission. It is now in the Great Western Museum. Desanges also painted a companion portrait of Lady Gooch. Sir Francis Grant, an even more eminent portraitist, was commissioned to paint another of Gooch as part of his testimonial. This is particularly fine and now hangs in the National Portrait Gallery. He is shown, a pleasant, confident, yet somehow shy figure, seated by an open window through which moorland hills can be seen. Norval is beside him, a huge, proud animal reflecting his master's strength.

During Gooch's tenure as chairman the Great Western gained its finest asset, the Severn Tunnel, the longest ever built for a railway in Britain and one of the supreme monuments of Victorian engineering.

Our forefathers gave railways nicknames. The GWR was the 'Great Way Round' because the route from South Wales stretched north-eastwards for forty miles before a convenient place to cross the Severn was reached and the line could swing towards London. To shorten the even more roundabout route to Bristol and the South-West Brunel started to build the Bristol and South Wales Union Railway, with a ferry from Portskewett, near Chepstow, on the Welsh side, to New Passage, 7 mls north of Bristol, on the English. At that point the estuary funnels from 5 mls wide to 2½ mls. The tidal range is 50ft. at the extreme

Charles Richardson

Sir John Hawkshaw

and the currents are fierce at most stages of the tide.

Brunel died before the line was opened. Charles Richardson, his resident engineer, who had worked with him on the Thames Tunnel, completed it. At Portskewett the currents had exposed the bedrock of hard, impervious strata across the whole width of the estuary. In 1862, whilst he was piling the ferry piers, it struck him that the Severn offered a better prospect for tunnelling than the quicksands of the Thames. He prepared a proposal which gained support from the merchants of Bristol. In 1864 he deposited a Bill for a tunnel and railway and on 6 January 1865 a meeting was held at which the prospectus of a £750,000 company was presented.

At that time the Great Western, under Potter's chairmanship, were involved in a project for a railway from Chepstow to Wootton Bassett which was to cross the Severn 6 mls upstream of the ferry by means of a 2¼ ml viaduct. The Tunnel Bill, Richardson's supporters said, was not being promoted to oppose this scheme, but to show the Great Western that there was a better one. They failed to convince them, however, and lack of funds caused the Bill to be withdrawn. Parliament sanctioned the

bridge proposal, but the Great Western's support was withdrawn when Gooch took over.

Richardson tried to revive his Bill in 1870 but again funds were not forthcoming. Then in 1871 he mounted a determined effort. He engaged Sir John Hawkshaw, the most eminent civil engineer in Britain, as a consultant. He also gained Gooch's support, telling him that a tunnel would cost over £200,000 less than a bridge.

Richardson and Hawkshaw prepared a joint report in which they estimated that a tunnel would cost £750,000 and a bridge £900,000, a lesser difference than Richardson had predicted to Gooch, and one that would be wiped out all too easily if difficulties were encountered. Richardson sent the report to Gooch but then had second thoughts, immediately writing to tell him that he greatly regretted having put his name to it. 'When I considered what my signature . . . involved and the kind trust you had so far placed in my opinion . . . I was greatly annoyed that I had been so hasty.' He dashed up to Paddington to discuss it with him.

Gooch gave the vacillating Richardson time to prepare a new statement. In this he stressed the impracticability of a bridge, because of the problems of building piers in such strong currents and depths of water. Gooch accepted the further report and the tunnel proposal was agreed, first by the board and then by the shareholders at the Annual Meeting in February 1872. The Bill was passed during that session. A competing Bill, involving a bridge at Sharpness, 15 mls nearer Gloucester, was also sanctioned.

Richardson, his obituarist said, was a man whose 'modest disposition prevented his being known to fame, and it was only those who were intimately acquainted with him who realised the nobility of his character'. This faint praise, his lack of skill over the report and weaknesses which he was to reveal later make it plain that it was Gooch's ability to convince both the board and the shareholders which launched the project.

The great difficulty to be faced was 'the Shoots', a ravine 100ft. deep half a mile from the Welsh side, through which 10 knot currents coursed even at low water. It determined the whole design of the tunnel. With only 30ft. between its crown and the bed at that point, and with gradients of one in a hundred on either side, the total length had to be over 4½ mls.

The approach which Gooch put to the shareholders was a cautious one. He pointed out that tunnelling under the Shoots was the only part of the project that was in any doubt, so they would start by driving a small pilot heading from the Welsh side until it was beyond the deep region, to make sure that there were no hidden difficulties. The cost of this was estimated as £30,000, a tiny fraction of the total for the whole job.

On 1 October 1872 Charles Richardson was appointed engineer for the Severn Tunnel Railway at £2,000 a year and Hawkshaw was engaged as a consultant. Alfred Gooch, who had been working in the engineer's office of the Great Western at Oxford since his adventures on the *Great Eastern*, was made Richardson's principal assistant. He moved into Ashfield House at Chepstow.

Their first task was to sink a 200ft. shaft at the water's edge at Sudbrook. Ground was broken on 18 March 1873. The contractors, who were small builders and miners, were Norris, who started by putting up cottages for the workmen, and Dennis and Perkins, who began on the shaft. Within three weeks they were 30ft. down and soon the first steam driven pump had to be installed to control the water that was seeping in.

By Christmas the shaft was 90ft. deep. Two tons of water were pouring in every minute, dashing Richardson's prediction that the tunnel would be 'a very dry one'. The contractors were in trouble as they had made no provision in their tenders for water. 'Without some allowance it is not possible for them to go on,' Richardson said, 'for they are men without capital, though good miners, and I should be sorry to lose them.' More pumps were provided and the work continued.

Richardson proved so indecisive that Gooch had to maintain a close involvement with the work. He had a difference of opinion with Hawkshaw over the type of brick to be used in the shaft and, instead of making up his own mind, told Gooch that he would have a drawing prepared to bring to his committee meeting. A few weeks later he was asking Gooch to clarify a matter left open at one of their meetings: 'I came about the question of lining the shaft . . . I wished to ask you if we should use the ⅛in. iron skin . . . Suppose we try a length of twenty feet?'. Gooch's exasperation at being bothered with such details can be imagined. He eventually confided to his journal that Richardson 'has no go in him and does not move without consulting me, making me almost the engineer'.

Full depth was reached in September 1874. Richardson then prepared for the driving of the heading. He tried to find a firm to take on the whole job, but the risks were too great. 'Several "miners" have been to look at it,' he told Gooch, 'But from what I hear I doubt if any **responsible** contractor will offer.' So again it was men without capital who began the task, the company providing them with the equipment and working methods. Techniques were used which were new to them. The shot holes were drilled with compressed air tools mounted on a carriage made at Swindon. Dynamite, invented in 1866, was used to blast down the hard Pennant sandstone. It took a compressor breakdown to convince them that the old hand methods were not the best. Nobel's explosive proved too effective at times. On one occasion a man was struck by a 17 lb. lump of stone when 95 yd. from the face.

By the end of 1875 they were approaching the near side of the Shoots. Hawkshaw, who was heavily engaged on the Channel Tunnel project, seldom found time to look at Richardson's reports but at length sat down with a batch of eleven. He was scathing, finding it incomprehensible that defective boilers had been holding up the work. But the heading was inching onwards through strong, self supporting rock and Gooch's worries were unfounded as yet.

Elsewhere on the Great Western other major gauge changes were undertaken. In 1874 all the lines south of the old main line were narrowed. No less than 208 mls were altered during the month of June, requiring meticulous planning and a superb organisation. The year ended sadly. On Christmas Eve a train was de-railed near Kidlington, north of Oxford, when a tyre on the front carriage broke. Three coaches fell from a canal bridge, thirty-four passengers being killed and sixty-five injured in the worst railway accident that had happened in Britain.

One of the matters which the Inspector criticised was the faulty operation of the 'Harrison cord', a crude device which enabled the passengers to sound a gong on the footplate in an emergency. At one time this had been a compulsory fitting as a result of a Private Member's Bill, but it had fallen into disrepute. When the Bill was going through Gooch had been infuriated. He went with deputations to the Board of Trade to point out how dangerous it was for passengers to stop trains. Before long, he said, they would find the cord being pulled 'by passengers suffering from the stomachache, or, what was quite as probable, for some young man to light his cigar'. His fear was of a collision from behind by a following train. The absolute block system had not yet been introduced to prevent such occurences, and this was another matter into which Parliament started to pry.

Opposition to governmental interference began to be organised by a committee of representatives of the major lines, the Railway Association. Gooch played an important part in its work, becoming vice chairman. The 'Railway Interest' in Parliament, those members who were active directors, were marshalled into a Parliamentary sub-committee. In 1873 they mounted their first attack, having some success over a Bill in which the Government proposed to encourage competition by setting up a powerful Railway Commission. At about this time *The Globe* published an article headlined 'Washing Dirty Linen At Home'. 'Sir Daniel Gooch,' said the editor, ' . . . indignantly resents Government interference, and considers that control over railways should be exercised through a board consisting of chief officers and engineers of the great lines. This suggestion shows ingenuity, altho' the public . . . will probably evince a considerable dislike to this novel Board of Control. Sheep can hardly be expected to elect themselves as shepherds.'

Safety on the railways had become a national scandal. Even the Queen complained of the attitudes of directors. The Government criticised methods of working trains and complained that safety devices were being introduced too slowly. When legislation was threatened Gooch reminded the minister of the gaffe over the Harrison Cord. His attitude should not be misunderstood. The companies were raising standards to a new level of public acceptability over a huge system using private capital. They could only progress slowly. The Railway Association succeeded in demonstrating that the most important improvements were going ahead as fast as could be expected. There were further disasters, however, and a Royal Commission was appointed. Their efforts concentrated on the introduction of automatic continuous brakes. The Newark Brake Trials were set up, but in the meantime the companies were putting their houses in order in their own ways. The Great Western tried eight different forms of brake, none of which was thought entirely satisfactory. Such efforts and skilful lobbying by the

Association caused Parliamentary intervention to be confined to a requirement for returns cataloguing progress to be made.

In the House Gooch opposed the Irish Church Bill. He was also against granting the vote to women who fell within the householder qualifications. When the age limit for the employment of boys in coal mines was raised to twelve he voted in favour of an exception for thin seams, where youngsters of ten were still to be allowed to work because of their small size. He was, however, also in favour of punishing those who knowingly employed under-age children. He took part in nineteen percent of the 384 divisions that session, rather less than in 1867, being at his most conscientious for the Bill which introduced the electoral procedures we now take for granted. The Conservatives fought the measure line by line. Gooch voted against the nomination of candidates in writing and against balloting being secret.

On 24 May 1874, to the astonishment of both sides of the House, Gladstone dissolved Parliament. He wished to abolish income tax but some of his ministers were not prepared to accept cuts in their budgets. Faced with such a split he decided to go to the country. After some urging Gooch decided to stand again. He was afraid that if there were two Conservatives neither would be elected, so when Goldney of Chippenham offered to join him he talked him out of the idea. Then, to his surprise, Goddard threw his hat into the ring. Gooch thought of withdrawing but the local party managed to persuade him that two candidates could be supported: 'The matter was so much pressed upon me that I made no further objections to going on and doing all I could to carry both seats'.

No less than four Liberals came forward. Cadogan and Henry Tucker were the official nominees. The Liberal electorate was divided over Gladstone's policies, especially regarding the licensing laws, so John Arkell, a local brewer, stood as an Independent Liberal and William Morris, the proprietor of *The Swindon Advertiser*, as a Radical and Working Men's candidate.

The Conservatives' tactics were to keep Morris in the fight to deprive the main Liberals of votes. 'He tried to get each side

to buy him,' Gooch wrote disgustedly. 'I am told he offered to retire if the Radicals would pay him £500. He sent to offer to continue to stand if I would pay him £250, which I, of course, declined.' Eventually all six were nominated, the formalities taking place quietly in a room, as required by the new laws. Gooch, after voting against the change for party reasons, found it a great improvement.

As usual he was well received at his meetings. Lady Gooch joined him on the platform with Mrs Swinhoe, the wife of the works' surgeon, to keep her company. They were not without courage. Cadogan and Tucker's meeting in the Drill Hall ended in a rumpus, the candidates and their committees being flung off the platform and Morris and his men installed in their place.

Gooch declared himself as in favour of abolishing income tax and leaving the liquor laws alone, two opinions likely to be popular. He believed that the Government should subsidise local services such as education and the police force, but that they should not meddle in parish matters: 'This is one of the many faults I have found with . . . Mr Gladstone's ministry. . . We don't want them to be our fathers, and as such to dictate what we shall and shall not do in our families'.

Polling took place on 4 February 1874. Gooch was delighted with the result. For the first time he headed the poll, and by a good margin. His 2,624 votes were followed by Goddard with 2,231, Cadogan with 2,092 and Tucker with 1,578. Morris polled only 497 and poor Arkell trailed with a mere 40. The two Conservatives were home with 4,855 between them to the Liberals' 4,207. Cricklade again reflected the national mood, Disraeli being swept to the Premiership.

By the early seventies submarine telegraphy had become routine. Telcon had sufficient expertise to dispense with the services of C.F. Varley and Sir William Thomson as consultants. 'It is Gouch (Bart) who objects to your and my names,' Varley told Thomson contemptuously, his words hinting at some of the jealousies of earlier expeditions. The *Great Eastern* continued to make her unique contribution, though Gooch never made a long voyage in her again. Her hull was painted grey in 1870 to fit her for the laying of the Bombay to Suez cable. In May 1873 he spent a few days on board prior to her successful voyage with the third Valencia to Heart's Content cable. An attempt was then made to repair the 1865 line but unfortunately this failed. 'What caused it to break is a mystery to us,' Gooch wrote. 'Is it from being stretched over a chasm and gradually weighted with shellfish and weeds, or has it become rotten and so broken with weakness?.'

During the spring of 1874 the Portugal to Brazil telegraph was laid but using three smaller vessels. Brunel's ship's days of usefulness were numbered. On 31 July 1874 she sailed from Sheerness to Portland with the fourth Atlantic cable. Gooch joined her for the short trip and watched her leave for Newfoundland. It was the last of her cable laying voyages. A year later, when the Telcon charter ended, Gooch was aboard for the sad trip from Sheerness to Milford Haven to lay her up. 'I do not know how we are to employ her in the future,' he wrote, 'but we will not give up hope . . . as she is a noble ship and has done good service in the past'. Her service to Gooch had indeed been good. The Great Eastern Steamship Company usually declared a dividend of fifteen percent or so. Telcon invariably paid twenty. There were also his investments in the companies which operated the cables she had laid. Gooch owed his baronetcy and at least £10,000 a year of his huge income to the ship which now rode at rusting mooring chains in the shelter of the Haven.

CHAPTER

30

In the mid-seventies the Great Western grew rapidly, absorbing other lines until it became the largest in Britain. The first major acquisition was the Monmouthshire, leased from 1 August 1875. Then in December the Bristol and Exeter was taken over to parry a thrust westwards by the Midland and London and South Western Railways. The settlement was so generous that Gooch was concerned at its effect on the next few dividends. Inevitably the South Devon, Cornwall and West Cornwall were drawn into the fold and during the first few weeks of 1876 all 443 mls of lines west of Bristol came under Great Western control. Charles Gooch was married at Plymouth on 4 January but because of the changes his father was not there. 'I am sorry it will not be possible for me to go,' he wrote, 'as it is . . . board week and important matters have to be settled.'

Charles, who was thirty, had returned from Russia in the previous May to become the Great Western's mineral engineer. He took a house at Cardiff, quite remote from the two collieries for which he became responsible. The Gyfeillon had been replaced in 1874 by the Cilely, a small pit at the head of the Ely Valley, just over the hills from the Rhondda. Mineral rights were also leased at Abergwynfi in the Llynvi Valley, where the company intended to open a large colliery. Gooch visited the locality, high amongst the mountains, in September 1876, just after his sixtieth birthday. He was still hearty enough, as his outing involved a seven mile ride by pony.

The Great Western's mileage had now passed the two thousand mark. The turnover increased from £4,900,000 in 1872 to £7,130,000. The takings per mile, however, dropped. The Victorian boom had given way to the Great Depression, the period from 1873 until the nineties when Britain lost her position as the workshop of the world. The railways began to feel the effects in 1876, when profits were poor everywhere. 'There seems little present prospect of improvement,' Gooch wrote. 'The world is unsettled by the prospect of war with Turkey . . . The value of money is nil.'

The following year business was even worse. The railways were hit hard, Great Western dividends, as Gooch had predicted, being low. 4% in 1876 was followed by 3⅞, 3¾ and 4⅛%. In 1880 there was a recovery to 5⅛%, the highest since 1848 apart from the two splendid years of 1872 and 1873. Gooch fought hard, continuing the development of the company during the slump. He followed the principle which he had urged in the late forties of investing during lean times in preparation for good. Repair and manufacturing activities were steadily centralised at Swindon, expenditure rising from £89,000 a year in the late sixties to £200,000 or so throughout most of the seventies.

By this time little of the broad gauge remained on the old Great Western system. Apart from the Windsor branch, left, it was said, in deference to Gooch's sentiments, there was only the original main line. This had to remain mixed as it provided the link with the Exeter to Truro sections, which were broad gauge throughout. Many of Gooch's locomotives were still in service. Most of the *Iron Dukes* were running and fifteen engines of the *Rover* class, the magnificent *Iron Duke* renewals, had been built before the end of the decade. Ten of his pre-1843 engines were still in operation in 1876, mainly *Fire Flies*, together with 122 of his later Great Western designs and most of the South Devon and Cornwall bogie-tanks.

In 1877 the Great Western suffered a severe blow when Joseph Armstrong died after a short illness. Gooch felt his loss deeply. 'His department was a very large and important one,' he wrote, 'and my anxiety will not be diminished by having to place it in the hands of a fresh man.' William Dean, who had been groomed for the position, took over.

Charles Gooch's work at Abergwynfi made encouraging progress. A railway was built through the district and his trial workings encountered the celebrated Four Foot vein of anthracite. The sinking of two shafts nearly 1,300ft. deep began on 4 May 1878, the chairman and his wife taking part in the ceremony of turning the first sod. Lady Gooch cut a good-sized piece of turf which was set into the lawn at Fulthorpe House.

Gooch maintained his level of attendance at the House of Commons. Between 1875 and 1879 he voted in twenty-two of the fifty-four divisions recorded in Hansard. He opposed the enfranchisement of female householders on two more occasions but was in favour of compulsory attendance at school. Foreign affairs predominated. 'War has been declared by Russia against Turkey,' he noted, 'a most unjustifiable war proclaimed in the name of Christianity by a nation as cruel and barbarous as savages in their dealings with the unfortunate people over whom they have obtained power.' By the end of the year he saw no gleam of sunshine for the future and could only hope that Britain might be spared a conflict.

His main work as an M.P. was once again in the committee rooms. In 1876 he was appointed to a Select Committee which considered the liability of employers to pay compensation to the victims of accidents. The carnage in industry was appalling. In 1875 767 men were killed on the railways alone – about three in every thousand. The unions felt that safety would only receive proper attention if this increased profits,

but at that time the employer was rarely left with a liability to the injured or their dependants. The law was that there was no entitlement to compensation unless the accident had been caused by the negligence of the employer in person or of someone who was not 'in common employment' with the victim. Case law had established the widest possible interpretation of 'in common employment' and the narrowest of 'employer'. If a shunter, for example, came to harm as a result of his own negligence or that of a fellow shunter or an engineman, signalman or stationmaster he had no hope of compensation. Only if the general manager, as his employer, or, say, a ticket clerk, whose work bore no relationship to his own, was at fault was there any hope of a claim succeeding. Between 1874 and 1876 Bills were drafted which would have given a fairer balance but were withdrawn after pressure from mining interests, where there were fears of an endless succession of expensive claims. The unions lobbied fiercely and eventually the Select Committee was appointed. Their task was to consider whether the employer's responsibility should pass downwards to his managers and foremen, and also to see whether the term 'common employment' could be better defined. Gooch was one of the Railway Association's four nominees. He worked hard, attending all but two of the fifteen meetings. Witnesses ranging from the Lord Chief Justice to leading trade unionists were examined.

Gooch's views are strange to our ears. 'Why should a master be responsible if you suppose that he has got proper and efficient men?', he asked. He was incensed at the suggestion that safety would only improve if compensation had to be paid. 'Have the railway companies no other reason for care and anxiety about the safety of the traffic and of their servants than the mere compensation they would have to pay their servants?,' he thundered. 'Do you think that the damage of railway stock and of railway plant . . . is not a much more serious matter than even compensation?' He also felt that most accidents on railways were caused by orders given by the masters being ignored: 'Even if you put a penalty . . . they could not do more than they do now.'

He regarded some of his men as already compensated for the dangers. 'Are not . . . the enginemen the highest paid men in the railway?,' he asked. 'Is there any other reason for their . . . higher wages than the extreme danger . . . because really there is no art in putting steam off and on?.'

'Yes,' was the answer. 'Shunting is far more dangerous and the goods guard's position is more dangerous. A platelayer's is a more dangerous duty than an engineman's and a platelayer only gets . . . 17s. or 18s. a week'.

'A platelayer's danger arises principally from not looking out,' Gooch shot back, determined to have the last word.

He also argued that the railways were meeting their obligations by contributing handsomely to the benevolent societies. Grierson told the committee that the Great Western put about £6,000 each year into the various provident and superannuation funds. This allowed Gooch to introduce a little blackmail.

'You are of opinion that if the companies were bound to compensate their servants . . . they would withdraw their subscriptions?,' he asked.

'I think it quite natural,' Grierson replied.

In the spring of 1877 the committee finalised their report. Gooch was on the winning side in twenty of the twenty-two divisions over amendments, the completed document being a close representation of his views. He and his colleagues pointed out that since the time of Charles II masters had been held liable for injuries caused by the negligence of persons not in common employment, and they were strongly against even this law. People were free to take work or not, and must suffer the consequences either way, they felt. They thought that a relaxation in the law would cause alarm and discourage investment. They nevertheless recommended a small step forward, their view being that the employers should bear the responsibility for the acts of any staff who acted directly for them, but the delegation ought to be established in each case.

To the Railway Association's concern the Bill which the Attorney General put forward was far more radical and was aimed exclusively at their industry. Gooch urged its withdrawal, saying that they had managed affairs with their men so well that on the Great Western there had not been a strike in forty years. The railwaymen's union, the Amalgamated Society of Railway Workers, were also unhappy about it and it was dropped.

The general secretary of the union was Edward Evans. He had been a clerk with the Great Western until dismissed for organising union branches. He had a revealing argument with Gooch after mentioning that he had taken up the case of an engineman (not one of the Great Western's) who had been ordered to take out an express after only four months experience on the footplate.

'You complained that you had written a letter to somebody who had not answered it,' Gooch said coldly. 'Is it usual for railway companies . . . to get the complaint made by someone outside the company?'

'It is usual for many companies to do so,' Evans replied.

'Take the Great Western Railway,' Gooch continued. 'Has it not been common for the men to make complaints and to meet the directors, and meet the principal officers, without interference by outside parties?.'

'I have known that bodies of men have . . . But I have also known other occasions where individuals have attempted to report their grievances to higher officers and have displeased intermediate officers by doing so.'

'Were they ever refused a hearing?,' Gooch asked.

'I may say that I believe the higher officers . . . are most anxious to do what is right for their servants, but there are others between them and the men who will punish the men for presuming to pass over their authority to the higher officers.'

According to the historian of ASLEF, the Associated Society of Locomotive Enginemen and Firemen, Gooch was 'the first chief adviser to an English railway to give employees the right of access to the Board of Management. This, of course, does not mean that he allowed trade union representation. But it was direct contact between men and management'. His methods, of which he was rightly proud, worked after the fashion of his day. The iron hand had to be shown at times, however, as it was in the only interchange between Gooch and his men which has been recorded in any detail. This occurred in 1879, when the outcome was momentous.

The Great Western's footplatemen were angry because their hours had been increased from ten to twelve a day. They organised a petition and sent a deputation to see Gooch. He was unmoved, so they reminded him that they had brought two thousand signatures with them. 'Damn the signatures! Have you got the men to back them up?,' he challenged. The crestfallen group, who knew that their society was not strong enough to call a strike, filed out. Amongst them was Charles Perry, who immediately set to work to form a more effective organisation and ASLEF, one of the most powerful unions of our own day, was born.

Throughout the late seventies the *Great Eastern* lay useless at Milford Haven. It had been a great shock to the company when Yates, their secretary, the son of the man who had bid for her in 1864, had embezzled a great deal of their money. At the shareholders' meeting in March 1876 Gooch was questioned about this and the ship's continuing idleness. The main attack came from a Mr Webber who, Gooch said angrily, would no doubt have discovered forgeries where he and his fellow directors had not: 'Perhaps forgery is not so patent to people who have been associated for many years as it may be to some who are suspicious.' He later reminded Webber that they had all had the whole of their capital back from the *Great Eastern* during the previous ten years.

'Not I!,' he shouted. 'I lost £1,000!'.

'I am speaking as a shareholder to the shareholders,' Gooch continued mildly. 'I have had the whole of my capital back, and I have had a very large interest in addition, therefore I am perfectly satisfied with the past history of the ship since the present company was formed.'

One of the shareholders suggested that they should fit her out to carry passengers to the Philadelphia Exhibition in the next year.

'I doubt whether anybody will employ her as a passenger ship,' Gooch replied. 'First of all, without she is kept perfectly clean . . . I do not think she would hold her own; the speed would be affected by the foulness of her bottom . . . Of course there is always this disadvantage; she is a single ship, and you would not creat a service by a single ship . . . It is quite true, when she did go for some time, no ship was so popular when she was obliged to discontinue.'

Perhaps Gooch would have been more enterprising if his coup of twelve years before had been less profitable. There was no point in his risking money to send her on some new venture, especially as Telcon continued to prosper. Dividends remained at 20%. In 1876 the Australia-New Zealand line was laid, followed by the Rangoon-Penang and Bombay-Aden the next year and the Aden-Durban in 1879. These four important links in the Empire's communications required over 8,000 mls of cable.

Gooch was proud enough of his numerous offices to list them in 1878. Including his seats as an M.P. and on the Windsor Bench, two masonic positions and his Deputy Lieutenantship there were thirty. Besides being chairman of the Great Western, the steamship company and Telcon he presided over the boards of the North Wales Coal and Coke Co., which owned the Ruabon collieries, and five small railway companies. The rest were alternate chairmanships of eight joint railway committees, directorships of three telegraph companies, the Telegraph Trust, two railways and the Great Western Hotel and the vice chairmanship of the Railway Association.

Gooch's health remained good as he entered his sixties. He caught a severe cold at the opening of the Westminster Aquarium in 1876 but was unaffected by a dousing later in the year when he slipped off a rock at Saundersfoot, having to climb the cliff-side and walk home in wet clothes. In 1878 he was out of condition and had to call in the doctor, but Emily still found it hard to keep up with him. At Bideford they were out for a walk when it came on to rain heavily. They had to run for it up the steep hill and were soaked. 'It did Bay no good,'

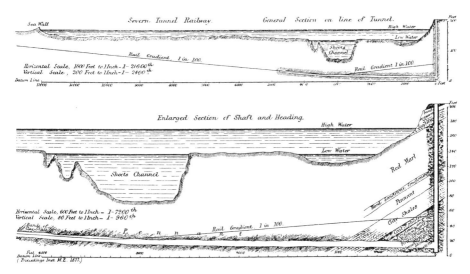

The Severn Tunnel. Progress to 1877

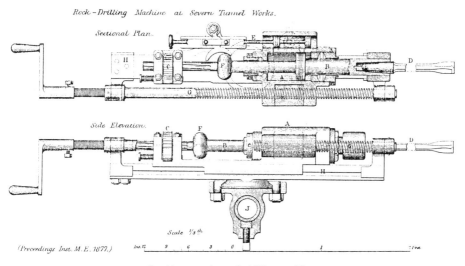

Geach's percussive rock drilling machine

Gooch commented, but it does not seem to have bothered him. Later in the year, however, he had congestion of the lungs, which kept him at home for three weeks and left him far from well. He had another attack at the end of 1879 when Emily, in addition to nursing him, was concerned for her mother. She died on 17 December. 'She was a truly worthy woman,' Gooch wrote, 'and my wife feels her loss very deeply.'

Their contacts with royalty continued. In 1878 the Levers invited them to follow the Boat Race in a steam launch along with a couple of dozen others, including the Prince of Wales, the Danish Crown Prince, the Prince of Teck and various Danish and

Swedish ministers. 'The day was all we could wish,' Gooch wrote, 'but although we had the privilege of following the race we really saw very little of it as the boilers of our steamer were priming badly and we got behind some other steamers . . . It was a very English sight to be sitting with the Prince of Wales smoking cigars very much as tho' he was of equal rank with us, yet there he was, the heir to . . . the finest kingdom in the world.' The next year they watched in only slightly less exalted company and were similarly lavishly entertained.

The work on the Severn Tunnel was progressing, but painfully slowly. As the heading crept outwards the seepage of water increased. By the end of 1875 Richardson needed an extra pump. 'There is no doubt something must be done. Shall I give the order?,' he asked Gooch, with customary indecision.

It was February 1877, almost four years after ground had been broken, before the Shoots were passed. Preparations were already in hand for the cutting of the main tunnel. Richardson was sinking a second shaft at Sudbrook for the pumping equipment and a draft specification had been written. Gooch wanted to divide the enormous job between two contractors. 'I have considered this but it seems to me to be impracticable,' Hawkshaw said. 'I do not know what your notion of letting the works is but I should invite tenders from a selected number of good contractors.'

During May Gooch paid his annual visit. The heading had advanced less than 650yd. in the previous twelve months. He must have asked some awkward questions, as only two weeks later Swindon produced a cost estimate for new percussive rock drilling machines which John Geach, one of Richardson's assistants, had designed. In August the tenders were received for the main tunnel. Richardson preferred William Lean's but Hawkshaw was determined to have Thomas A. Walker, who had been his contractor when the Thames Tunnel had been turned into a part of London's railway system.

Richardson had not been able to prepare a complete specification, as he knew nothing of conditions beyond the Shoots. He was afraid that costs would mount each time difficulties were encountered, especially with Hawkshaw involved. 'What power should I or any one else have,' he asked Gooch, 'to reduce the work to . . . fair proportions with Sir John himself as final arbitrator in points of dispute? – Sir John, recollect, with his very large ideas of the work, and his own contractor, accustomed to carry out those ideas of very heavy work – a sort of work that pays the contractor well.' Gooch shared Richardson's concern as neither tender was accepted. Instead smaller contracts were placed with Norris and a newcomer called Brotherhood to drive pilot headings to explore the rest of the ground, both under the estuary and inland. Five shafts were to be brought into use, greatly speeding the tunnelling, and when the headings were finished it would be possible to write a full specification and place a firm contract.

Alfred Gooch – 'Billy' – was still working as Richardson's assistant. In September 1877, whilst he was on holiday in Ireland, Gooch had rather a shock. 'I have had a letter from Alfred,' he wrote, 'telling me about his marriage, foolish boy, but as an honourable man he could not have done otherwise. May they be happy and all will be well. I should have felt it much more had he acted dishonourably in the matter.' His son was born barely four months later and on 30 April 1878 Gooch saw his latest grandchild for the first time: 'Billy met us in his trap near Tintern. We found his wife and baby very well, the latter a very good specimen of infant humanity. Very glad to find Billy happy and comfortable in his home'.

The next day Gooch visited the tunnel. The main heading was 2,200 yds. long but less than half a mile had been driven in the previous year. In his journal he made the scathing comment quoted previously that Richardson 'has no go in him'. His criticisms were not confined to the privacy of his journal, however, as amongst the Great Western's archives is the laconic note, 'Chs. Richardson. Severn Tunnel Railway. £2,000 from 10 October 1872 to 30 April 1878. £1,000 from 1 May 1878'. From the day of Gooch's visit his salary was halved.

By October 1879 the headings under the estuary were within 130 yd. of one another.

On the Welsh side, however, serious difficulties had developed. In the heading inland from Sudbrook shaft the water was under such pressure that it forced its way through fissures in jets which shot horizontally for many yards. To prevent the rock walls from breaking up strong timbering was erected. A transverse fracture was passed successfully but beyond this the seepage increased. After another ten yards they came to a second fracture. Richardson hurriedly began to arrange for more pumps, but it was too late. On the evening of Thursday 16 October 1879 the pressure shattered the rock between the two breaks. A huge mass of rock burst through the wood lining with a noise like the firing of a gun. Water began to flood in, gaining rapidly on the pumps. Richardson tried to build a timber dam to hold it back, but within 28 hr. the works on the Welsh side were drowned out.

On the Friday morning Gooch was 15 mls away and ignorant of their plight. It was the day of the opening of the Severn Bridge, the rival scheme at Sharpness which Parliament had approved in the same year as the tunnel. The Midland Company were triumphant, as they anticipated a heavy traffic in Forest of Dean coal. At the celebration luncheon Gooch had to make a speech. He invited the guests to visit the Severn Tunnel within a few weeks and take a walk under the river. 'It will be rather wet and you had better bring your umbrellas,' he joked.

Removing spoil from the Severn Tunnel workings

CHAPTER

31

The flooding, rather than deterring Gooch, galvanised him into action. On 28 October 1879, less than two weeks after the water had burst in, he asked Sir John Hawkshaw to take over as chief engineer. Hawkshaw had a few reservations, but Gooch soon

The intention was to start the main tunnel as soon as the headings were cleared of water. On 2 December Hawkshaw told Gooch that he was not yet happy about the Shoots and proposed to construct the first length of full-sized tunnel there. He also

Sudbrook village

satisfied him and he accepted. The board confirmed his appointment on 12 November at a salary of £2,000 a year. His staff were Richardson, still on £1,000, Alfred Gooch on £450 and a brickwork inspector.

wanted Thomas Walker to be given the contract for the whole works. Gooch agreed and on 15 December Walker submitted a tender for £949,959. Even at that stage the work could not be specified in detail, so there were still great financial risks to be borne by the Great Western. Already a major change had been introduced, just as Richardson had feared. Hawkshaw was insisting on a minimum of 45ft. between the tunnel crown and the bed of the Shoots instead of 30ft. This required the English side to be lowered by 15 ft. and the gradient on the Welsh side to be increased to one in ninety.

Walker set to work with great energy. Four new shafts were started and far larger pumps were ordered for draining the headings. By 6 June a 75 in. engine had been run at Sudbrook. Soon afterwards its plunger-pump burst, hurling a huge lump of cast iron past a workman's ear. Nearly three months elapsed before repairs were complete. The water level was then soon reduced to 40ft. above the heading, but it was only after great heroism that the rest was cleared.

Three hundred yards along the heading there was a strong flood door. This had to be closed and so Walker engaged a diver called Lambert. When he tried to reach it his air pipe floated so firmly against the rough roof that he had to turn back, groping his way through the inky darkness, untangling the pipe as he went. Walker had heard of a new diving suit with a built-in air supply. He brought Fleuss, its inventor, to Sudbrook but when Lambert took him to the mouth of the heading he was horrified, saying that he would not do the job even for £10,000. Lambert, with the coolest of courage, borrowed his gear. After one abortive attempt he was successful.

By 7 December 1880, fourteen months after the flooding, the works were dry. Walker's men were able to start in earnest but after only a few weeks the sea broke in at the Salmon Pool, close to the Gloucestershire shore. Walker plugged the hole with bags of clay. A second breach occurred a few hundred yards away and again he used clay as a temporary plug before sealing both cavities with gravel and coarse sand. All then went well and in September 1881 the two headings met. After eight and a half years it was at last possible to walk under the estuary, but an immense amount of work remained to be done before the first train could pass through.

During the early eighties Gooch was far from well. He found it hard to shake off the effects of his chest infections. Emily's concern shows in two exquisite cards which she sent him. The first, written at Malvern in 1881, was 'to my darling husband with all loving wishes for a happy peaceful Easter'. Their holiday came up to her hopes as they returned refreshed, though Gooch had found a favourite walk 'a sharp pull for an old fellow'. In the May her message was 'to my darling husband with fondest love, and all blessings be his, wake and sleep – such prays his devoted wife'. She must have been thankful that he had given up a little of his work. During 1880 the Ruabon collieries were sold and he resigned from the board of the Great Eastern Steamship Company. 'I did so with great reluctance,' he wrote. 'I . . . do not feel equal to so many cares as I have lately had upon me and feel compelled to give up some of them.' By the beginning of 1882 he was much better, his only recorded trouble over the next few years being tooth-ache in May 1884, when he was nearly sixty-eight. Emily's health, however, remained a constant source of worry to him.

Gooch's slow recovery had serious effects on his activities as an M.P. During the opening weeks of the 1880 session he voted in only one division.

Then, on 8 March, Disraeli, now the Earl of Beaconsfield, announced that Parliament was to be dissolved. There had been two promising by-election results, so the Cabinet decided to chance the polls. Gooch did not feel up to either a campaign or the night work of the House. He had a meeting with the main members of the Cricklade Conservative Association on 15 March. They felt sure that both seats would be lost if he did not stand and offered to take all the work of the contest from him, so he was left with little choice. On 20 March his election address appeared. It is remarkable for both its brevity and its complete lack of content. 'My political opinions during the many years I have represented you have become well known to you,' he said, 'and they remain unaltered; therefore they need not be fully stated at the present time. I shall support any measure of domestic legislation which may be brought forward to promote the moral and social welfare of the people.' He closed by asking the electors to support him in his absence, as they had in 1865.

A.W. Neeld stood as the second conservative. The Liberals, because of the grip which they believed Gooch to have at New Swindon, only put up one candidate, Neville Story Maskelyne. Gooch, though re-elected, was most disappointed at the result. Maskelyne, as expected, was an easy winner, with 4,350 votes. Gooch was a poor second with 2,441, Neeld trailing with 1,748. 'One bad feature was the breach of good faith on the part of the voters', Gooch complained, 'so large a number making promises which they did not perform'. Maskelyne's included 3,771 'plumpers', whose second votes would have been more than enough to have elected a second Liberal. Only 493 'split' for Gooch and Maskelyne. With secret balloting Gooch's personal standing had counted for very little.

Polling day was spoilt by Liberal roughs, who went on the rampage in the evening, wrecking public houses whose landlords had dared to show support for Gooch or Neeld. They were eventually confronted by forty policemen. The order to disperse was met by shouts and stones, so the police charged, striking out mercilessly with their truncheons. The mob soon fled.

Cricklade was yet again an indication of the national mood. Beaconsfield had mis-judged the electorate's views, the Liberals romping home by 353 to 238. Gooch put the defeat down to the distress amongst all classes and a feeling that any change might do good.

The new Commons met for the first time in May. Gooch, still in poor health, voted in only eight of the 164 divisions that session. Over the rest of the Parliament he took part in eighteen of the seventy-three recorded in Hansard, the same proportion as in earlier years, showing that he had made a complete recovery. He found the House less mannerly: 'What a wonderful change do I see since I entered . . . then a body of gentlemen, now a body of roughs, or little better.' This he blamed on Glad-stone, for whom he had nothing but contempt. He still enjoyed the social aspects of the House, particularly the new smoking room: 'I have very often gone . . . for an hour . . . and have enjoyed the fun more than the House'. He was one of the privileged cronies of the Serjeant at Arms, Captain Gosset, spending many pleasant evenings in his quarters. They were a convivial crowd, as when Gosset retired and the ceiling was redecorated it was rumoured that the whisky fumes had made the painter faint.

Gooch's most important Parliamentary work was again for the Railway Interest. On 13 January 1881 he was made chairman of the Railway Association and was selected as one of their seven nominees to a Select Committee on passenger and freight rates. He attended forty-eight of the sixty-three meetings, missing only three during the second session. A carefully prepared case demonstrated a responsible approach by the companies, the Committee finding that charges were usually much lower than the maxima fixed by Parliament.

In 1884 he became a member of a Committee which inquired into the letting of contracts for naval vessels. He was again horrified at the inefficiency of the Royal Dockyards: 'A private establishment would soon be ruined if it carried on . . . in such a manner'. Their report proposed that the government establishments should stick to repairs and the building of experimental ships, leaving new construction to con-tractors.

This was Gooch's last special task as an M.P. In 1885 his career in the Commons came to a close. Gladstone's cabinet became divided over Irish affairs but, ironically, it was a budget proposal to increase the tax on wines and spirits which brought them down. Poor Gooch, now sixty-nine, was asked to stand yet again. He told the secretary of the local Association that if he were twenty years younger he would gladly do so, but his mind was made up. He had accepted the inevitable. The borough had lost its second seat in a further reform measure and on 5 December Maskelyne was returned as the sole Member. He won by 4,541 to 2,770 in a straight fight, far too great a majority for Gooch to have over-turned.

His chairmanship of the Great Western

View over the canal basin at the turn of the century. Fulthorpe House is the one on the left.

continued to dominate his life. Under his firm hand the rest of the Great Depression was weathered well. Dividends were good, rising to 6⅜% in 1883, the highest since 1848. After a slight drop they reached 6¾% in 1889, the best in the seventy years from 1848 to 1918.

Gooch's success at looking after the shareholders' interests is apparent from the average dividends in successive periods from 1860 to the end of the century. In the five years before he took the chair the figure was 2.37%. During the critical years from 1866 to 1870, when bankruptcy was barely staved off, it dropped to only 2.05%. In the seventies 4.68% was averaged, rising to 5.89% in the eighties, nearly ½% higher than his successors managed in the following decade. Receipts per mile rose from £3,100 in 1866 to £3,890 in 1873, a 25% increase at a difficult time. The Great Depression then began to bite and this figure was not exceeded until well after his time. It reached a low of £3,240 in 1881 before rising to £3,520 in 1889, a total increase of only fourteen percent in his long tenure of the chair. Passengers carried showed a fairly steady rise from 19½ mil-

lions in 1866 to 55 millions in 1889. Goods traffic over the same period climbed from 8.4 to about 26 million tons per year. Gooch also had the difficult task of improving the railway without over-straining its purse. Gauge changes, the quadrupling of lines, short cuts and better brakes and signalling equipment were all introduced.

MacDermot, the historian of the Great Western, called the latter part of Gooch's era the 'years of prosperity and repose' and the period which followed it 'the great awakening'. It was undeniable, he felt, 'that Gooch's rooted dislike of innovations and policy of rigid economy, especially in train mileage, so necessary, no doubt, in the sixties and early seventies, were carried on too long and were the chief cause of the unpopularity of the Great Western among the commercial classes and the travelling public'. G.N. Tyrell, who was Superintendent of the Line from 1864 to 1888, was at the root of much of the dissatisfaction, as he was incurably conservative and reduced speeds to the minimum. The more venturesome Grierson could not shift him. Gooch appears to have admired his approach, so different from his own in earlier days.

Perhaps, as with Richardson, he was too busy to see past the caution of an unimaginative subordinate. MacDermot did not pay due regard to the effects of the long slump in trade on Gooch's policies. His objective was a good dividend, not growth or speed, unless these were essential to profits. His great achievements were the survival of the financial crisis, the improving profitability during the Great Depression, the fusing of the many companies into a unified whole, and the Severn Tunnel, a priceless asset in peace and war until the juggernaut took over. He left a magnificent line for his successors to exploit.

The shareholders, if they had disagreed with his policies, could have voted him from the board. Instead they chose to honour him. In 1883 they passed a resolution asking the directors to commission a bust as a companion to Brunel's in their new meeting room. 'It is pleasant to feel that all my anxiety and work for the company is appreciated,' he wrote. Edward Wyon was chosen as the sculptor. At the annual meeting in the following February it was in place and much admired. It is now in the Gooch Gallery at Swindon.

On the remaining 500 mls of 7ft. gauge many of Gooch's engines continued to run. Although a generation had passed since his last had been built his prowess was remembered. D.K. Clark published a work on steam engines in 1889, once again including the indicator cards from *Great Britain*. 'They may be taken as standards of the performance of locomotives having well protected inside cylinders,' he wrote, 'for though these diagrams were taken more than thirty-six years ago, the performance indicated by them has not been surpassed in locomotive practice.'

Telcon remained outstandingly successful under his chairmanship. 'Our difficulty here has been to keep the dividends down,' he wrote. During the eighties they took on a new challenge, building what was then Britain's largest power station.

Gooch's interest in electricity went back to his youth, when he experimented with galvanic batteries at Tredegar, building a small motor. In later years he was interested in several similar ideas, but all proved too heavy and costly to compete with steam.

Electric lighting was more promising, however, and the invention of lamps and dynamos made a great impression on him. In 1880 an arc lighting system was installed at Paddington Station by the Anglo-American Brush Corporation, but there were difficulties over patents and the terminus reverted to the dimmer light of gas.

J.E.H. Gordon, a brilliant young Cambridge graduate, became the head of a new electric lighting department at Telcon. He built a 350 kW dynamo, the largest in the world, to supply arc lights at the East Greenwich works. His work was so successful that a Bill was put through to extend the company's operations to include electric lighting. Gooch was an enthusiastic supporter of the move, as their first contract was for a complete power-house and lighting system for the Great Western, serving the terminus, hotel and goods yard at Paddington and the Westbourne Park and Royal Oak stations. Well over four thousand incandescent and a hundred arc lamps were required, which was a gigantic installation in its day.

To generate the power Gordon and his colleague Frank Bailey built three immense alternators – 350 kW, 68 Hz, 146 r.p.m., two phase. Each weighed 45 tons. They were driven by Rennie vertical steam engines supplied by nine large locomotive boilers. There were no condensers, the steam and flue gases exhausting into 90 ft. stacks.

Paddington Power Station was the first in Britain for electric lighting on a large scale. It was commissioned in April 1886. Not surprisingly there were difficulties, but the Great Western took it over at the end of 1887. It remained in service for about twenty years, a remarkable testimony to its designers. Throughout its life the local people fought its noise, vibration and smoke in the courts, but without success.

Unfortunately Telcon lost a good deal of money on the contract. A concession which had been obtained to light the St. James's district was abandoned. Early in 1888 Gordon and Bailey left to start their own business. The imaginative venture fizzled out. By 1895 power stations in Britain totalled well over 100,000 hp. Gordon and Bailey remained prominent in the new industry and Gooch and his colleagues had made a sad mistake.

Excellent progress was maintained with the Severn Tunnel until Walker had to start working inland from Sudbrook. On 10 October 1883, at a point a hundred yards short of where the previous flooding had occurred, the water burst in. Once more the works were inundated.

A few days later there was a second disaster. Richardson had predicted that under extreme conditions of wind and tide the sea-banks along the shore on the Welsh side could be over-topped and the tunnel flooded. He used the spoil from the workings to build embankments 16ft. high around the entrance as additional protection. When Gooch saw these he was amused as in the whole of the time that he had known the nearby South Wales line there had never been a flood, yet it was only protected by a 10ft. bank. On 18 October 1883, however, a violent storm coincided with an extra high spring tide. The railway was soon inundated and the sea began to pour into the Marsh Shaft, which was not yet connected to the main heading. Fifty men were at work below. One was swept from a ladder whilst trying to escape and was killed. The remainder fled to scaffolding in the higher parts of the tunnel, spending a terrifying night before being brought out by boat.

The Marsh Shaft was soon pumped out but at Sudbrook Lambert again had to be sent for to close a flood door. With two other divers to handle his air line he managed to reach it. When it slammed shut the concussion was so terrific that, he said, he 'saw all the stars of heaven inside his helmet'.

As completion was neared Walker attacked the tunnel with a huge workforce. At the peak 3,628 men were at work, laying as many as a third of a million bricks each week. He had a continuous struggle against the water pressure in the 'very dry' workings, twenty-seven pumps being installed in twelve shafts to handle 20,000 gall./min., but no further major problems were encountered. On 27 October 1884, when Gooch and Lord Bessborough, a fellow director, were at Sudbrook, the last two sections were about to meet under the Welsh shore. With his sixty-eighth birth-

day recently behind him Gooch went below. 'The men had got a small hole through, making the tunnel open throughout,' he wrote. 'I was the first to creep through and Lord Bessborough followed me. It was a very difficult piece of navigation, but by a little pulling in front and pushing behind we managed it, and the men gave us some hearty cheers.'

By April 1885 the tunnel was almost finished and it was anticipated that the Prince of Wales would open it on 1 August. In mid-July it was rumoured that there was a delay, because the approach cuttings were not ready. There were also arguments about ventilation, the technical press stating that the Board of Trade would be unlikely to allow traffic until the fans were supplemented by a mid-channel shaft. This absurd suggestion came to nothing. When the first train steamed through on 5 September there was little ceremony as, Gooch said, 'it will be some months yet before we can open to the public as the permanent pumping and ventilation machinery has to be arranged and fixed'. On board with him were Lady Gooch, Charles Richardson, Sir John Hawkshaw, Thomas Walker, Alfred Gooch and about forty other guests. To the disappointment of the neighbourhood and the press all outsiders were excluded. 'No reason for this course was assigned,' *The Engineer* said, 'and as it would be absurd to suppose the directors and engineers feared to expose their work to critical eyes, it can only be presumed that the desire to be exclusive was stronger than the wish to gratify those upon whom the ultimate success will depend.' The press were so piqued that only brief notices appeared, *The Illustrated London News* giving it no mention at all. One assumes that the Great Western had no right to allow any form of public use at that time and preferred not to say so.

On 9 January 1886 a coal train was worked through as an experiment, Gooch hoping that goods working would commence in March. His troubles were not yet over, however, and he became irritated with Hawkshaw. At the shareholders' meeting in February he had to announce a further postponement, as Hawkshaw would not hand over until a pump had been dismantled. Six months later he again had to blame him for delays. The water had to be under control before traffic could start. Gooch told the shareholders that 'the spring . . . was gradually diminishing, but although he personally would now run a goods train through, Sir John Hawkshaw, who was responsible, will not allow it to be done'. In fact it was 1 September before goods services started and not until 1 December that the first passenger train ran. Nearly fourteen years of toil ended without the accolade of a royal opening, no ceremony of the magnificence due to such an achievement ever taking place. This must have been Gooch's doing and it seems probable that he was not prepared to arrange for a great fuss to be made of Hawkshaw.

The Severn Tunnel had cost £1,806,248, two and a half times the original estimate and nearly double Walker's contract price. Most of the work had been done in six intensive years. Gooch must bear much of the blame for the half-hearted start, which put at least four years onto the programme. The approach of exploring the ground and preparing firm specifications cannot be faulted, but he put up with Richardson for too long. His greatness, however, was that he launched the project and persevered with it throughout all the difficulties. 'This has been a very anxious work for me', he wrote. 'One has felt a doubt whether we ought to persevere with so large an expenditure, but I never lost hope of succeeding in the end.'

CHAPTER

32

During the eighties Gooch's fame reached its peak. In December 1882 Spy, the brilliant caricaturist, drew him as one of his series for *Vanity Fair*. A good many magazines published articles about him. Though outwardly a modest man he took pride in them, keeping a list with his memoirs. They range from *Engineering's* of 1868 to the last, '*Railway Herald*, with portrait, May 1888'. He was also one of those included in 1888 in Barraud's *Men and Women of the Day*, a collection of superb photographic portraits accompanied by well written biographical sketches.

In the latter part of the decade important events in the history of the Great Western were marked. On 13 August 1886 there was the hundredth half yearly meeting and then on 14 August 1887,[*] when he was nearly seventy-one, he reached his Great Western jubilee day, 'it being fifty years since I entered the service . . . I have seen great changes'.

The jubilees were outnumbered by sadder occasions. On 23 November 1882 Tom Gooch died peacefully after a few days illness. 'He has been a good son and a good and loving brother,' Gooch wrote, 'and few men are more fitted to meet the Great Change.' Gooch had a bad cold, so his doctor would not let him attend the funeral at Kensal Green. Only a few weeks later his sister Jane passed away. Both had been deeply committed christians. Gooch himself had the unquestioning faith of most

Victorians but shared neither Tom's fervour nor Jane's pious dedication.

Steadily his family, friends and colleagues slipped away – Whitworth, Grierson and then, hardest of all, Alfred Gooch, who had given most of his short adult life to the Severn Tunnel. The years began to tell on him, but still he maintained his detailed contact with the affairs of the Great Western. In December 1887 Charles Gooch wrote, complaining that if he was only allowed to increase production at the Avon he would be able to show costs as low as anyone's. Early in 1888 William Dean had to offer an explanation for an increased consumption of coal and on 8 July Charles Gooch wrote again, thanking him for permission to order some trams. These are the last of the letters amongst his personal papers, for the shadows, Sir Theodore Martin said, 'were beginning to close round a long and crowded life . . . The energy of quiet enthusiasm which had carried him through his toilsome and honourable career began to flag and health failed'.

His decline began on 17 January 1889 when he caught a cold which soon turned to bronchitis. He recovered sufficiently to attend the February board and to take the chair at the shareholders' meeting on 14 February.

He 'got through pretty well', he said, not surprisingly, as he declared the best dividend for four years. Then on 4 March he

---

[*] This conflicts with the starting date of 18 August 1837 given in his memoirs and which has usually been quoted. This was a Friday, a most unlikely day to start a new job, whereas 14 August 1837 was a Monday. The jubilee is noted in his journal on the actual day. On all counts the fourteenth seems the more probable.

'Spy's' 1882 cartoon of Gooch – 'The Great Western'.

developed gout in his left foot which soon spread to his right.

On 11 April Frances, his youngest sister, died, a grim portent. He was improving a little at the time, so on 13 April Emily took him to Hastings. 'I can now walk a little – but very little – and am sent down here to effect a cure,' he said. After a fortnight they returned to Fulthorpe House, but he was no better. 'I hope I will feel the benefit of the change now I have got back to my home,' he wrote sadly, but for the next four months he was housebound at Paddington.

In August he was well enough to be taken to his beloved Clewer. This raised his spirits and he was able to take an occasional drive in the carriage, but as autumn drew on and the weather grew colder he had a relapse. His complaint developed rapidly, bringing suffering which he bore with patience and courage.

By 30 September his condition had become serious enough for *The Times* to commence issuing daily bulletins. They announced that he had rallied, but the improvement was brief. On Monday 7 October it was stated that gouty phlebitis had developed from the attacks to his feet, leading to weakness of the heart. He was in a gravely critical state.

After a restless weekend Gooch became more tranquil but was less able to take food. His strength ebbed away and by Wednesday he was failing rapidly. The end was not far distant.

A year previously the *Great Eastern* had been sold to the shipbreakers. Now she lay on a mud flat on the Mersey, being torn to pieces by a horde of workmen. She was so stoutly built that this proved difficult, but in the very week that Gooch was fading from life *The Illustrated London News* published a last picture of her, showing her raddled form, her dignity past recovery. Brunel's ship and the man who had given her purpose were nearing their end together.

Emily fought hard for him. By Sunday Prince Christian's surgeon was in residence at Clewer, supplementing the efforts of Dr Pavy, his friend and London physician, and Dr Ellison, surgeon to the Queen's Household at Windsor. Their patient, however, was beyond recall and by Monday evening was very weak. He survived the long night and the next morning, but at two in the afternoon of Tuesday 15 October 1889 he died. 'Had he been a judge or a bishop,' said *The Times*, 'he would hardly have passed as an old man; he was only seventy-three. But few men reach great age who are exposed to the constant strain of railway work, and if he was not a very old man, he was, at least, a very old railway servant.'

Lady Gooch did not believe in the elaborate Victorian funerals. It was announced that Sir Daniel's would take place quietly at Clewer on the Saturday, with no processions of any kind.

On the morning of the funeral the principal obituaries appeared in the newspapers and technical press. Their words, though fulsome, carry conviction, their very volume a proof of his stature. 'It will be hard indeed to fill the void,' said *Herapath's Railway Journal*. 'We do not often see

The *Great Eastern* as she was in the last week of Gooch's life

men like the chairman of the Great Western – solid, silent, unobtrusive, a great man truly, who veritably has left his footsteps in the sands of time . . . He was a strict disciplinarian but ever just; he heard what every man had to say . . . It has been a matter of surprise to some that Gooch should have made so able a chairman and administrator. It is not always so with engineers, but then it is to be borne in mind that he had been the superintendent of great works in which he was particularly compelled to practise every economical device, and it was this training that made him a man of business.'

The Times saw the Great Western not only as the largest, but as one of the most prosperous of English railways, owing largely to his able, though at times perhaps somewhat over-conservative, management. The Severn Tunnel they regarded as existing only because of his dogged perseverence and unconquerable faith. *The Engineer* observed that 'so many years have elapsed since he practised . . . that the present generation has probably forgotten

that he was a great mechanician . . . Sir Daniel was a very remarkable man, far more than is generally known. He made surprisingly few mistakes in his work. His career is another proof that genius is . . . independent of opportunity.'

The directors and senior officers of the railway were taken to Windsor by special train. It was pouring with rain and on their arrival they hurried into the waiting cabs, which splashed through the streets and sodden countryside to the church. The coffin lay in the library at Clewer. Shortly before mid-day it was borne to the open hearse and covered with wreaths, the main one a crown of gardenias, tuberoses and maidenhead fern from Lady Gooch. The four horses drew their light burden down the short drive and across the lane to St. Andrew's. In the carriages which followed were his widow, Charles Gooch and his two sisters and their husbands, together with William Frederick and John V. Gooch and Mr D.F. Gooch, the new heir to the baronetcy. Sir Henry Gooch and Frank Gooch were both not well enough to attend, and nothing was said of George Henry.

The short pathway from the lychgate to the porch was lined by twenty-four Freemasons, all in mourning dress and white gloves, bearing sprigs of acacia. Sir Daniel's body was carried between them to the door, where it was met by the rector, the curate and a Minor Canon from St. George's Chapel, Windsor.

During the service the choir sang the hymn *Art Thou Weary* before all followed the coffin to the churchyard. More wreaths lay on the massive slab of polished stone which had been drawn to one side to reveal the vault. The weather had worsened and rain was lashing down as the choir sang *Jesus Lives*. The coffin was then lowered into its last resting place at the spot which he had chosen so long ago.

New Swindon paid its tribute next day at St. Paul's Church. The vicar preached on Daniel, xii, 4: 'Many shall run to and fro, and knowledge shall be increased'. At the close the densely crowded congregation stood in tribute whilst the *Dead March in Saul* was played.

Soon the slab was replaced over the vault. A new inscription had joined Peggy's:

Sir Daniel Gooch, Baronet
of Clewer Park, Windsor
Born 24 August 1816. Died 15 October 1889
'I know that my redeemer liveth'

Epilogue

After the next board meeting the Deputy Chairman of the Great Western sent formal condolences to Lady Gooch. She replied with a heavy heart, paying her husband the tribute which he would most have valued.

12 November 1889
My Dear Sir Alexander Wood,
You so kindly transmitted to me the resolution of the Great Western Board recording their deep sorrow at the death of my dear Husband . . . I feel I must ask you *to express my thanks to* 'The Board' *and please tell one and all of* 'My Friends' *round you that I do truly appreciate their acknowledgement of the great services of my dear Husband's administration of the* Great Western Railway. *Words cannot express what I feel.* The Railway! *has lost a great good man! but my loss is far, far greater. Forgive me – I cannot write more – only I do beg of you to accept my most heartfelt thanks for* your *constant kind* attention *and great thoughtfulness at all times to Sir Daniel and to me.*

Believe me,
Dear Sir Alexander,
Yours very sincerely,
Emily Gooch.

In the meantime Gooch's will was read and his executors and trustees set to work to fulfil his wishes. His personal estate – all that he owned except Clewer Park and his other freehold possessions – was valued at £669,658 0s. 7d. Including his heirlooms and his real estate he had been worth perhaps three quarters of a million, the equivalent of thirty or forty millions today. After taking good care of Lady Gooch his main concern had been to endow the baronetcy with property. This he did with typical pragmatism. Only a sixth of his fortune was shared between his four younger children and Alfred's widow. The rest was entailed to his successors.

From the distance of almost a century we can look back on Gooch's achievements with awe. From 1880 to 1899 only 223 men besides the great landowners left more than half a million – eleven a year, or about one in every thirty thousand adult deaths. He had risen from a workman's wage to become one of the richest five hundred or so in the land. Many of his fellow engineers left large fortunes – Brunel £90,000, Robert Stephenson £400,000, Tom Gooch £51,000, John V. Gooch £84,000. His flair for financial matters, a measure of luck and a longer working life enabled him to accumulate even greater wealth. He was both the Great Western's longest serving locomotive engineer and its longest serving chairman. Only three or four others ever held a chief officer's post and then a chairmanship in a railway. At his death he was amongst the handful who held the power in the two vital services of railways and submarine telegraphy, and he was unique in being involved at such a level in both.

From such a man arrogance or ostentation might have been understandable. Whilst he maintained the dignity of his position the panoply of wealth meant little to him. He was wealthy before he bought his first carriage. His Paddington house was that of a well-to-do, rather than extremely rich, man. Clewer was not kept up in great country-house style, his needs remaining modest in relation to his means. He enjoyed the position which his success gave him, but did not strive for status. His wealthy and aristocratic friends were made because of his worth and ability, not because he bought, or even charmed, them. He had the confidence to regard the great people he encountered as no more than equals in a different field, as we see from his letter to Disraeli and his cool attitude to royalty. Though he used power well he did not seek it, as his initial reluctance to become chairman of the Great Western and his role as a useful but silent back-bencher show.

Parris, in a short biographical study, suggests that Gooch wished to found a dynasty. His careful entailing of his estate may seem to indicate this, but it was not a driving force. His title came without his seeking it and after the bulk of his fortune was made. He saw a duty to endow his baronetcy with appropriate dignity, but no more than that. His keen sense of history left him in no doubt of the importance of the events in which he had been involved and of the people he had known, hence his memoirs and instructions to his descendants on the heirlooms which he wished them to treasure – a piece of Birkinshaw rail, his Masonic regalia, a sofa from the Royal saloon, souvenirs from the telegraph expeditions and so on.

Central to Gooch's life was work. He believed that without it there was no true security and so ensured that his sons were trained to good careers, though none inherited his talents. He enjoyed engineering but management, business and investment brought him even greater pleasure. Few have shown such outstanding flair in all four fields, the combination making him one of the first engineer-managers and certainly the first to lead great concerns. It was his interests in management and business which caused him to stay at Paddington rather than move to Swindon.

Gooch had three driving forces. The first was his need for financial security, common to his time and class. The second was duty. Duty to shareholders, family, friends and colleagues show through his life, and it was this, rather than ambition, which made him take the chairmanship of the Great Western. It kept him in Parliament into his

seventieth year, doing something for which he had no great inclination and less time.

His third and greatest impetus came from his interest in making money. He had the nose for an opportunity and always put investment before possessions. In his business affairs he was shrewd and, on occasion, incisive to the point of brutality, but he had a firm moral code. 'Altho' I feel it is not possible for all men to succeed in life,' he wrote, 'yet I am sure few need fail to do well if they will win for themselves a character of strict honesty, and by this I do not mean that they will not steal, but that in their dealings with men they will act with honour, not seeking to obtain an advantage by either supressing or magnifying the truth.' His code, however, allowed him the South Devon contract and the *Alma* barge, which would not be regarded as ethical in these days and were close to the wind even then, judging by his caution. His shrewdest stroke, the purchase of the *Great Eastern*, brought no conflict with his morality. There was no way forward for the shareholders he represented and whose plight he shared. The rules of the game were that the debenture holders came first, and so he used the rules.

Lady Gooch continued to live at Fulthorpe House for some years, moving eventually to 109 Eaton Place in Belgravia, where she died on 19 May 1901, shortly before her sixtieth birthday. Her grave is beneath a simple stone in the corner of the churchyard at Clewer, barely a yard from the vault where her predecessor and her husband lie, but which was not for her. She did all that she could to ensure that his fame lived on. In accordance with his wishes she had extracts from his memoirs and journals published. Her main concern, and that of the friends who helped her, was that he should gain proper credit for his part in Atlantic Telegraphy.

As a result of his sense of history both *North Star* and *Lord of the Isles* were preserved at Swindon. In 1905 William Dean's successor, the great G.J. Churchward, found himself short of room. He solved his problem by an act of vandalism for which he has been soundly, though not entirely justly, castigated. He tried to find a proper home for the two engines but on 16 December wrote to the board to say that they were occupying valuable space: 'They have been offered to several Institutions without success and I beg to recommend that authority be given for them to be destroyed'. So the board, Churchward and, above all, the un-named Institutions share the shame of scrapping the finest relics of the broad gauge. They were the last victims of the Gauge War, for in 1892 the remainder of the 7ft. gauge had been torn up and the stock had gone the way of the *Great Eastern*. 'No traveller on the line . . .

will see without a pang the stately *Iron Duke*, the wandering *Tartar* or the swift-flying *Swallow* disappear', one who knew them well said just before their end. 'They look today, with their great 8-feet driving wheels and their old-world brass-mounted boilers . . . just as they must have looked . . . when our forefathers gaped open-mouthed at the tale of their achievements. And indeed their achievements were, in sober earnest, remarkable enough'. But so were all the achievements of their creator.

Sources and Acknowledgements

The principal sources available for a study of Daniel Gooch are, firstly, the edited version of his writings prepared shortly after his death by Lady Gooch and others, published as *Diaries of Sir Daniel Gooch, Baronet* by Kegan Paul, Trench and Trübner in 1892. They are accompanied by an introduction written by his friend Sir Theodore Martin, a parliamentary solicitor who was also a literary figure of sufficient distinction to be selected by Queen Victoria to write Prince Albert's biography.

The *Diaries* would have served as an excellent framework for a definitive biography and are still of great value, as they include extensive extracts from Gooch's journals written on board the *Great Eastern* during the 1865 and 1866 Atlantic Telegraph Expeditions. Lady Gooch, however, preserved the manuscripts of Sir Daniel's memoirs and his later journals, apart from the volumes for 1870–3 and 1886–9, which were presumably of a specially personal nature, as they covered their courtship and Sir Daniel's final illness. They passed into the family of Charles Fulthorpe Gooch, Sir Daniel's second son. Their existence was unknown to outsiders until 1969, when they appeared at Sotheby's for auction. They contain much valuable new information. By the most wonderful chance they were purchased by Roger Burdett Wilson, an author and antiquarian bookseller, who produced a painstakingly edited transcription, published by David and Charles in 1972 as *The Memoirs and Diaries of Sir Daniel Gooch*. Only four years later Roger Wilson died. He had the forethought, wisdom and generosity to bequeath the Gooch Manuscripts to the City of Birmingham Reference Library. My personal debt extends even beyond access to these, as his Introduction to the *Memoirs* is of great interest and his editorial notes embody an extensive and well-researched bibliography. He gave me a flying start, and I thank him for this and honour the memory and labours of a kindly and respected man.

The most important remaining primary sources are the numerous files of Gooch documents held at the Public Record Office, Kew. They are so pertinent that he himself must have had a hand in their selection, as is confirmed by the note with the Geelong and Melbourne Railway papers stating that these were 'some of the collection of Sir Daniel Gooch's correspondence left in the custody of the Great Western Railway when Sir Daniel's estate was liquidated at the date of his death'.

I am grateful to Mrs Gillian White, Sir Daniel's great-great-grand-daughter, the only child of Sir Robert Gooch, the Fourth Baronet, for her kind interest and for sending me copies of the writings of John Gooch, which Sir Daniel entered into his Family Bible.

Two other invaluable sources are Gooch's *Sketch Book* and his *Great Eastern Notebook*. The former, though only pocket-sized, contains enough information to enable any of his broad gauge engines to be built. It is held at the National Railway Museum, York. The *Great Eastern Notebook* was auctioned at the same time as the manuscripts but passed out of this country. Fortunately its exportation was conditional upon a microfilm being lodged with the Department of Manuscripts of the British Library.

Though relatively brief it contains unique information, in particular a previously unknown report on the ship's engines prepared after her trial trip.

It gave me great satisfaction to unearth several sources of especial fascination. T.L. Gooch's *Diaries, 1823–1833,* and his manuscript autobiography in the Library of the Institution of Civil Engineers appear to have been overlooked by previous researchers. *The Notebooks of Thomas Ellis* were found as a result of patient work by Miss M.L. Gibbens of Gwent County Library. *The Diaries of Edward Snell,* which had been lost sight of in Great Britain, came to light as a result of most enjoyable correspondence with John Arnold, Tom Griffiths and Alannah Kelly of the State Library of Victoria, Melbourne. Tom Griffith's enthusiasm and interest has been of great value in the finalising of my manuscript.

I am aware that there is other material at Swindon and amongst Brunel's papers which time and expense have prevented me from researching. I have, however, had the benefit of a mass of excellent publications by other workers. I gratefully acknowledge my debt to those supreme examples of engineering scholarship, James Warren's *A Century of Locomotive Building by Robert Stephenson and Company* and E.T. MacDermot and C.R. Clinker's *History of the Great Western Railway.* Other works which I have relied upon are listed in the Bibliography, and I thank their authors for both the assistance and the pleasure which they have given me.

I have been fortunate in having ready access to the libraries of the Universities of Glasgow and Strathclyde. The ability to both browse and borrow amongst their huge collections has been of enormous value. I thank the Librarians and their staffs for their courtesy and for making me welcome.

Finally I offer my most grateful thanks to all those other Institutions and people to whom I have turned for advice or help. Frequently they have undertaken gems of research whose outcome has been most exciting and illuminating. I am also indebted to those who have given permission for the use of material for illustrations. I am particularly pleased to be able

to include Peter Holt's superb line drawing of *North Star*(page 39). My especial thanks are due to: Marion E. Allen; Rev. P. Amor; Berkshire County Library; Berkshire Record Office; Birmingham Reference Library (and for the illustrations on pages 10 (top) and 168); The Bodleian Library; R.A. Bowden, Archivist, Marylebone Library, and Staff (and for the illustration on page 189); The British Library, Dept. of Printed Books; The British Railways Board for permission to quote from the RAIL series at Kew; The Secretary of the Carlton Club; Gordon Cullingham; Mrs J.L. Drury, University of Durham; Dundee Museums and Art Galleries; Durham County Archivist; Eccles Public Library; Librarian and Curator, Freemasons' Hall; Gateshead Library (illustrations on pages 28 and 29, top); James Guilbeau, New Orleans; A. Lisle Harvey; Central Librarian, Hastings; House of Lords' Library; R.L. Jenkins (and for the illustration on page 15); Leningrad Museum of Railway Transport; Liverpool Record Office; David Lyall and his co-executors for permission to quote from the Gooch Manuscripts; Ewen McEwen; Angus Macnaghten; F.W. Manders, Local Studies Librarian, Newcastle Central Library; Merseyside County Museums (and for the illustration on page 138); W.A. Morris, Archivist, The Institution of Civil Engineers; S.G. Morrison, Librarian, The Institution of Mechanical Engineers; The National Library of Wales; The National Maritime Museum, Greenwich; The National Portrait Gallery (frontispiece); Newton-le-Willows Library; Northumberland Record Office; Hon. G.W.N. Palmer, OBE, TD, Lord Lieut. of Berkshire, and his Clerk; Public Record Office, Kew; Marian Roberts, Area Librarian, Wrexham; Michael Rutherford, The National Railway Museum, York (and to the Museum for the illustrations on pages 96 and 104); The Science Museum, South Kensington (and for the illustrations on pages 18, 88 and 123); The Scottish Record Office; William Serjeant; Allan H. Shaw; Rev. Denis Shaw, Rector of Clewer; Mrs Margaret M. Snell (and for the illustration on page 75, bottom); Suffolk County Archivist; The Director of Libraries, Sunderland; Divisional Librarian, Swindon;

Dr Hugh Torrens; Librarian of University College, London; Warrington Central Library; Mrs M.F. Weldon, MBE; Dr J.N. Westwood; Staff at Wigan Reference Library; Robertson Wilkie; Maurice Williams; S.J. Woodward, Curator, Museums and Art Gallery, Borough of Thamesdown (and for the illustration on page 131).

The writing of a biography is, like love, an obsession with one person. I close by thanking my family for their forbearance during the five years and more of my spare time which I devoted to the memory of a great man.

A.P., 1987

Appendix

Gooch's Locomotive Designs

Class		Number Built	Month/Year	Driving Wheel dia. ft. in.				Bore × Stroke in.	
Broad Gauge									
Great Western Railway									
Fire Fly	2-2-2	(62)	3/40–12/42	7	0			15(15¼)	18
Sun	2-2-2	(21)	4/40– 1/42	6	0			15 or 14	18
Leo	2-4-0	(18)	1/4 – 7/42	5	0			15	18
Hercules	0-6-0	(4)	7/42–10/42	5	0			15(16?)	18
Great Western	2-2-2	1	4/46	8	0			18	24
	(4-2-2)								
Iron Duke	4-2-2	22(7)	4/47– 7/55	8	0			18	24
Prince	2-2-2	6	8/46– 3/47	7	0 (7	6)		16	24
Avalanche	0-6-0t	(1)	2/46	5	0			17	24
Premier	0-6-0	12	2/46– 5/47	5	0			16	24
Pyracmon	0-6-0	6	11/47– 7/48	5	0			16	24
Bacchus	0-6-0	1	5/49	5	0			16	24
(built from Thunderer)									
Corsair	4-4-0bt	2(13)	8/49– 3/55	6	0 (5	9)		17	24
Waverley	4-4-0	(10)	2/55– 6/55	7	0			17	24
Victoria	2-4-0	18	8/56– 5/64	6	6			16	24
Caesar	0-6-0	8	6/51– 2/52	5	0			16(17)	24
Banking	0-6-0t	4	10/52–10/54	5	0			17	24
Standard Goods	0-6-0	102	5/52– 3/63	5	0			17	24
Metropolitan	2-4-0t	10(12)	6/62–10/64	6	0			16	24
(condensing tank engines)									
Bristol and Exeter Railway									
	4-2-2	(20)	1849	7	6			16½	24
	0-6-0	(8)	1849	5	0			16	24
Vale of Neath Railway									
	4-4-0bt	(6)	10/51–12/51	5	6			17	24
South Devon and Cornwall Railway (Contract)									
	4-4-0bt	(12)	10/51– 4/53	5	9			17	24
	0-6-0bt	(4)	12/54– 9/55	4	9			17	24
	4-4-0bt	(16)	4/59– 6/65	5	6			16½	24
	0-6-0bt	(8)	3/60–12/64	4	6			16½	24

Total Broad Gauge 192 + (215) = 407

Narrow Gauge
Great Western Railway

0-6-0	12	1855–6	5	0	15½	24
2-2-2	(8)	1855–6	6	6	15½	24
0-6-0	(2)	1857	5	0	16½	24
0-6-0	12	1857–8	4	6	16½	24
0-4-2t	(2)	1857				
0-6-0t	2	1860				
0-6-0	18	1861–2				
0-6-0	(12)	1862				
2-4-0	(8)	1862				
2-2-2	(10)	1862				
0-6-0	10	1864–5				
2-4-0t	2	1864	Metropolitan Tank Engines			

Total Narrow Gauge   56 + (42) = 98

Bracketed figures in 'Built' column are the number built by contractors. Unbracketed are the number built at Swindon.

t = saddle tank
bt = saddle tank, leading bogie

Information from the Railway Correspondence and Travel Society's *The Locomotives of the G.W.R., Parts 1 and 2* and, for the narrow gauge engines, from H. Holcroft's *An Outline of Great Western Locomotive Practice*.

Bibliography

P.R.O. = Public Record Office, Kew.

Used Throughout

Gooch, Sir D., (ed. Lady (Emily) Gooch, Sir Theodore Martin and friends), *Diaries of Sir Daniel Gooch, Baronet.* Kegan Paul, Trench and Trubner, 1892.

Wilson, R.B., *Sir Daniel Gooch – Memoirs and Diary.* David and Charles, 1972.

Gooch, Sir D. Manuscripts of Memoirs and Diaries. Birmingham Reference Library.

Marshall, John., *A Biographical Dictionary of Railway Engineers.* David and Charles, 1978.

Chapter 1

Deeds, etc, Scottish Record Office, re. Devon Iron Works.

'Description and Valuation of Bedlington Iron Works', *c* 1840. Durham Bishopric Estate Papers, University of Durham.

Dron, R.W., *The Coal Fields of Scotland.* Blackie, 1902.

Gooch, T.L. MSS Autobiography, Library of the Institution of Civil Engineers.

Hamilton, H., *The Industrial Revolution in Scotland.* Frank Cass, 1966.

Martin, E., *Bedlington Iron and Engine Works, 1736–1867: a New History.* 1974. Frank Graham.

Waters, R.E.C., 'Genealogical Notes of the Kindred Families of Longridge, Fletcher and Hawks, with Pedigrees'. *c.* 1880.

Chapter 2

Previously cited: Gooch, T.L.; Martin;

Birkinshaw, John and Longridge, Michael, 'Remarks on the Comparative Merits of Cast Iron and Malleable Iron Railways'.

Fordyce, W., *A History of Coal, Coke and Coal Fields and the Manufacture of Iron in the North of England'.* 1860, rep. Frank Graham, 1973.

Gooch, T. L., Diaries, 1823–1833. Library of the Institution of Civil Engineers.

Marshall, C.F. Dendy, *A History of British Railways Down to the Year 1830.*

Memoir of John Viret Gooch. *Institution of Civil Engineers, Min. and Proc.* 1900.

Parson, W. and White, W., *History, Directory and Gazetteer of the Counties of Durham and Northumberland.* Vol II. W. White and Co., 1828.

Rolt, L.T.C., *George and Robert Stephenson. The Railway Revolution.* Longmans, 1960

Skeat, W.O., 'George Stephenson, the Man and his Letters'. *Institution of Mechanical Engineers*, 1973.

Stevenson, D, *Life of Robert Stevenson, Civil Engineer.* Adam and Charles Black, 1878.

Warren, J.G., *A Century of Locomotive Building by Robert Stephenson and Company, 1823–1923.* Andrew Reid, 1923.

Chapter 3

Gooch, T.L., (Diaries); Rolt; Warren.

Ashton, T.S., *Iron and Steel in the Industrial Revolution.* Manchester University Press, 1924.

Barrie, D.S. and Lee, C.F., *The Sirhowy Valley and Its Railways.* The Railway Publishing Co., 1940.

Dickinson, H.W., and Titley, A., *Richard Trevithick: the Engineer and the Man.* Cambridge University Press, 1934.

Edwards, N., *The Industrial Revolution in South Wales.* The Labour Publishing Co., 1924.

Ellis, C.W., 'Early Locos in Monmouthshire'. Letter, *Monmouthshire Evening Post,* 23 Feb. 1912.

Ellis, T., 'Notebooks'. National Library of Wales.

John, A.H., *The Industrial Development of South Wales.* University of Wales Press, 1950.

Jones, O., 'The Sirhowy Tramroad and Its Locomotives'. J. Monmouth-shire Local Hist. Council, No. 2, Autumn 1965.

Penny Magazine, Feb 1844. 'A Day at the Butterley Ironworks, Derbyshire'.

Powell, E., *The History of Tredegar.* South Wales Argus, Ltd., 1902.

Report of the Commissioners for Enquiring Into the Employment and Condition of Children in Mines and Manufactories. Brit. Parl. Papers, 1842 (380) XV, 1. and Report and Evidence of Sub-Commissioners, 1842 (381, 382) XVI, 1 and XVII, 1.

Scrivenor, H., *History of the Iron Trade.* Longmans, Brown, Green and Longmans, 1854.

Trevithick, F., *The Life of Richard Trevithick.* E. and F.N. Spon, 1872.

Wilkins, C., *The South Wales Coal Trade and Its Allied Industries.* Daniel Owen and Co., 1888.

Chapter 4

Warren.

Ahrons, E.L., *The British Steam Locomotive, 1825–1925.* Ian Allan, 1927.

Anon., *The Vulcan Locomotive Works, 1830–1930'.* The Locomotive Publishing Co., 1931.

Brown, F.A.S., *Great Northern Locomotive Engineers,* Vol 1. Allen and Unwin, 1966.

Bruce, G.B. Presidential Address to the Institution of Civil Engineers, 8 November 1887.

Carmichael, P., (ed. Gauldie, E.,) 'The Dundee Textile Industry, 1790–1885; From the Papers of Peter Carmichael of Arthurstone'. *The Scottish History Soc.*, 1969.

Carvel, J.L., *One Hundred Years in Coal.* Privately printed, T. and A. Constable, University Press, Edinburgh.

Donaghy, T.J., *Liverpool and Manchester Railway Operations, 1831–1845.* David and Charles, 1972.

'Dundee and Newtyle Railway, 150'. Information Pack published by Dundee Museums and Art Galleries Extension Services, 1981.

'Dundee Directory and General Register, 1834'. Archibald Allardice.

'Dundee Directory for 1837–8'. James Chalmers, 1837.

Dundee, Perth and Cupar Advertiser.

Great Western Railway Magazine, Nov. 1890. 'Interview with Jim Hurst, the Great Western Railway Company's First Engine Driver'.

'Hand List of the Vulcan Collection'. Merseyside County Museums.

Memoir of James Stirling. *Min. Proc. I.C.E.*, 1875–6.

Railway Gazette, 14 Nov. 1947. 'Memoirs of Archibald Sturrock'.

Shaw, A., 'The Vulcan Foundry – a Case Study of the Location and Growth of a Locomotive Building Firm'. Padgate College of Higher Education B. Ed. Dissertation, May 1977 [unpublished].

Smiles, S., *Lives of the Engineers. The Locomotive. George and Robert Stephenson.* John Murray, 1879.

Thomas, R.H.G., *The Liverpool and Manchester Railway.* Batsford, 1980.

Thomson, J. and MacLaren, J., *The History of Dundee.* John Durham and Son, 1874.

Chapter 5

Vulcan Handlist; Warren; Waters.

Bruce, The Rev. J. Collingwood, *A Handbook to Newcastle-on-Tyne.* Longmans, Green, Longmans, Roberts and Green, 1863.

'Directory of Newcastle and Gateshead, 1833'. Alexander Ihler.

Fleming, H.M. le, and Price, J.H., *Russian Steam Locomotives.* David and Charles, 1960.

Gooch-Barbara Gooch, letter of 1836 amongst MSS Memoirs and Diaries, Birmingham Reference Library.

Haywood, R.M., *The Beginning of Railway Development in Russia in the Reign of Nicholas I, 1835–42.* Duke University Press, N. Carolina, 1969.

History and Directory of Newcastle upon Tyne. T. Bulmer and Co., 1887.

'Improvements in Steam (Locomotive) Engines: Gray v. London and North Western Railway Co'. Transcript of evidence, 1851. Library of the Institution of Mechanical Engineers.

Maclean, J.S., *The Newcastle and Carlisle Railway, 1825–1862.* R. Robinson and Co., 1948.

Manders, F.W.D., 'A History of Gateshead'. Gateshead Corporation, 1973.

Penny Magazine, Sept. 1844. 'A Second Day at the Tyne Factories'.

P.R.O., RAIL 1008/1. Hawks and Thompson.

Rogers, F., *Gateshead – An Early Victorian Boom Town.* Priory Press, 1974.

Sunderland Herald, 5 Nov. 1858. 'Death of Henry Tanner, Esq. J.P.'.

'The Conversion of the Gauge on the Great Western'. *The Engineer*, 13, 20, 27 May 1892.

Westwood, J.N., *A History of Russian Railways.* Allen and Unwin, 1964.

Young, R., 'Timothy Hackworth and the Locomotive'. Shildon Stockton and Darlington Railway Jubilee Committee, 1923. 1975 edition.

Chapter 6

Gooch, T.L. (Autobiog); Conv. of Gauge articles; Hurst Interview; *The Vulcan Locomotive Works*; Vulcan Collection; Warren.

Gooch-Brunel, 18 July, 1837. G.W.R. Museum, Swindon.

Guilbeau, J.L., 'The St. Charles Street Car, or The New Orleans and Carrollton Rail Road'. The Author, 1977 edition.

MacDermot, E.T., revised Clinker, C.R., *History of the Great Western Railway.* 2 Vols. Ian Allan, 1964.

P.R.O. RAIL 1008/83. Gibbs-Saunders, 9 July 1837.

Rolt, L.T.C., *Isambard Kingdom Brunel.* Longmans, Green, 1957.

The Locomotive, 15 Jan. 1926. 'A Link With Brunel and Stephenson'.

The Locomotive, Vol. VI, 1901. Series of articles, 'The B.G. Locomotives of the Great Western'.

The Railway Correspondence and Travel Society. 'The Locomotives of the Great Western Railway – Part Two – Broad Gauge'. *The Society*, 1952.

Wood, N., *A Practical Treatise on Rail Roads.* Longmans, Orme, Brown, Green and Longmans, 1838

Chapter 7

Hurst Interview; MacDermot; Rly. Corresp. and Travel Soc.; Rolt (Brunel).

Gibbs, G.H., (ed. Simmons, J.), *The Birth of the Great Western Railway: Extracts from the Diary and Correspondence of George Henry Gibbs.* Adams and Dart, 1971.

Horsley, F. and S., (ed. Gotch, Brunel R.), 'Mendelssohn and his Friends in Kensington: Letters written by Fanny and Sophy Horsley in 1833–6'.

P.R.O., RAIL 1008/25. Gooch's first GWR letterbook, 1837–8.

Chapter 8

Conv. of Gauge articles; Gibbs; MacDermot; Rolt (Brunel); Wood.

Babbage, C., *The Life of a Philosopher.* Longman, Green, Longman, Roberts and Green, 1864.

Hyman, A., *Charles Babbage, Pioneer of the Computer.* Oxford University Press, 1984.

National Railway Museum, York. 'Correspondence etc. in Connection with the Reconstruction of *North Star*, 1925'. Transcript of Brunel correspondence.

P.R.O., RAIL 1008/17; 1008/26; 1008/82. Rep. to Directors; letterbook, 1839–41; engine alterations, 1839.

Sketch Book of Sir Daniel Gooch. Nat. Rly. Mus., York.

The Vulcan Papers. Newton-le-Willows Library. Untitled copies of the reports submitted at the meeting of 9 Jan. 1839.

Whishaw, F., *Railways of Great Britain and Ireland*. 1842. David and Charles reprint.

Chapter 9

MacDermot; Rly. Corresp. and Hist. Soc.; Trevithick; *Great Western Railway Magazine*.

Harrison, F., *Autobiography*.

Jefferies, R., 'The Story of Swindon'. *Frasers' Magazine*, May 1875.

Parris, H., 'Sir Daniel Gooch. A Biographical Sketch'. *J. Transport History*, Feb. 1976.

Peck, A.S., 'The Great Western at Swindon Works'. Oxford Publishing Co., 1983.

Public Record Office, Kew, RAIL 1008/5. Steel tyres, 1840–44,

Public Record Office, Kew, RAIL 1008/26. Gooch's letterbook, 1839–41.

Public Record Office, Kew, RAIL 1008/83. Letters of complaint, 1839–40.

Public Record Office, Kew, RAIL 1014/6. Tanner and T.L. Gooch to Gooch.

Robins, W., 'Paddington, Past and Present'. The Author, 1853?

The Engineer, Vol. CX, supplement p. xix. 'The Great Western Railway'.

Chapter 10

Brown; MacDermot; Rly. Corresp, and Hist. Soc.; Ellis, C.H.; Robins; Rolt (Brunel); *Civil Engineer and Architects' Journal*, Aug. 1839, 281–3. 'Lord Willoughby de Eresby's Patent Machinery for the Compression of Peat'.

The Illustrated London News.

Longford, E., *Victoria R.I.*. Pan Books edition, 1964.

Public Record Office, Kew, RAIL 1008/5. Tyre patent, 1840–44.

Public Record Office, Kew, RAIL 1008/6. Peat experiments.

Public Record Office, Kew, RAIL 1008/18. J.V. Gooch.

Public Record Office, Kew, RAIL 1014/6. Letters from Tanner, T.L. Gooch and A. Gooch.

Queen Victoria, (ed. Benson, A.C.), *The Letters of Queen Victoria*. Vol. 1. John Murray, 1907.

Railway Gazette, 14 Nov. 1947. 'Memoirs of Archibald Sturrock'.

Rolt, L.T.C., revised Kichenside, G., *Red for Danger*. Pan Books edition, 1978.

Chapter 11

Babbage; Improvements in Steam (Locomotive) Engines; MacDermot; Warren; *British Railways Magazine*, Vol. 3, 30–31, 1952. 'Gooch has a Good Day'.

Clark, D.K., *Railway Machinery*. 2 Vols. Blackie and Son, 1855.

Engineering, 15 June 1900. 'The Late John Viret Gooch'.

Gage, J., *Turner: Rain, Steam and Speed*. Art in Context series, 1972.

Gooch *v*. Banks. *The Times*, Law Reports, 25 November 1842.

Great Western Railway Magazine, March 1936. 'An Historic Model of a Broad Gauge Locomotive'.

Marshall, W.P., 'Evolution of the Locomotive Engine'. *Min. Proc. I.C.E.*, 1897–8, Pt. III, pp. 241–301.

Public Record Office, Kew, RAIL 1008/5. Tyre patent, 1840–44.

Public Record Office, Kew, RAIL 1008/18. Marshall-Gooch.

Public Record Office, Kew, RAIL 1008/26. Haigh Foundry expansion gear,

Public Record Office, Kew, RAIL 1014/6. Letters from Tanner.

Roe, J.W., *English and American Tool Builders*. University Press, 1916.

Rolt, L.T.C., *Tools for the Job*. Batsford, 1965.

The Illustrated London News.

Chapter 12

MacDermot; Rolt (Brunel); Warren.

Anon., (Conder, F.R.), *Personal Recollections of English Engineers and of the Introduction of the Railway System in the United Kingdom*. Hodder and Stoughton, 1868.

British Parliamentary Papers, 1845 (317) XL, 1; 1845 (625) XL, 153; 1846 (473) XXXVIII, 1. (Lists of Railway Subscribers).

Hansards' Parliamentary Debates.

Lewin, H.G., *The Railway Mania and Its Aftermath*. David and Charles, 1968. Reprint of 1936 edition.

Public Record Office, Kew, RAIL 1008/2. *Red Star* letter.

Public Record Office, Kew, RAIL 1014/6. Letters from Tanner.

Report of the Gauge Commissioners. Brit. Parl. Papers, 1846 (684, 699, 700) XVI 1, 29, 383.

Sekon, G.A., [i.e., G.A. Nokes], *A History of the Great Western Railway*. Digby, Long and Co., 1895.

Sidney, S., *Gauge Evidence*. Edmunds and Vacher, 1846.

Chapter 13

Rep. Gauge Comm.; Warren.

Bidder, G.P., 'On Mental Calculation'. *Min. Proc. I. C. E.*, XV, 1855–6, p. 251.

'Observations on the Report of the Gauge Commissioners as Presented to Parliament'. (The Great Western, 1846).

Public Record Office, Kew, RAIL 1008/2. Gooch-Hammond.

Public Record Office, Kew, RAIL 1008/18. Reid letter.

Chapter 14

MacDermot; Obs. on Rep. of Gauge Comm.; Peck; Rly. Corresp. and Hist. Soc.

Bourne, J.C., *History and Description of the Great Western Railway*. David Bogue, 1846.

Clark, D.K., *Railway Machinery*. 2 Vols. Blackie and Son, 1855.

Grinsell, L.V., Wells, H.B., Tallamy, H.S. and Betjeman, J., *Studies in the History of Swindon*. Borough Press, Swindon.

Hudson, K., 'The Early Days of the Railway Community in Swindon'. *Transport History*, Vol. 1, No. 2, July 1968.

'Improvements in Steam (Locomotive) Engines. Gray v L&NWR'. I. Mech. E. library.

Jefferies, Richard, *The Story of Swindon*. Frasers' Magazine, May 1875.

Morris, W., 'Swindon, Fifty Years Ago (More or Less)'. The Author, 1885?

North Wilts Herald.
Public Record Office, Kew, RAIL 1008/2. Gooch letters.
Public Record Office, Kew, RAIL 1014/6. Henry Tanner letter.
Public Record Office, Kew, RAIL 1014/8. Nasmyth letters.
Snell, E., diaries at The State Library of Victoria, Melbourne.
'Supplemental Observations on the Published Evidence and Appendix of the Gauge Commissioners'. Great Western, 1846.
The Illustrated Exhibitor and Magazine of Art, 3 Jan 1852, pp 101–105. 'The Great Western Railway Company's Locomotive Factory at Swindon'.
The Illustrated London News.
The Locomotive, Vol. VI, 1901. Series of articles, 'The B.G. Locomotives of the Great Western'.
Williams, A., *Life in a Railway Factory*. Alan Sutton, 1984.

Chapter 15
Gooch, T.L. (Autobiography); MacDermot; Rly. Corresp. and Travel Soc.; Rolt, 'Red for Danger'; *The Locomotive*, Vol. VI.
Hadfield, C., *Atmospheric Railways*. David and Charles, 1967.
Holcroft, H., 'An Outline of GWR Locomotive Practice'.

Chapter 16
Clark; Ellis, T. (Notebooks); Hadfield; MacDermot.
Gooch, D., 'Observations on the Resistances to Railway Trains at Different Velocities'. *Min. Proc. I. C. E.*, 1848, pp 292–326.
Harding, W., 'On the Resistances to Railway Trains at Different Velocities'. *Min. Proc. I. C. E.*, 1846, p. 369.
Marshall, C.F. Dendy, 'The Resistance of Express Trains'. *The Railway Engineer*, 1925.
Public Record Office, Kew, RAIL 1008/18. Manby-Gooch.
Report of the Commissioners of Railways Respecting Railway Communication Between London and Birmingham, 1848.
The Morning Herald, 22 April 1848. 'On the Resistances to Railway Trains at Different Velocities'.
The Morning Herald, 25 May 1848. 'Resistance to Railway Trains at Certain Velocities'.

Chapter 17
Jefferies; MacDermot; Rly. Corresp. and Travel Soc.; Snell.
Darwin, B., 'A Century of Medical Service, the Story of the Great Western Medical Fund, 1847–1947'. Swindon 1947.
Public Record Office, Kew, RAIL 1005/454. Gooch-Sturrock.
Public Record Office, Kew, RAIL 1008/7. B. and E. engines.
Public Record Office, Kew, RAIL 1008/19. Gooch-Saunders, Rea's house.
White, A.J.L., 'Swindon Works', 11 articles in *G.W.R. Mag.*, 1911–14.

Chapter 18
Clark; Gooch, D.,(Sketch Book); Hadfield; Mac-

Dermot; Rly. Hist. and Travel Soc.; Rolt, (Red for Danger); Snell;
Abbott, G. Blizard, *Masonic Portraits: Sketches of Distinguished Freemasons*. W.W.Morgan, 1879.
Ahrons, E.L., *Locomotive and Train Working in the Latter Part of the Nineteenth Century*. Heffer, 1953.
Bonnet, H., 'Saga of the Steam Plough'.
Clark, D.K., 'Experimental Investigation of the Principles of the Boilers of Locomotive Engines'. *Min. Proc. I. C. E.*, 8 March 1853.
Cooke, C.J.B., *Round the Works of our Great Railways*. Arnold, n.d.
Public Record Office, Kew, RAIL 1008/7. G.W.R. staff.
Public Record Office, Kew, RAIL 1008/15. Letterbook, S. Devon Railway contract.
Public Record Office, Kew, RAIL 1008/27.
Public Record Office, Kew, RAIL 1014/8. Committee of Consultation Report, 1849.
G.W.R. Mag.
The Morning Herald.

Chapter 19
Cooke; Gooch, D., (Sketch Book); Gooch, T.L., (Autobiography); Rolt, (Brunel); Rolt, (Red for Danger); Williams;
Hobsbawm, E.J., *Industry and Empire*. Pelican Books, 1969.
'Improvements in Steam (Locomotive) Engines. Gray v L&NWR'. I. Mech. E. library.
Rolt, L.T.C., *Victorian Engineering*. Allen Lane, The Penguin Press, 1970.
The Illustrated Exhibitor and Magazine of Art, 3 Jan 1852, pp 101–105. 'The Great Western Railway Company's Locomotive Factory at Swindon'.
The Illustrated London News.

Chapter 20
Gooch, D., (Sketch Book); MacDermot; Rly. Corresp. and Travel Soc.
Harrigan, J., 'Victorian Railways to '62'. Victorian Railways Public Relations and Betterment Board, 1962.
Holcroft, H., *The Armstrongs of the Great Western*. Railway World, Ltd., 1953.
Hunter *et al.*, *The Streets of Windsor and Eton*. Windsor Local History Publications Group, 1980.
Lerry, G.G., *The Collieries of Denbighshire, Past and Present*. Wynn Williams, Wrexham, 1968 edition.
Macnaghten, A., 'Windsor in Victorian Times'.
Public Record Office, Kew, RAIL 1008/11. 'Cornwall Engines. Specification for Eight Wheel Locomotive Bogie and Tank Engines'. Initialled 'D.G.'.
Public Record Office, Kew, RAIL 1008/24. *Alma* barge.
Public Record Office, Kew, RAIL 1008/28. Geelong and Melbourne Railway.
Silto, J., 'A Swindon History, 1840–1901'. The Author, 1981.

Chapter 21
Rolt, (Brunel).
Beaver, P., *The Big Ship. Brunel's* Great Eastern — *A Pictorial History*. Evelyn, 1969.
Dodd, George, *Railways, Steamers and Telegraphs*. Chambers, 1867.

Emmerson, G.S., *The Greatest Iron Ship: S.S. Great Eastern*. David and Charles.

Gooch, Sir D., Notebook of the P.S.S. *Great Eastern*. Dept. of Manuscripts, British Library.

Public Record Office, Kew, RAIL 1014/8. Ticket prices.

The Illustrated London News.

Chapter 22

Emmerson; Gooch, D., (Sketch Book); MacDermot; Rly. Corresp. and Travel Soc.

Public Record Office, Kew, RAIL 1008/2. West Mid. Rly. Rep. of 1863 and Gooch's reply. Gooch-Potter Report.

Public Record Office, Kew, RAIL 1008/3. Cost of rolling rails.

Public Record Office, Kew, RAIL 1008/16. South Dev. Rly.

Public Record Office, Kew, RAIL 1008/82. Resignation letter.

Chapter 23

Emmerson; Gooch, D., (Notebook).

Anon., 'The Telcon Story, 1850–1950'. The Telegraph Construction and Maintenance Co. Ltd., 1950.

Barty-King, H., *Girdle Around the Earth: the Story of Cable and Wireless*. Heinemann, 1979.

Bright, E.B. and Bright, C., *The Life Story of the Late Sir Charles Tilston Bright*. Constable, n.d.

Field, H.M., *The Story of the Atlantic Telegraph Cable*. New York, 1893.

Russell, W.H., *The Atlantic Telegraph*. Day and Sons, 1866.

The Manchester Guardian.

The Times.

Thompson, S.P., *The Life of William Thomson, Baron Kelvin of Largs*. 2 Vols. Macmillan, 1910.

Chapter 24

Emmerson; Russell.

MacDermot; 'The Vulcan Loco. Works'.

Hanham, H.J., 'Elections and Party Management: Politics in the Time of Disraeli and Gladstone'. 1959.

North Wilts Herald. Various, incl. 10 June 1865, 'Grand Demonstration at New Swindon'.

Swindon Advertiser.

The Engineer.

The Vulcan Papers. Newton-le-Willows Library.

Thomson, T.R., (ed.), 'Materials for a History of Cricklade'. Cricklade Historical Society, 1958–61.

Chapter 25

Emmerson; Field; Russell.

Elliot, G., 'Description of the Paying-out and Picking-up Machinery Employed in Laying the Atlantic Telegraph Cable'. *Proc. I. Mech. E.*, 1867.

O'Neil, Henry, The Laying of the Atlantic Cable. *Blackwoods' Edinburgh Magazine*, Oct. 1865.

The Illustrated London News.

The Times.

Chapter 26

Elliot; Field; MacDermot; Thompson.

Briggs, A., *Victorian People*. Pelican Edition, 1965.

Eversley, D.E.C., 'The Great Western Railway and the Swindon Works in the Great Depression', article in *Railways in the Victorian Economy*, (ed. Reed), M.C., David and Charles.

Hansards' Parliamentary Debates.

Public Record Office, Kew, RAIL 1014/8. Chairman's salary.

The Illustrated London News.

The Times.

Thomson, Prof. W., 'The Forces Involved in the Lifting and Laying of Deep Sea Cables'. *Proc. Roy. Soc.*, Dec, 1865.

Chapter 27

Briggs; Emmerson; Hanham; Harrison; Lerry; MacDermot.

Bagwell, P.S., *The Railwaymen: The History of the National Union of Railwaymen*. Allen and Unwin, 1963.

Houses of Parliament. Division Lists.

Kelvin Papers, University of Glasgow.

McKillop, N., *The Lighted Flame: a History of the Associated Society of Locomotive Enginemen and Firemen*. Thomas Nelson and Sons, 1950.

Public Record Office, Kew, RAIL 1008/82. Disraeli re. loan.

Paris, le Comte de, *The Trade Unions of England*. Smith, Elder, 1869.

Reports of the Commissioners Appointed to Inquire Into the Organisation and Rules of Trades Unions, etc. Brit. Parl. Papers, 1867 (3873, 3893, 3910, 3952) XXXII, 1; 1867–8 (3980-I–VI) XXXIX, 1; 1868–9 (4123) XXXI, 235; 1868–9 (4123-I) XXXI, 363.

The Illustrated London News.

Windsor, Eton and Slough Express, 30 May 1868. 'Death of Lady Gooch'.

Chapter 28

Briggs; Emmerson; Hanham; Harrison; Kelvin Papers; MacDermot; Reports of the Commissioners Into Trades Unions.

Gooch-Disraeli, 25 Oct 1868. Disraeli Papers, Bodleian Library.

Gray, J. McFarlane, 'Description of the Steam Steering Engine in the *Great Eastern* Steamship. *Proc. I. Mech. E.*, 1867 p 267.

Hansards' Parliamentary Debates.

North Wilts Herald.

Chapter 29

Briggs; Darwin; Emmerson; Kelvin Papers; MacDermot; Rolt, (Brunel); Rolt, (Red for Danger). 'The Telcon Story'.

Alderman, Geoffrey, *The Railway Interest*. Leicester University Press, 1973.

Arnold, Matthew, *Culture and Anarchy*, 1875 edition.

Hansards' Parliamentary Debates.

Houses of Parliament. Division Lists.

The Illustrated London News.

Inst. of Civil Eng., Min. and Proc. 1895–6. Memoir of Charles Richardson.

Martin, Sir T., in 'Diaries of Sir D. Gooch', 1892.

North Wilts Herald.

Public Record Office, Kew, RAIL 250/308; 257/1; 1008/21. Severn Tunnel.

Richardson, C., 'The Severn Tunnel'. *The Engineer*, 24 Sept. 1875.

Richardson, C., 'The Severn Tunnel'. *British Association*, Bristol, 1875.

Richardson, C., 'The Severn Tunnel'. *Clifton Scientific Club*, 12 March 1887.

Rolt, L.T.C., *Victorian Engineering*. Allen Lane, The Penguin Press, 1970.

Swindon Advertiser.

Touchstone, Vol IV, No. 104, 29 March 1879. 'Sir Daniel Gooch, Bart., M.P.'.

Chapter 30

Emmerson; MacDermot; Rly. Hist. and Travel Soc.; Richardson (3).

Geach, J.G., 'On the Mechanical Appliances Used in the Construction of the Heading Under the Severn for the Severn Tunnel Railway'. *Proc. I. Mech. E.*, July 1877.

Hansard.

The Illustrated London News.

Public Record Office, Kew, RAIL 250/308; 257/1; 257/2. Severn Tunnel.

Report from the Select Committee on Employers' Liability for Accidents to Their Servants. Brit. Parl. Papers, 1876 (372) IX, 669; 1877 (285) X, 551.

The Bullionist, 4 March 1876. 'The Great Eastern Steamship Company (Limited)'.

Chapter 31

Briggs; Emmerson; Eversley; Lerry; MacDermot; Rly. Hist. and Travel Soc.; Rolt, (Victorian Engineering).

Hansard.

Hawkshaw, J. C., 'The Severn Tunnel Railway'. *The Engineer*, 26 Sept. 1884.

Houses of Parliament. Division Lists.

North Wilts Herald.

Parsons, R.H., *The Early Days of the Power Station Industry*. Cambridge University Press, 1940.

Public Record Office, Kew, RAIL 250/308; 250/309; 257/1. Severn Tunnel.

Report of the Committee Appointed to Inquire Into the Conditions Under Which Contracts are Invited for the Building or Repair of Ships of the Navy. Brit. Parl. Papers, 1884–5 (c.4219) XIV, 125.

Report from the Select Committee on Railways (Rates and Fares). Brit.Parl. Papers, 1882 (317) XIII, 1.

Tweedie, M.G., 'Gordon Electric Light Installation at Paddington'. *Great Western Railway Magazine*, 1906.

Walker, T.A., *The Severn Tunnel, Its Construction and Difficulties, 1872–1887*. Richard Bently and Sons, 1888.

Chapter 32

Gooch, T.L., (Autobiography); Martin.

Barraud, *Men and Women of the Day*, Vol. 1, 1888.

Clark, D.K., *The Steam Engine*. 1889.

Engineering, 21 December 1868. 'Sir Daniel Gooch, M.P.'.

Engineering, 18 October 1889. 'Sir Daniel Gooch'.

Public Record Office, Kew, RAIL 1008/21.

The Illustrated London News.

The Times.

Epilogue

Public Record Office, Kew, RAIL 1008/82. Lady Gooch-Sir A. Wood.

Rogers, H.C.B., *G.J. Churchward – A Locomotive Biography*. Allen and Unwin, 1975.

Rubinstein, W.D., *Men of Property*. Croom Helm, 1981.

Index